ROBLEMS IN ADVANCED ORGANIC CHEMISTRY

PROBLEMS IN ADVANCED
ORGANIC CHEMISTRY

Toshio Goto and Y. Hirata
Nagoya University

George H. Stout
University of Washington

HOLDEN-DAY

San Francisco, Cambridge, London, Amsterdam

This is a revised, updated, and expanded edition of TECHNIQUES AND REACTIONS
IN ORGANIC CHEMISTRY: A PROBLEMS APPROACH, by Toshio Goto and Yoshimasha Hirata,
originally published in Japanese by Nankodo Company Limited, Tokyo.

Second Printing . . . . October, 1969

Library of Congress Catalog Card Number: 67-13842

Printed in the United States of America

PREFACE

The modern organic chemist requires a knowledge of electronic theory, reaction mechanisms, stereochemistry, and the interpretation of physical data, as
well as the older areas of synthetic and degradative reactions. This knowledge
should be practical as well as theoretical and can only be developed by application to actual problems, either in the laboratory or as examples drawn from the
work of others. It is the intention of this book to provide such problems, to allow the student to struggle with them and exercise his skills in arriving at his
own conclusions, and then to provide him with answers and references for check-
ing and further instruction.

A word of caution is in order with regard to the answers. Most of these are
drawn more or less directly from the literature, at least as far as the basic arguments are concerned. A few have been modified when, in the view of the authors, other conclusions appeared justified. It is most probable that some answers
are incorrect, particularly with regard to mechanisms proposed for reactions
for which only a limited amount of information is available; but they represent
the best thought at the present time. Continued study has also shown that many
reactions originally viewed as rather simple are, in fact, highly complex; this
will doubtless prove true for many of those discussed in the problems. In many
cases, too, alternative answers are possible. An attempt has been made to indicate these where possible, but some have certainly been omitted. It should be
noted, however, that the number of *reasonable* alternatives is very much smaller
than the number of different answers which may be obtained by students, so other
conclusions should be carefully scrutinized before they are accepted as "just as
good" as the ones given.

The problems are intended either for self-study or for group discussion by
graduate students in their first year and beyond. A good background in organic

chemistry at the second-year level is required for the problems to have much meaning, although they may be used in conjunction with an advanced course to point up strong and weak points in one's knowledge. The form and difficulty of the problems most closely resemble those of questions appearing on "cumulative examinations" or "preliminary examinations," common hurdles in doctoral programs, and they should be most useful to students studying for these.

An effort has been made to provide each problem with references which afford the student further reading on the topics covered. These are intended as instructional guides and ignore any questions of priority, although in many cases they do lead to the original work. Some of the commonest secondary references are cited simply by the author's name; these and the equivalent full references are listed on page viii. Additional general references for study in various special fields are given at the beginnings of some of the chapters.

The problems are divided into groups based, very roughly, on the kinds of reactions involved. Many of the choices are quite arbitrary, since one problem may include a number of different reaction types. An alternative classification, based on the kinds of problems (mechanism, synthesis, road-map, and so on) is given in Index 1, while the details of the individual problems are used as the basis for Index 2.

Some of the problems are quite easy; some are very difficult. It cannot be recommended too strongly that the student resist for the longest possible time the temptation to consult the answers, since the maximum gain is obtained only by thinking at length about the questions involved. One problem a day, mulled over in spare moments, would be none too slow a pace to follow through much of the book.

This book was first published in Japanese, and represents selected problems chosen from those discussed in graduate-student seminars with the guidance of Dr. Kiyoshi Hattori, Dr. Kiyoyuki Yamada, Dr. Shoji Eguchi, and Dr. Shosuke Yamamura, whose help we gratefully acknowledge. It has been extensively revised and the answers expanded during the course of translation. This revision has been greatly facilitated by the extensive and penetrating comments of Professor Peter Yates, to whom we express our gratitude. Finally, thanks are due to Professor C. Djerassi and Professor K. Nakanishi, who suggested the translation of this book into English, and to Holden-Day, Inc., and Nankodo Co., Ltd., who gave us an opportunity to publish it.

T. Goto
Y. Hirata
Nagoya, Japan
G. H. Stout
Seattle, Washington

October 1967

CONTENTS

BASIC REFERENCE LIST

Bellamy, L. J. *The Infra-Red Spectra of Complex Molecules*, 2nd ed., Wiley, New York, 1958.

Eliel, E. L. *Stereochemistry of Carbon Compounds*, McGraw-Hill, New York, 1962.

Gould, E. S. *Mechanism and Structure in Organic Chemistry*, Holt, New York, 1959.

Hine, J. *Physical Organic Chemistry*, 2nd ed., McGraw-Hill, New York, 1962.

Jackman, L. M. *Applications of Nuclear Magnetic Resonance Spectroscopy in Organic Chemistry*, Pergamon, London, 1959.

Nakanishi, K. *Infrared Absorption Spectroscopy*, Holden-Day, San Francisco, 1962.

Royals, E. E. *Advanced Organic Chemistry*, Prentice-Hall, New York, 1954.

CHAPTER 1

GENERAL PROBLEMS

These problems cover some of the general background information which should be part of the tools of any organic chemist. Much of the required knowledge can be obtained from any advanced text in the field, e.g., Hine or Gould. Other, and more specific, references are as follows:

1. P. H. Hermans, *Introduction to Theoretical Organic Chemistry*, Elsevier, Amsterdam, 1954. An early and comparatively little-known text which contains much useful material on the theoretical bases of physical properties.
2. G. W. Wheland, *Advanced Organic Chemistry*, 3rd ed., Wiley, New York, 1960. Particularly useful for resonance theory and tautomerism.
3. E. L. Eliel, *Stereochemistry of Carbon Compounds*, McGraw-Hill, New York, 1962. An extensive survey.
4. K. Mislow, *Introduction to Stereochemistry,* Benjamin, New York, 1965. A short but comprehensive introduction to symmetry and its effects in organic chemistry. Many problems.
5. H. C. Brown, D. H. McDaniel, and O. Hafliger in *Determination of Organic Structures by Physical Methods* (E. A. Braude and F. C. Nachod, eds.), Academic Press, New York, 1955, pp. 567-662. An exhaustive review of dissociation constants and their applications.

PROBLEM 1.   Arrange the groups in each set in increasing order of magnitude for the effect indicated.

(1.1) $-I$ effect (R = alkyl) $-SO_3^{\ominus}$, $-SR$, $-\underset{\underset{O}{\parallel}}{S}R$, $-SO_2R$

(cont.)

(1.2)   + M effect

$$\underset{R}{-N\overset{\overset{\displaystyle NR}{\|}}{C}OR}, \quad \underset{R}{-N\overset{\overset{\displaystyle NR}{\|}}{C}R}, \quad \underset{R}{-N\overset{\overset{\displaystyle ||}{}}{C}H_2R}, \quad \underset{R}{-N\overset{\overset{\displaystyle \overset{\oplus}{N}R_2}{\|}}{C}R}$$

(1.3)   − M effect

$$-CO\underset{\underset{NR}{\|}}{N}R_2, \quad -C\underset{\underset{\oplus NR_2}{\|}}{N}R_2, \quad -C\underset{\underset{\oplus NR_2}{\|}}{N}R_2$$

ANSWER 1.   [See C. K. Ingold, *Structure and Mechanism in Organic Chemistry,* Cornell University Press, Ithaca, 1953, pp. 60-90.]
The notation is that of Ingold, and although it is not so much used in the U.S., it is often encountered in the foreign literature. I refers to an inductive effect, whereas M is a mesomeric or resonance effect in the ground state of the molecule. A plus sign indicates electron donation, and a minus sign signifies electron withdrawal.

(1. 1)

$$-SR < -\underset{\oplus}{S}-R < -\overset{\overset{\displaystyle O^{\ominus}}{|}}{\underset{\underset{O^{\ominus}}{|}}{S}}{}^{\oplus\oplus} -O^{\ominus} < -\overset{\overset{\displaystyle O^{\ominus}}{|}}{\underset{\underset{O^{\ominus}}{|}}{S}}{}^{\oplus\oplus} -R$$

The electron-withdrawing inductive effect increases with the formal positive charge on the sulfur. The net negative charge on $-SO_3^{\ominus}$ reduces its effect, however, in comparison with the sulfone, $-SO_2R$.

(1. 2)

$$-\underset{\underset{\oplus}{\underset{NR_2}{R}}}{\overset{..}{N}}-C-R < -\underset{\underset{O}{R}}{\overset{..}{N}}-C-R < -\underset{\underset{NR}{R}}{\overset{..}{N}}-C-R < -\underset{R}{\overset{..}{N}}-CH_2R$$

The ability of the nitrogen to donate electrons by contribution from the resonance form A increases as the importance of form B decreases.

$$\overset{\frown}{\underset{\underset{X}{R}}{\overset{..}{N}}}-C- \longleftrightarrow \overset{\oplus}{\underset{\underset{X}{R}}{N}}=C- \longleftrightarrow \underset{\underset{:X:^{\ominus}}{R}}{\overset{\oplus}{N}}=C-$$

$$\qquad\qquad A \qquad\qquad\qquad B$$

If X is strongly electron-withdrawing, B will be a major contributor; if it is not, A will be more important. The electron-attracting powers ($-M$) of the groups shown are ($=\overset{\oplus}{N}R_2 >\ =O >\ =NR >> H_2$).

(1.3)

$$-\overset{\overset{NR}{\|}}{C}NR_2 < -\overset{\overset{O}{\|}}{C}-NR_2 < -\overset{\overset{\oplus}{N}R_2}{\overset{\|}{C}}-NR_2$$

The importance of resonance form A will increase with the ability of the atom X to accommodate the electrons transferred to it. This increases

$$=N- <\ =O <\ =\overset{\oplus}{N}< .$$

$$\overset{..}{Y}\diagdown\overset{\overset{X)}{\|}}{C}-NR_2 \longleftrightarrow Y=\overset{\overset{\displaystyle :\overset{..}{X}:\ \ominus}{|}}{\overset{\oplus}{C}}-NR_2$$
$$A$$

PROBLEM 2. Predict which compound in each of the following pairs has the larger dipole moment:

(2.1) m-Chloronitrobenzene and p-chloronitrobenzene

(2.2) 3,5-Dimethylnitrobenzene and 3,6-dimethylnitrobenzene

(2.3)

(2.5)

(2.4)

(2.6)

ANSWER 2. [See Gould, Chap. 3; C. P. Smyth, *Dielectric Behavior and Structure,* McGraw-Hill, New York, 1955, Chaps. 8-11.]
The net dipole moment can often be considered as the vector sum of the individual moments of the various bonds. This method will break down if there are interactions between the bonds which change their electron distributions, but is approximately applicable otherwise.

(2.1)

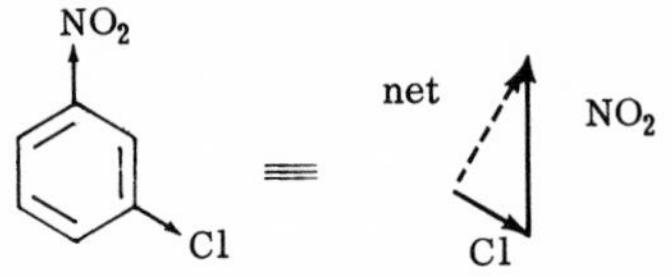

Therefore, A > B
observed A = 3.69 D
            B = 2.78 D

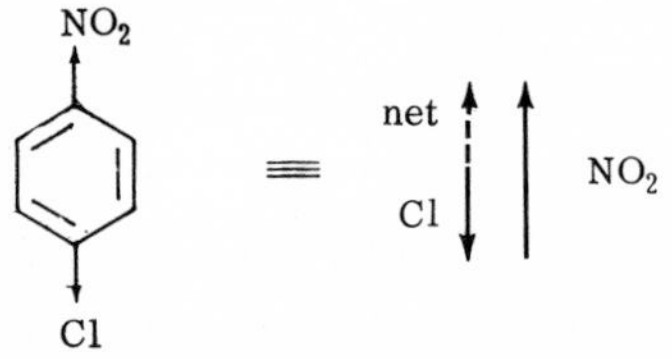

(2.2)

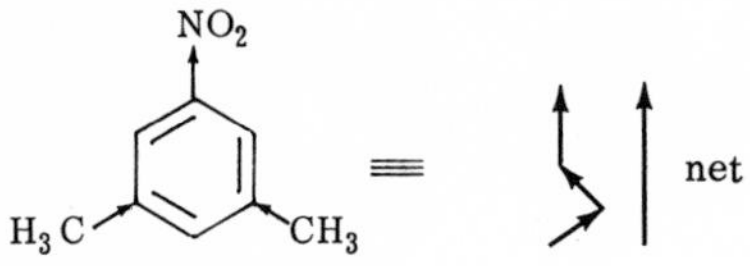

Therefore, A > B

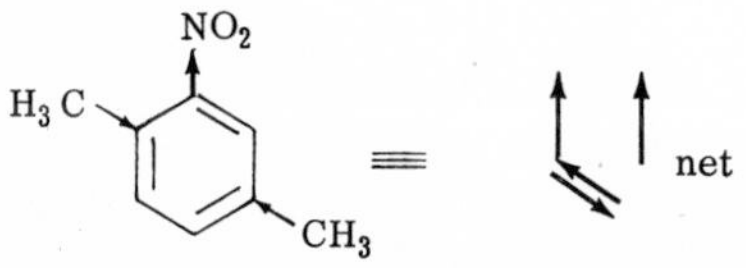

The dipole moments of the CH_3-C bonds are toward the ring, while those of $C-NO_2$ are away. In B the two methyl contributions cancel, but in A they partially reinforce.

(2.3)

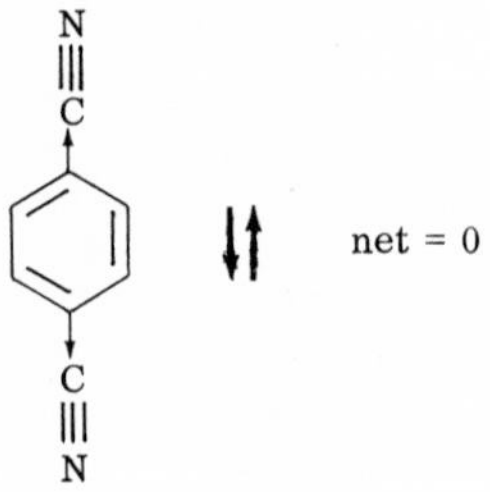

net = 0

Therefore, B > A

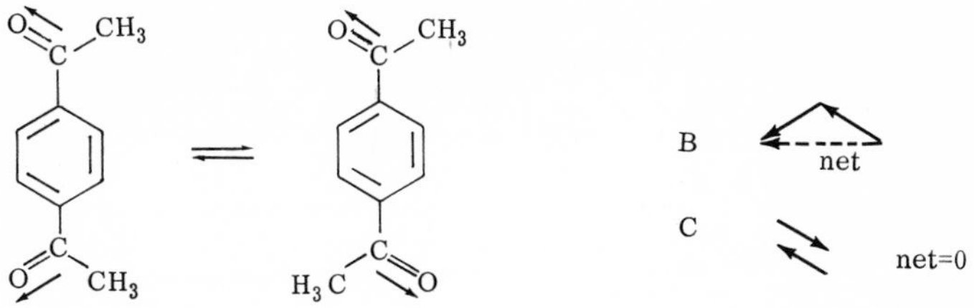

B

C

The dipole moments of the acetyl groups are oriented approximately along the
$\diagdown\overset{+\to}{C}{=}O$. In one conformation (C) these cancel, but in the other (B) there is a
net resultant. Since both forms exist in solution, there will be some dipole moment observed. The linear cyano groups in A, however, cause the net moment
to be zero at all times.

(2.4)

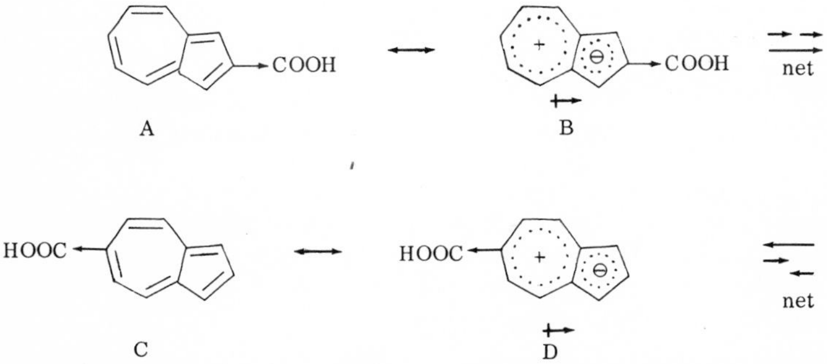

A   B

Therefore,
A > C

C   D

The azulene system has a dipole moment for the parent hydrocarbon as a
result of contributions from the resonance form shown in B.

(2.5)

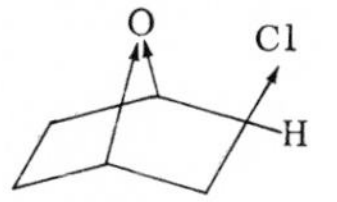

A

A > B

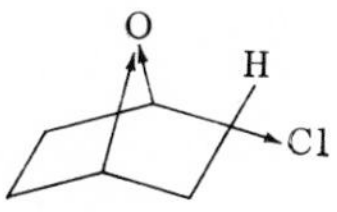

B

In A the C → O and C → Cl bonds are pointing roughly in the same direction; in B they are more nearly opposed.

(2. 6)   Cyclopropane shows properties which are intermediate between those of ethylene and the normal saturated hydrocarbons. In particular, the cyclopropyl group is more electronegative than an alkyl group and has a lesser tendency to give up electrons. This effect may be ascribed either to conjugation, which brings electrons back to the ring, or to increased *s* character of the exterior bonds of the cyclopropane system. Whatever the exact cause, the dipole moment of cyclopropyl chloride (1.76 D) resembles that of vinyl chloride (1.44 D) more than that of isopropyl chloride (2.15 D).

PROBLEM 3.   Predict for each of the following pairs which compound will have the larger heat of hydrogenation:

(3.1)   1,4-Pentadiene, 1,3-pentadiene

(3.2)   4,4-Dimethyl-trans-2-pentene, 4,4-dimethyl-cis-2-pentene

(3.3)   1-Butene, trans-2-butene

(3.4)   Ethylidenecyclohexane, 1-ethylcyclohexene-1

(3.5)   Bicyclo[2,1,0]pentane, cyclopentene

ANSWER 3.   [See R. B. Turner in *Theoretical Organic Chemistry,* Butterworth, London, 1959, pp. 67-83.]
      The relative heats of formation of two isomeric unsaturated compounds may be compared if they can be hydrogenated to the same product and the heat evolved measured. The less stable isomer will have the greater heat of hydrogenation, since it gives up the most stored energy in the process. Since heat is evolved, the heats of hydrogenation are negative.

(3. 1) $CH_2{=}CH{-}CH_2{-}CH{=}CH_2$ $\Delta H = -60.8$ kcal/mole

            $CH_2{=}CH{-}CH{=}CH{-}CH_3$ $\Delta H = -54.1$ kcal/mole

      The conjugated diene is stabilized by resonance, and hydrogenation is a relatively less favorable process than with the unconjugated isomer.

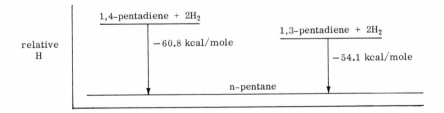

(3.2)   [R. B. Turner, D. E. Nettleton, Jr., and M. Perlman, *J. Am. Chem. Soc.,* **80**, 1430 (1958).]

$\Delta H = -26.5$ kcal/mole

$\Delta H = -30.8$ kcal/mole

Cis-alkenes are less stable than their trans isomers because of the greater steric strain occasioned by having two bulky groups on the same side of the double bond. The difference in cis/trans energy varies from ca. 1 kcal/mole in the 2-butenes to 9.3 kcal/mole for the 1,2-di-t-butylethylenes.

(3.3)   [G. B. Kistiakowsky, J. R. Ruhoff, H. A. Smith, and W. E. Vaughan, *J. Am. Chem. Soc.,* **57**, 876 (1935).]

$CH_3CH_2CH=CH_2$ $\Delta H = -30.3$ kcal/mole

$\Delta H = -27.6$ kcal/mole

Except for special cases in which strain plays a role, the stability of olefins goes up and the heats of hydrogenation go down as the extent of substitution increases. For alkyl substituents there is disagreement about the cause of this effect, but it is undoubtedly real.

(3.4)   [R. B. Turner and R. H. Garner, *J. Am. Chem. Soc.,* **80**, 1424 (1958).]

$\Delta H = -26.3$ kcal/mole

$\Delta H = -25.1$ kcal/mole

It is clear both from heats of hydrogenation and from equilibration experiments that a double bond within a six-membered ring (endocyclic) is energetically favored over one adjacent to the ring (exocyclic). The causes are probably steric, since moving the bond into the ring reduces the number of axial-axial hydrogen contacts. A similar effect may account for the greater enol content of cyclohexanones as compared with acyclic ketones.

(3.5)

$\Delta H = -55.1$ kcal/mole

$\Delta H = -25.7$ kcal/mole

The strain in the bicyclopentane is very great, and this is reflected in the heat of hydrogenation. Note by way of comparison that the calculated ΔH for cyclopropane is -37.6 kcal/mole, considerably greater than that for propylene (-30.1 kcal/mole).

PROBLEM 4.   Deduce from the following dipole moment data the directions of the dipoles in the parent compounds and suggest an explanation.

1a X = H 3.71 D	**2a** X = H 1.24 D	
1b X = Br 2.07 D	**2b** X = Br 2.52 D	

ANSWER 4.   [W. R. Brasen, H. E. Holmquist, and R. E. Benson, *J. Am. Chem. Soc.*, **83**, 3125 (1961).]

The bond moment for bromine on an aromatic system is ca. 1.5 D, with bromine at the negative end. It may be seen that bromine substitution reduces the net moment of tropolone (**1**) but increases that of the nitrogen analog (**2**). Thus the unsubstituted compounds have their dipoles oriented oppositely.

3   1.0 D

The tendency of seven-membered unsaturated rings to approach the positively charged six π-electron tropenium (tropylium) system is well known (see
azulene, **3**) and is shown by **1**. The amino system (**2**) apparently does not do this,
however. Instead, there is a transfer of electrons from the nitrogens toward the
ring. It is suggested that this involves a contribution from the resonance form
shown, which provides a possible ten π-electron system. The molecule may also
be thought of as a bent polyene chain corresponding to **4**, in which the dipole moment arises from the transfer of an electron

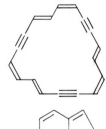

4

from the proton to the conjugated system.

PROBLEM 5.   Which of the following compounds can be classified as aromatic?

(5.1)   1,2,3-Triphenylcyclopropenium cation

(5.2)   Cyclooctatetraenyl dianion

(5.3)   Cyclobutadiene

(5.4)   2,4,6-Cycloheptatriene-1-carboxylic acid

(5.5)   p-Benzoquinone

(5.6)   Azulene

(5.7)   Sydnone

(5.8)

(5.9)

ANSWER 5.   [See Gould, pp. 412ff; D. P. Craig in *Non-Benzenoid Aromatic
Compounds* (D. Ginsburg, ed.), Wiley-Interscience, 1959, pp.
1-42.]
A fundamental problem related to this question is defining what is meant

by aromatic. Perhaps the best definition is that an aromatic compound is one which is significantly more stable than would be predicted on the basis of a hypothetical-model molecule having the same structure and a fixed electron distribution corresponding to normal single and double bonds. The difference in energy between the real molecule and the model is known as the "delocalization energy." Experimentally, aromatic compounds show less reactivity than would be predicted for their fixed-bond models, and often react by substitution (which preserves the aromatic system) rather than addition (which destroys it). A modern criterion for aromaticity is whether or not the compound shows evidence in its NMR spectrum of the presence of a ring current, i.e., delocalization of the electrons in the cyclic unsaturated system in the presence of a magnetic field.[1]

Hückel's rule, which is based on simple quantum-mechanical calculations, states that aromatic character is associated with those compounds which possess $(4n + 2)$ π-electrons in a planar, fully conjugated ring system. There are hidden snags in the general application of this rule, particularly with regard to predicting planarity, but it can often provide a good guide.

(5.1)   [R. Breslow and C. Yuan, *J. Am. Chem. Soc.*, **80**, 5991 (1958).]

This fits the Hückel rule with $n = 0$ and appears to be aromatic.

(5.2)   [T. J. Katz, *J. Am. Chem. Soc.*, **82**, 3784 (1960).]

The relatively ready formation of this dianion and the presence of a ring current speak for its aromatic character. As a 10π-electron system it fits the Hückel rule with $n = 2$. It should be noted that the uncharged precursor, cyclooctatetraene, is nonplanar and nonaromatic. This is attributed to the presence of only eight π-electrons $(4n)$ in its unsaturated system.

---

[1]J. A. Pople, W. G. Schneider, and H. J. Bernstein, *High-Resolution Nuclear Magnetic Resonance*, McGraw-Hill, New York, 1959, pp. 180–183.

(5.3)   [See W. Baker and J. F. W. McOmie in *Non-Benzenoid Aromatic Compounds*, pp. 43-105.]

Although simple benzene-like conjugation can be written for cyclobutadiene, it does not fit the Hückel rule and is extremely unstable. Both calculations and physical measurements suggest that it is rectangular rather than square, and that resonance does not occur.

(5.4)

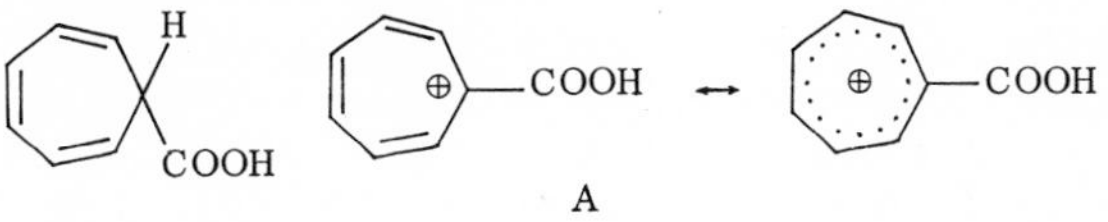

A

This molecule does not have a closed resonance system and is not aromatic. Loss of H⁻, however, leads to A, which contains the six π-electron tropenium (tropylium) system and is aromatic.

(5.5)

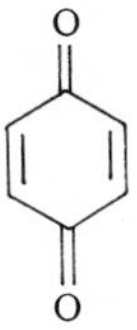

Although p-benzoquinone has considerable delocalization energy (16 kcal/mole), this is much smaller than that of benzene, and the molecule is perhaps best considered as a combination of $\alpha\beta$-unsaturated ketone systems with relatively little additional interaction in the ground state.

(5.6)   [See E. Heilbronner in *Non-Benzenoid Aromatic Compounds*, pp. 171-276.]

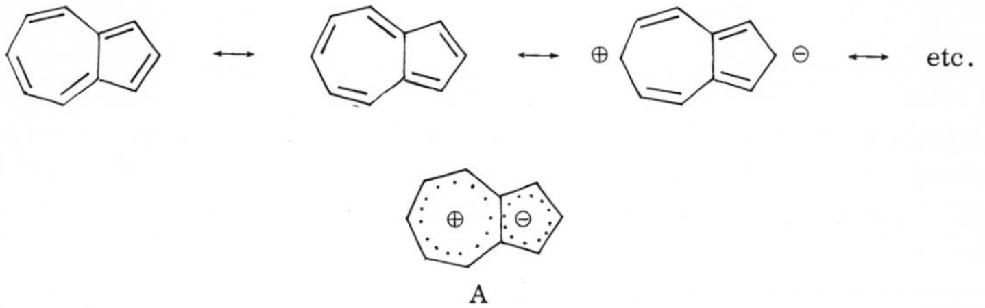

A

Azulene is definitely an aromatic hydrocarbon, similar in many ways to naphthalene, although with less stabilization. It is a 10π-electron system which may be viewed either as a combination of tropenium and cyclopentadienide moieties (A) or, roughly, as a single conjugated cyclodecapentaene tied across by one bond.

(5.7)   [See W. Baker and W. D. Ollis, *Quart. Rev.*, **11**, 15 (1957).]

The sydnones[1] are members of the class of "meso-ionic compounds" which cannot be satisfactorily represented by any single valence bond picture not involving separated charges. Instead they are hybrids of a large number of dipolar and tetrapolar forms. They may also be considered to be aromatic, since the five-membered ring contains six π-electrons.

(5.8)   [F. Sondheimer and R. Wolovsky, *J. Am. Chem. Soc.*, **84**, 260 (1962).]
If the acetylenic bonds are considered as contributing two π-electrons to the conjugated system (the other π-bond is in the nodal plane and does not interact), this tridehydro-[18]-annulene meets the Hückel rule with n = 4. It shows an aromatic ultraviolet spectrum, the presence of a ring current, and is significantly more stable than its open-chain analogs.
Partial hydrogenation of the acetylenic groups[2] leads to [18]-annulene (A), which also shows aromatic properties, although it is not very stable.

A

---

[1] F. H. C. Stewart, *Chem. Rev.*, **64**, 128 (1964).
[2] F. Sondheimer, R. Wolovsky, and Y. Amiel, *J. Am. Chem. Soc.*, **84**, 274 (1962).

(5.9)   [R. J. Windgassen, Jr., W. H. Saunders, Jr., and V. Boekelheide, *J. Am. Chem. Soc.*, **81**, 1459 (1959).]

This cyclazine shows marked aromatic properties, as might be expected, since it is planar and its periphery contains ten π-electrons, thus fitting the Hückel rule. Such a picture is an oversimplification, and more specific calculations indicate a large gain in resonance energy results from the interaction of the nitrogen electrons with the periphery. This view is supported by the very low basicity of this system.

PROBLEM 6.   For each of the following, state which of the structures in parentheses would make the greater contribution to the resonance hybrid of the indicated molecule. Justify your choice.

(6.1) CH_3CN ($CH_3\overset{\ominus}{C}=\overset{\oplus}{N}$, $CH_3\overset{\oplus}{C}=\overset{\ominus}{N}$)

(6.2)

(6.3) $CH_3COCH=\underset{\underset{OH}{|}}{C}C_2H_5$ $\left(CH_3C=CHCOC_2H_5,\ CH_3\underset{\underset{OH}{|}}{C}=CH\overset{\oplus}{C}C_2H_5\right)$

(6.4)

ANSWER 6.   [For extensive discussions of the conditions for reasonable resonance contribution, see G. W. Wheland, *Advanced Organic Chemistry*, 3rd ed., Wiley, New York, 1960, pp. 112-125; Hine, pp. 1-17.]

(6.1)   The location of the unshared electrons in the two structures should be considered.

$$CH_3-\overset{\ominus}{\ddot{C}}=\overset{\oplus}{\ddot{N}}\ CH_3-\overset{\oplus}{C}=\overset{..}{\underset{..}{N}}\ \ominus$$

A   B

Each has one atom with an octet and one with a sextet, and they are equivalent in this respect. Although neither is good, the negative charge on the more electronegative nitrogen and the positive charge on carbon (B) is to be preferred over the reverse arrangement.

(6.2)

A   B

In A, the chlorine, despite its positive charge, has a full outer shell of eight electrons. Such an arrangement is energetically much favored over that in B, in which the chlorine has only six electrons. (This is a very general phenomenon; compare the difference between the relatively stable species $R\overset{+}{O}H_2$ and the extremely reactive one RO^+.)

(6.3)

A   B

Of these only B has any possibility of contributing to the resonance hybrid. A is a *tautomer* of the original structure, a chemically different species resulting from the shift of a proton.

(6.4)

A   B

Of these A involves a nitrogen atom with five bonds, i.e., ten electrons. Elements of the first row of the periodic table lack the extra low-lying orbitals which would be required for such bond formation; so such forms do not contribute. B, in fact, represents one of the two major contributors to the ground-state hybrid of aliphatic diazo compounds, the other being that given in the problem.

PROBLEM 7.   For each of the following show the principal structures which contribute to the resonance hybrid.

(7.1)   (7.3) $CH_2{=}CHCOO^{\ominus}$

(7.2)   (7.4) $CH_2{=}CH\overset{\oplus}{C}HR$

ANSWER 7.

(7.1)

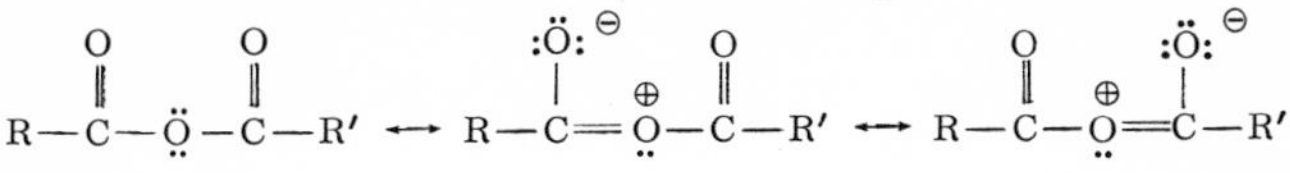

(7.2)

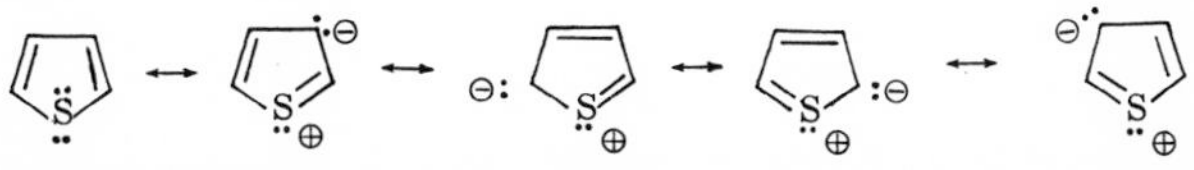

Because sulfur is in the second row of the periodic table, it can use 3d orbitals to expand its octet. Thus additional forms which should be considered are A and B.

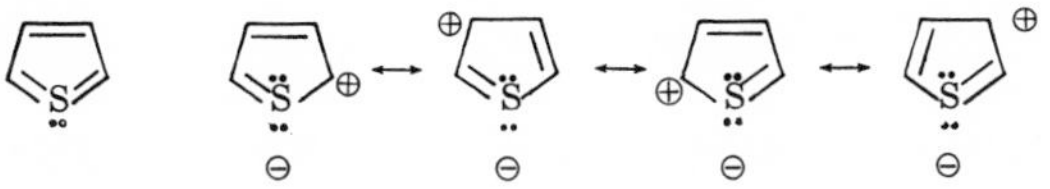

A   B

(7.3)

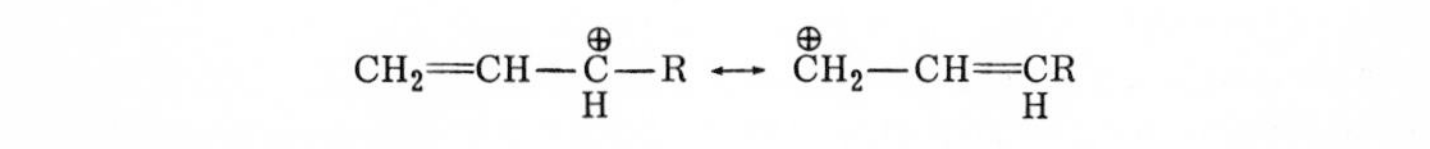

The first two forms contribute equally; the third is much less important.

(7.4)

$$CH_2=CH-\overset{\oplus}{\underset{H}{C}}-R \longleftrightarrow \overset{\oplus}{CH_2}-CH=\underset{H}{CR}$$

If R = alkyl, the first form is somewhat more important than the second, because electron release by R stabilizes the secondary ion with respect to the primary one.

PROBLEM 8.   Arrange the following compounds in order of increasing pK_a (decreasing acidity):

(8.1)
$$C_6H_5OH, \ CH_3COOH, \ CH_3SO_2CH_2COOH, \ CH_3CH_2OH,$$

$$p\text{-}CH_3C_6H_4OH, \ (CH_3)_3CCOOH, \ (C_6H_5)_3CH$$

(cont.)

(8.2)   The conjugate acids of

CH_3NH_2, H_2NNH_2, H_2NOH, $C_6H_5NH_2$, CH_3CN, $(CH_3)_2NH$, NH_3, H_2NCNH_2,

$$\underset{\text{NH}}{\|}$$

$H_2N-\!\!\!\!\bigcirc\!\!\!\!-NO_2$,

(8.3)

ANSWER 8.   [See H. C. Brown, D. H. McDaniel, and O. Hafliger in *Determination of Organic Structures by Physical Methods,* Vol. 1 (E. A. Braude and F. C. Nachod, eds.), Academic Press, New York, 1955, pp. 567-662; Hine, pp. 58-65.]

The acidity of a compound is determined by the relative stabilities of the acid and base forms. Any factor which tends to stabilize one more than the other will shift the equilibrium between the two. In general, electron-withdrawing substituents tend to destabilize acids and stabilize their conjugate bases, whereas electron-donating groups have the opposite effect.

(8.1) $CH_3SO_2CH_2COOH$ (pK$_a$ 2.36) CH_3COOH (pK$_a$ 4.76) $(CH_3)_3CCOOH$ (pK$_a$ 5.05)

C_6H_5OH (pK$_a$ 9.95)   p-$CH_3C_6H_4OH$ (pK$_a$ 10.19)

CH_3CH_2OH (pK$_a$ 15.8) $(C_6H_5)_3CH$ (pK$_a$ ~ 25)

These compounds may be divided into three groups. The first, carboxylic acids, are the most acidic largely because of the stabilization of the basic ion by carboxylate resonance, which spreads the charge over two oxygens.

The electron-withdrawing effect of the sulfone removes electrons inductively from the carboxyl system, thus destabilizing the acid form and stabilizing the anion. Both effects lead to an increase in the acidity. Alkyl substituents, on the other hand, are electron-donating, have opposite effects on the species in the equilibrium, and decrease the acidity.

In the case of phenols, the aromatic ring is not as electron-withdrawing as a carbonyl group and does not have as great a destabilizing effect on the hydroxyl to which it is joined. Furthermore, the resonance forms of the phenoxide ion distribute the charge onto carbon atoms, which are less effective receptors than the much more electronegative oxygen atom of a carboxylate ion. The net effect is to make the hydroxyl less acidic than in a carboxylic acid. Alkyl substitution on the aromatic ring of a phenol reduces the acidity still further, for the reasons given above.

The acidities of the last two compounds are determined mainly by the stabilities of their ions and demonstrate that a charge localized on a single oxygen is more stable than one which can be distributed over a large number of carbon atoms.

(8.2)

$$CH_3C\overset{\oplus}{\equiv}NH \quad (pK_a < 0) \qquad H_3\overset{\oplus}{N}OH \quad (pK_a\ 6.0) \qquad CH_3\overset{\oplus}{N}H_3 \quad (pK_a\ 10.6)$$

$$O_2N-\langle\!\!\bigcirc\!\!\rangle-\overset{\oplus}{N}H_3 \quad (pK_a\ 1.0) \qquad H_3\overset{\oplus}{N}NH_2 \quad (pK_a\ 8.2) \qquad (CH_3)_2\overset{\oplus}{N}H_2 \quad (pK_a\ 10.8)$$

$$C_6H_5\overset{\oplus}{N}H_3 \quad (pK_a\ 4.6) \qquad H_4\overset{\oplus}{N} \quad (pK_a\ 9.3) \qquad H_2NCNH_2 \quad (pK_a\ 14)$$
$$\overset{\|}{\underset{\oplus NH_2}{}}$$

$$\langle\!\!\bigcirc\!\!\rangle_{\overset{\oplus}{N}H} \quad (pK_a\ 5.2)$$

The effects of substituents on the acidities of these ammonium ions should be considered in terms of both the acid and its conjugate base.

The basicity of an atom decreases as the hybridization of the orbital containing the unshared electron pairs changes from sp³ to sp² to sp (see $CH_3^{\ominus}$ and $CH\equiv C^{\ominus}$). Correspondingly, the strengths of the conjugate acids *increase*. This effect accounts for the relative order

$$CH_3C\overset{\oplus}{\equiv}NH \ > \ \langle\!\!\bigcirc\!\!\rangle_{\overset{\oplus}{N}H} \ > \ NH_4^{\oplus}$$

In anilines, conjugation of the nitrogen electrons with the ring stabilizes the base and decreases its tendency to donate electrons. Adding a p-nitro group both withdraws electrons inductively, destabilizing the positively charged ammonium ion (acid), and provides additional resonance forms to tie up the electron pair of the base and make them unavailable for bonding.

The basicity of the simple amines is affected by electron-withdrawing (O > N > H) or electron-donating (C > H) substituents. These serve, respectively, to decrease or increase the stability of the positively charged acid and so increase or decrease its acidity.

The guanidinium ion is particularly stable because its structure allows the equidistribution of the charge over three nitrogens.

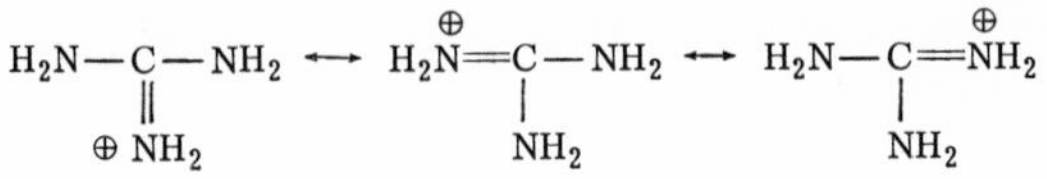

$$H_2N-\overset{\overset{\displaystyle \parallel}{C}}{\underset{\oplus NH_2}{}}-NH_2 \longleftrightarrow H_2\overset{\oplus}{N}=\overset{\underset{\displaystyle NH_2}{|}}{C}-NH_2 \longleftrightarrow H_2N-\overset{\underset{\displaystyle NH_2}{|}}{C}=\overset{\oplus}{N}H_2$$

(8.3)

NO₂ — (pK_a 7.16) phenol

NO₂ with H₃C and CH₃ — (pK_a 8.25)

H₃C and CH₃ — (pK_a 10.18)

CN — (pK_a 7.95)

phenol — (pK_a 9.95)

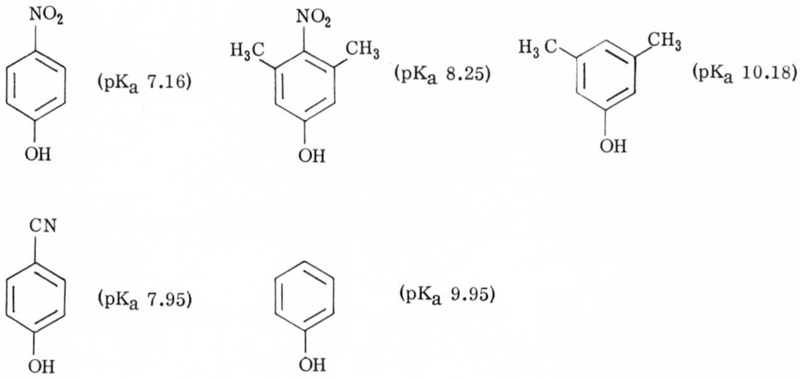

The acidity of substituted phenols is determined mainly by the effects of the substituents on the distribution of the charge into the ring (forms **1** → **3**):

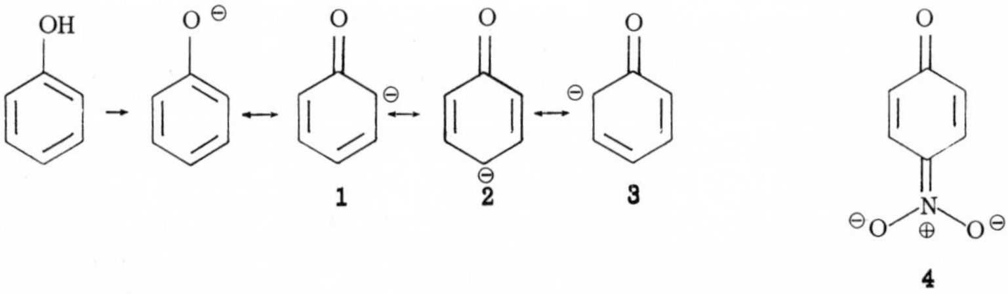

Addition of a para electron-withdrawing group increases this charge distribution, stabilizes the ion, and increases the acidity. The — NO₂ group is more powerfully electron-withdrawing than — CN, so the effect is larger. It depends largely, however, on the contribution from an additional resonance form **4**; and if two methyl substituents are added ortho to the nitro group, steric hindrance reduces the contribution of **4**, and the acidity decreases. It is still greater than that of unsubstituted phenol, however, both because of some residual resonance interaction and because of the direct inductive effects of the nitro group.

Substitution by electron-donating groups such as methyl tends to increase the electron density in the ring and reduce the stability of the ion.

PROBLEM 9.   Arrange the following compounds in order of decreasing
basicity:

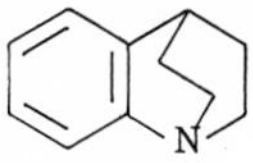

A    B 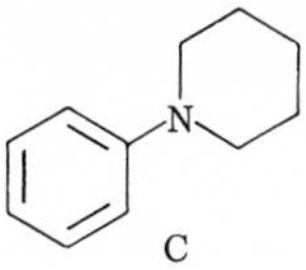   C

ANSWER 9.   [B. M. Wepster, *Rec. Trav. Chim.*, **71**, 1171 (1952).]

$(pK_b = 3.35)$

B

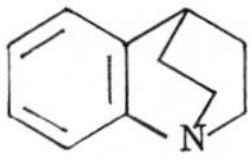

$(pK_b = 6.21)$

A

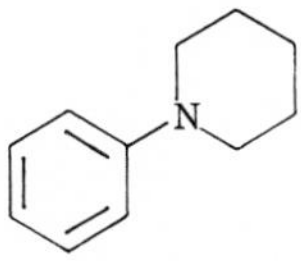

$(pK_b = 8.80)$

C

The phenyl group is electron-withdrawing both by resonance and inductively.
In A only the inductive effect is operative, because the electron pair of the nitrogen is in the plane of the benzene ring and cannot interact with the π-electron
system. In C, on the other hand, the phenyl group reduces the electron density
on nitrogen both inductively and by the participation of resonance forms such
as D.

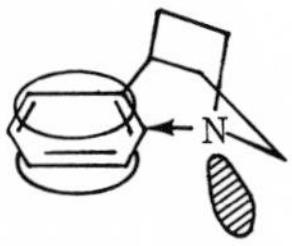

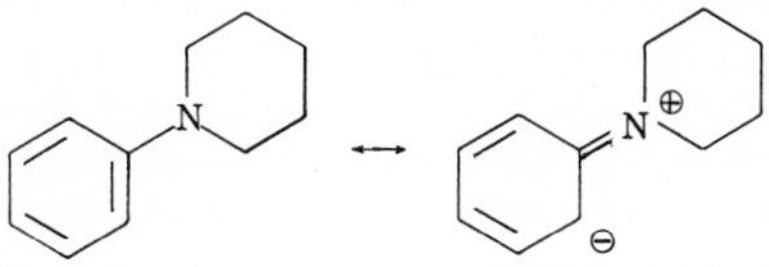

D

PROBLEM 10.   Predict which of the following compounds are optically active.

(10.1)

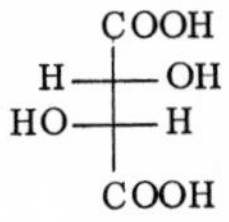

COOH
H——OH
HO——H
COOH

A

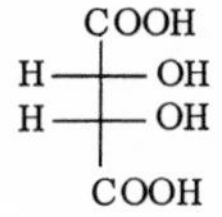

COOH
H——OH
H——OH
COOH

B

(10.2)

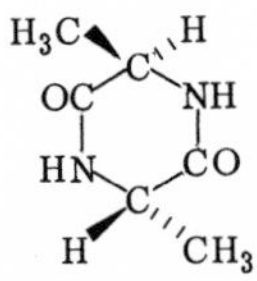

A

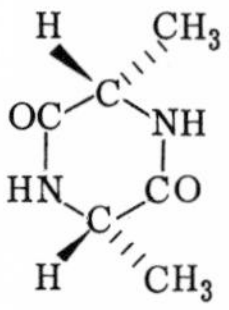

B

(10.3)

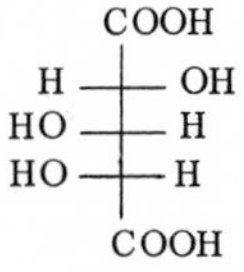

COOH
H——OH
HO——H
HO——H
COOH

A

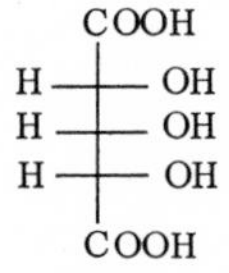

COOH
H——OH
H——OH
H——OH
COOH

B

COOH
H——OH
HO——H
H——OH
COOH

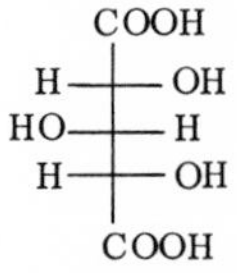

C

(10.4)

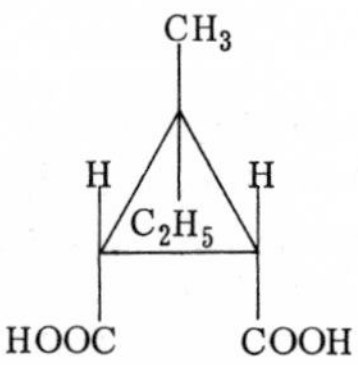

A 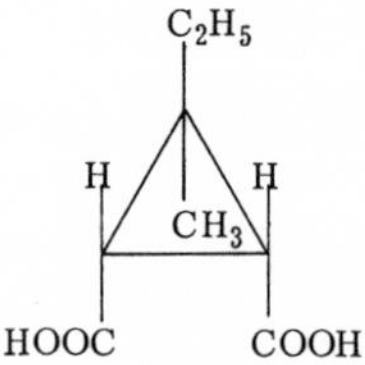   B 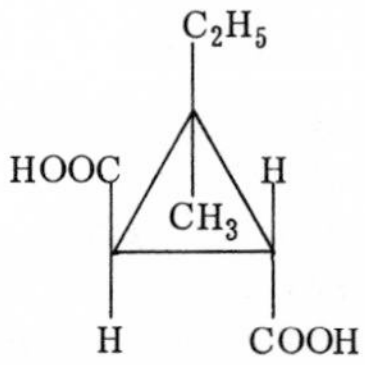   C

ANSWER 10.   [Eliel, Chaps. 2, 3; K. Mislow, *Introduction to Stereochemistry,* Benjamin, New York, 1965.]

The fundamental condition for a compound to be resolved into optically active forms is that it not be identical with its mirror image, or, more commonly, not be convertible into its mirror image by any process which is energetically possible under the conditions of observations. The job of determining this convertibility is often, but not always, simplified by noting whether any possible (even if improbable) conformation exists which possesses a center of symmetry or a mirror plane. If it does, the conformation is identical to its mirror image, and no optical activity will be found. If the conformation is of relatively high energy, it may be possible to resolve the compound, but a slow racemization may then occur as individual molecules achieve the symmetric form.

(10.1)

A   A'   B   B'

A is not identical with its mirror image A' and cannot be converted to it. B is identical to B' (rotate one in the plane of the paper) and also has a mirror plane within it.

(10.2)

A   A'   B   B'

A has a center of symmetry (indicated by the dot) and can be shown to be identical to the mirror image A' by being rotated about a horizontal axis in the plane of the paper. Because of the cis arrangement of the methyls, B has no center of symmetry and cannot be converted by any rotation (or by chair-chair inversion) into B'.

(10.3)   As in the case of 1B, B and C have mirror planes and are optically inactive. In these cases the planes pass through the central carbon in the chain; so it is only pseudoasymmetric. A contains no plane and is optically active.

(10.4)   This is similar to the preceding problem. A and B have mirror planes, C does not.

PROBLEM 11.   How many stereoisomers are possible for each of the following compounds, and which are optically active?

(cont.)

(11.1)

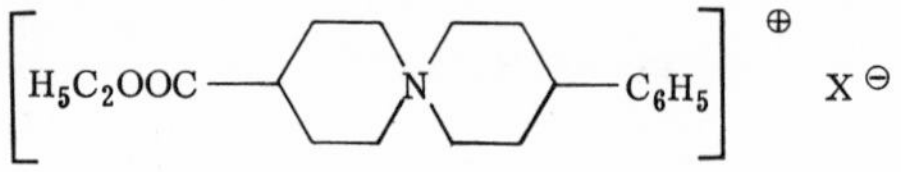

$$\left[H_5C_2OOC - \underset{N}{\bigcirc\bigcirc} - C_6H_5 \right]^{\oplus} \quad X^{\ominus}$$

(11.2)

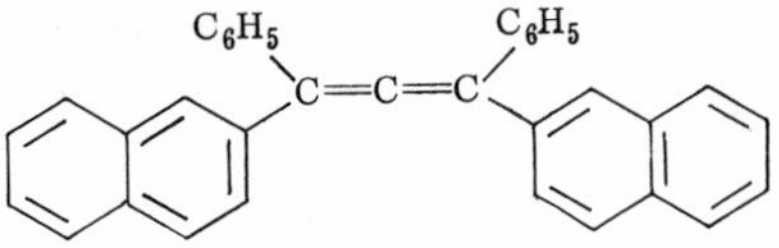

(11.3)

$$\left[\begin{array}{c} CH_3 \qquad CH_3 \\ \underset{N}{\bigcirc\bigcirc} \\ CH_3 \qquad CH_3 \end{array} \right]^{\oplus} \quad TsO^{\ominus}$$

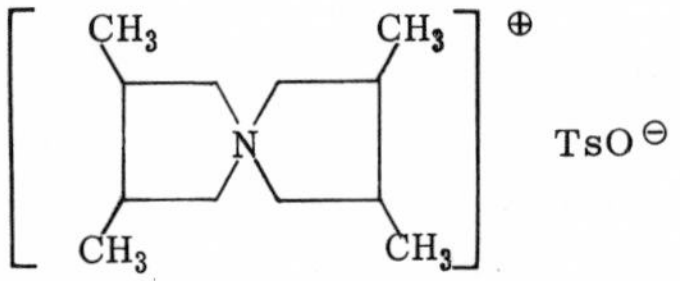

ANSWER 11.   [Eliel, Chap. 11.]

(11.1)   There are just two isomers, A and A', which constitute a dl pair. The alternatives, with the phenyl group down, can be obtained simply by flipping the first two over.

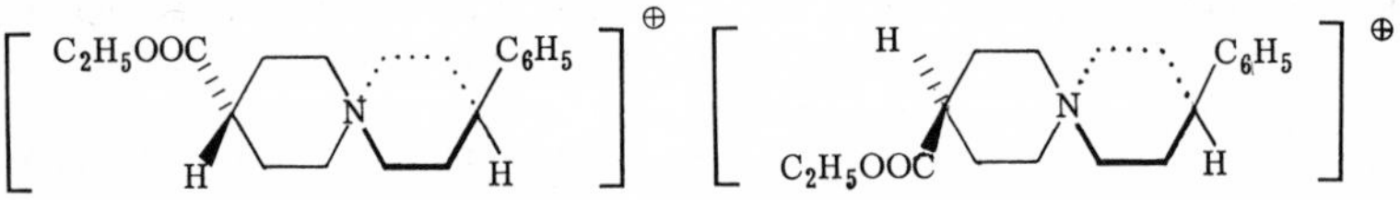

A   A'

(11.2)   This is actually the same as part (1), because allenes consist of two double-bond systems with their π-bonds and terminal bonds at right angles. Thus

A   A'

This system will have one dl pair if a ≠ b.

(11.3)   [G. E. McCasland and S. Proskow, J. Am. Chem. Soc., 78, 5646 (1956).]
The general structure of this compound is

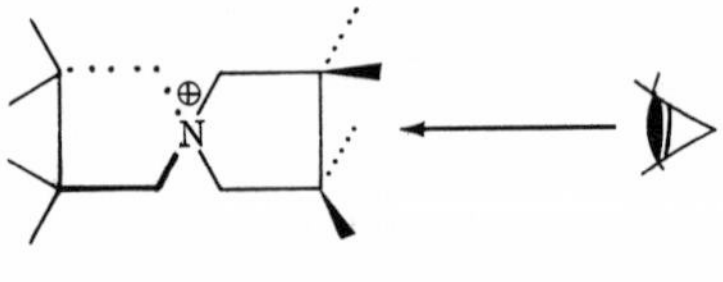

and the various isomers may be represented as though viewed from one end down the central axis of the molecule. The possible isomers may be deduced and classified by considering the various combinations of cis and trans methyl substitutions in the two rings, or by writing out all 16 possible combinations and determining which are the same. There are three dl pairs (**1** − **3**) and one meso form (**4**):

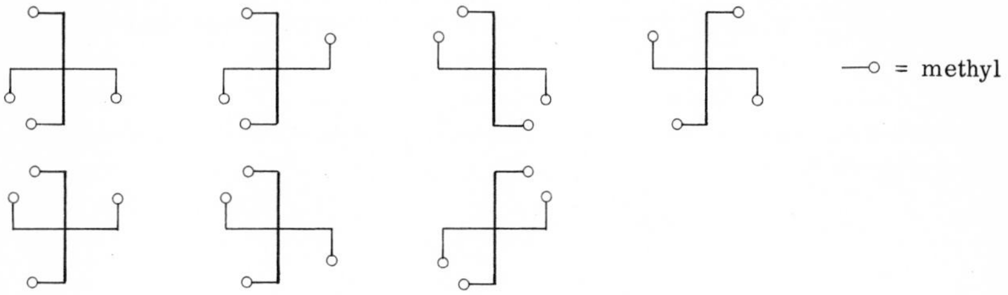

—○ = methyl

(dl) cis–cis	(dl) cis–trans	(dl) trans–trans	(meso) trans–trans
1	**2**	**3**	**4**

The meso form (**4**) is of particular interest because it contains an uncommon symmetry element, a fourfold rotary inversion axis, which, like a center or a mirror, renders a structure identical to its mirror image.

PROBLEM 12.   Which of the following compounds can be resolved into optically active forms?

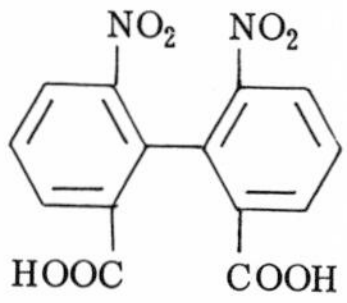

(12.1) 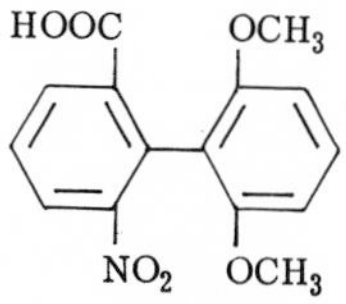   (12.2) 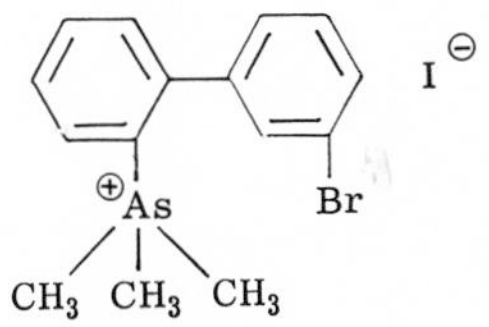   (12.3) 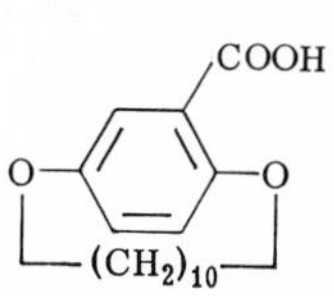   (12.4)

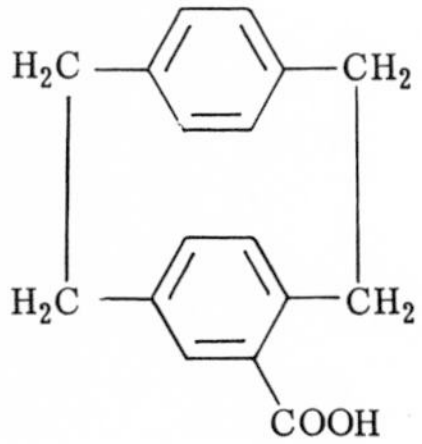

(12.5) 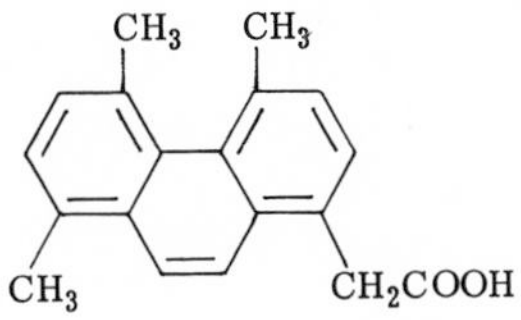   (12.6) 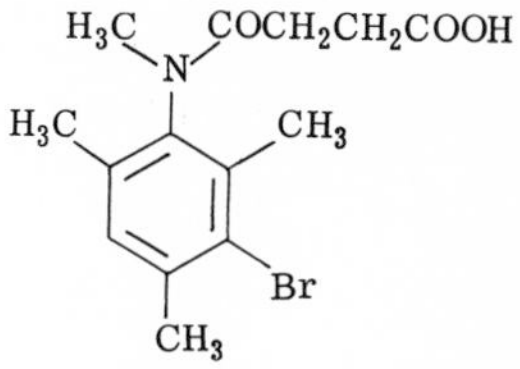   (12.7)

ANSWER 12.   [Eliel, pp. 156–179.]

None of these compounds contains an asymmetric carbon atom, so any possible optical activity must arise from an over-all molecular asymmetry which produces nonsuperimposable mirror images.

(12.1)   [See R. Adams and H. C. Yuan, *Chem. Rev.*, **12**, 261 (1933).]

Biphenyls which contain bulky substituents in the 2,2′,6,6′-positions are prevented from assuming a planar, symmetric configuration. Instead, the rings are approximately at right angles and two optical isomers are possible (see allenes, Problem 11). Spontaneous racemization occurs in some cases if the sizes of the substituents are such that there can be a slow equilibration past the rotation barrier.

(12.2)   This would appear to be the same as (1), since free rotation is also restricted here; but since the two substituents in one ring are identical, the compound has a mirror plane and is inactive.

(12.3)   [M. S. Lesslie and E. E. Turner, *J. Chem. Soc.*, **1933**, 1588.]

The trimethylarsonium group is so large as to provide a significant barrier to rotation even when it has only hydrogen to pass. Consequently this compound can be resolved, although it racemizes rapidly in solution.

(12.4)   [A. Lüttringhaus and H. Gralheer, *Ann.*, **557**, 112 (1945); A Lüttringhaus and G. Eyring, *Ann.*, **604**, 111 (1957).]

In this case the question is whether optical isomers will arise because of the inability of one side of the benzene ring to rotate through the polymethylene bridge.

If n = 10, rotation is free and the compound cannot be resolved; if n = 9, it may be resolved but racemizes on heating; and if n = 8, no racemization can be found.

(12.5)   [D. J. Cram and N. L. Allinger, *J. Am. Chem. Soc.,* **77**, 6289 (1955).]
Resolvable. The close approach of the two benzene rings makes rotation from one form to the other impossible.

(12.6)   [M. S. Newman and A. S. Hussey, *J. Am. Chem. Soc.,* **69**, 3023 (1947).]
The two methyl groups in the 4 and 5 positions overlap and are forced out of the plane of the ring system. This results in the two mirror-image forms A and A′. Resolution is possible, but the compound racemizes fairly easily.

A   A′

(12.7)   [R. Adams and L. J. Dankert, *J. Am. Chem. Soc.,* **62**, 2191 (1940).]
Free rotation about the central C—N bond is restricted by steric hindrance between the ortho methyl groups and the substituents on nitrogen; the compound is resolvable. Bromination of **1** gave **2**, which was optically inactive because it is symmetric with respect to rotation about the C—N bond. If the optical activity had been due to an asymmetric nitrogen atom, it would not have been affected.

1   2

PROBLEM 13.   Arrange the following compounds in order of increasing enol content:

(a)   Acetone

(b)   Ethyl acetoacetate

(cont.)

(c) Diethyl malonate

(d) Acetylacetone

(e) Cyclopentanone

(f) Biacetyl

(g) Cyclopentane-1,2-dione

ANSWER 13.   [Gould, pp. 376-380; G. S. Hammond in *Steric Effects in Organic Chemistry* (M. S. Newman, ed.), Wiley, New York, 1956, pp. 444-454; G. W. Wheland, *Advanced Organic Chemistry*, 3rd ed., Wiley, New York, 1960, pp. 681-702.]

(a) $(2.5 \times 10^{-4}\%$ enol$) <$ (e) $(4.8 \times 10^{-3}\%) \sim$ (f) $(5.6 \times 10^{-3}\%) <$ (c) $(0.1\%) <$ (b) $(7.5\%) <$ (d) $(80\%) <$ (g) (100%)

The enol content of compounds containing isolated carbonyl groups (e.g., acetone) is very low. Placing the group in a five- or six-membered ring increases the extent of enolization markedly (see cyclohexanone, $2 \times 10^{-2}\%$ enol), but the actual content is still small. The origin of the effect is complex, but presumably reflects a decrease in H—H repulsions brought about by introducing a second trigonal carbon into the ring (cf. the relative stabilities of endo- and exocyclic olefins).[1]

Acyclic α-diketones such as biacetyl (f) normally assume a transoid arrangement and show relatively little tendency to enolize. In rings, however, the dipoles of the two carbonyl groups are constrained to lie more or less parallel and coplanar. The repulsion between the like charges destabilizes the keto form and increases the enolization greatly.

β-Dicarbonyl compounds are the most common source of enols. Roughly, the extent of enolization increases as the carbonyl groups involved go from

$$\underset{\text{RCOR}'}{\overset{\overset{\displaystyle O}{||}}{}} \rightarrow \underset{\text{RCR}'}{\overset{\overset{\displaystyle O}{||}}{}} \rightarrow \underset{\text{RCH}}{\overset{\overset{\displaystyle O}{||}}{}}$$

----

[1] R. B. Turner and R. H. Garner, *J. Am. Chem. Soc.*, **80**, 1424 (1958).

Thus

$$
\underset{(c)}{CH_2 \overset{COOEt}{\underset{COOEt}{<}}}
\quad < \quad
\underset{(b)}{CH_2 \overset{COOEt}{\underset{COCH_3}{<}}}
\quad < \quad
\underset{(d)}{CH_2 \overset{COCH_3}{\underset{COCH_3}{}}}
$$

CHAPTER **2**

SPECTRAL PROBLEMS

The problems in this chapter deal with various physical methods for study-ing the nature and structure of organic molecules. There are a great number of references available on most of these topics, and those given below represent only a partial selection.

General surveys of spectral methods:
1. R. M. Silverstein and G. C. Bassler, *Spectrometric Identification of Organic Compounds*, 2nd ed., Wiley, New York, 1967. Covers MS, IR, NMR, and UV. Contains some discussion together with worked-out examples and problems based on reproduced spectra.
2. J. C. P. Schwarz, *Physical Methods in Organic Chemistry*, Holden-Day, San Francisco, 1965. Covers UV, IR, NMR, ORD, MS, and other physical methods. A good introduction to a wide range of techniques.
3. John R. Dyer, *Applications of Absorption Spectroscopy of Organic Compounds*, Prentice-Hall, Englewood Cliffs, N.J., 1965. Covers mainly IR and NMR with a little on UV. Very good introduction, with some problems involving actual spectra. Inexpensive paperback volume.
4. D. W. Mathieson, *Interpretation of Organic Spectra*, Academic Press, New York, 1965. Covers NMR, IR, and MS. Resembles Silverstein and Bassler in using actual examples as a basis for discussion. Contains a somewhat more complete coverage of NMR, and some problems, but does not use all methods simultaneously for studying a single compound.

Ultraviolet and visible spectroscopy (UV):
1. A. I. Scott, *Interpretation of the Ultraviolet Spectra of Natural Products*,

Macmillan, New York, 1964. The best and most extensive discussion of the
interpretation of UV spectra of complex systems.
2. H. H. Jaffe and M. Orchin, *Theory and Applications of Ultraviolet Spectroscopy*, Wiley, New York, 1962. A very clear exposition of the theoretical
bases for electronic spectra and their application to various systems.

Infrared spectroscopy (IR):
1. K. Nakanishi, *Infrared Absorption Spectroscopy*, Holden-Day, San Francisco,
1962. Extensive tables of group frequencies. A large number of problems
based on actual spectra. More readable than Bellamy but has fewer references.
2. L. J. Bellamy, *The Infra-Red Spectra of Complex Molecules*, 2nd ed., Wiley,
New York, 1958. Undoubtedly the standard reference for discussions of group
correlations of all kinds.
3. R. N. Jones and C. Sandorfy in *Chemical Applications of Spectroscopy*, Vol. IX
of *Technique of Organic Chemistry* (A. Weissberger, ed.), Wiley-Interscience,
New York, 1956, pp. 247–580. Particularly good on C—H and C=O absorp-
tions. More detailed than Nakanishi but easier to read than Bellamy.

Nuclear magnetic resonance (NMR):
1. L. M. Jackman, *Applications of Nuclear Magnetic Resonance Spectroscopy in
Organic Chemistry*, Pergamon, London, 1959. A brief but thorough introduction to the method and its uses.
2. N. S. Bhacca and D. H. Williams, *Applications of NMR Spectroscopy in Organic Chemistry*, Holden-Day, San Francisco, 1964. Examples of the use of
NMR methods for the solution of structural problems. Although drawn from
the steroid field, much of the information is more generally applicable.
3. J. A. Pople, W. G. Schneider, and H. J. Bernstein, *High-Resolution Nuclear
Magnetic Resonance*, McGraw-Hill, New York, 1959. Somewhat broader in
coverage and more theoretical than the preceding works, this is probably
the fundamental reference in the field.

Optical rotatory dispersion (ORD) and circular dichroism (CD):
1. C. Djerassi, *Optical Rotatory Dispersion*, McGraw-Hill, New York, 1960.
2. P. Crabbé, *Optical Rotatory Dispersion and Circular Dichroism in Organic
Chemistry*, Holden-Day, San Francisco, 1965.

Mass spectrometry (MS):
1. J. H. Beynon, *Mass Spectrometry and Its Application to Organic Chemistry*,
Elsevier, Amsterdam, 1960. An exhaustive study of the techniques in the field
and their application.
2. K. Biemann, *Mass Spectrometry*, McGraw-Hill, New York, 1962. Covers
equipment, technique, and interpretation of fragmentation patterns.
3. H. Budzikiewicz, C. Djerassi, and D. H. Williams, *Interpretation of Mass
Spectra of Organic Compounds*, Holden-Day, San Francisco, 1964. Concerned
only with fragmentation patterns, but of a wider range of compounds.
4. H. Budzikiewicz, C. Djerassi, and D. H. Williams, *Structure Elucidation of
Natural Products by Mass Spectrometry*, Vols. I and II, Holden-Day, San

Francisco, 1964. Extensive discussion of actual mass-spectral findings on many classes of natural products, especially alkaloids.

PROBLEM 14.   Calculate λ_{max}^{EtOH} (UV) for the following compounds:

(a)   (b)   (c)   (d)

(e)   (f)   (g)

ANSWER 14.   [For discussion and tables of substituent contributions see A. I. Scott, *Interpretation of the Ultraviolet Spectra of Natural Products*, Pergamon, London, 1964, Chap. 2.] The UV maxima of simple alicyclic conjugated polyenes and enones can be predicted with surprising accuracy by using a basic system value and additive constants for substituent effects.

(a)   215 ($\alpha\beta$-unsaturated ketone) + 12 (β-ring residue) = 227 mμ
       Found: 225 mμ,[1] 230 mμ[2]
(b)   215 + 12 (β-ring residue) + 10 (α-ring residue) + 5 (double bond exocyclic to cyclohexane) = 242 mμ
       Found: 241, 243 mμ[1]
(c)   215 + 2 × 12 (2 β-groups) + 35 (α − OH) = 274 mμ
       Found: 268 mμ
(d)   253 (homoannular diene) + 4 × 5 (2 ring residues + 2 substituents) = 273 mμ
       Found: 262 mμ
(e)   214 (heteroannular diene) + 4 × 5 (4 substituents and ring residues) + 5 (1 exocyclic double bond) = 239 mμ
       Found: 238 mμ

---

[1] Model compounds with the same chromophore taken from *Constants of Organic Compounds* (M. Kotake, ed.), Asakura Publishing Co., Tokyo, 1963.
[2] Model compounds from A. I. Scott, loc. cit.

(f)   253 (homoannular diene — in center) + 2 × 30 (double bonds extending con-
      jugation) + 5 × 5 (substituents) + 3 × 5 (exocyclic double bonds) = 353 $m\mu$
      Found: 355 $m\mu^2$ (for 3-OAc derivative, contribution of —OAc $\approx$ 0)
(g)   215 + 30 (conjugated double bond) + 2 × 18 (γ,δ-ring residues) + 5 (exo-
      cyclic double bond) = 286 $m\mu$
      Found: 290 $m\mu^2$

PROBLEM 15.   Suggest an explanation for the fact that substituting hetero-
atoms for the —CH_2 —at position X in A causes the UV maximum to shift toward shorter wavelengths.

$\lambda \begin{smallmatrix}95\% \text{ EtOH}\\ \max\end{smallmatrix}$

(1)   X = —CH_2—   238 $m\mu$

(2) $>$N—CH_3 232.5 $m\mu$

A

(3) $>\overset{\oplus}{N}\overset{CH_3}{\underset{CH_3}{}}$ $ClO_4^{\ominus}$ 229 $m\mu$

ANSWER 15.   [E. M. Kosower and D. C. Remy, *Tetrahedron,* **5**, 281 (1959).]
      The transition being observed is the $\pi \rightarrow \pi^*$ excitation of the $\alpha\beta$-unsatu-
rated ketone system.[1] This may be represented very roughly as A $\rightarrow$ B, at least
to the extent that there is greater charge separation in the excited state than in
the ground state.

A $\xrightarrow{h\nu}$ B

It has been suggested that this dipolar contribution to the excited state is decreased by the presence of a close positive charge as in **3**, that the energy of
the excited state is thereby increased, and that the excitation wavelength is
consequently shortened. The case of **2** is less clear, but may reflect a similar
interaction involving the dipole of the $R_3\overset{++}{N}$: group, the positive end of which is
closer to the charged bridgehead of B than the negative.

---

[1] H. H. Jaffe and M. Orchin, *Theory and Applications of Ultraviolet Spectroscopy,*
Wiley, New York, 1962, Chap. 10.

PROBLEM 16.   Normally, Δ^4-3-ketosteroids show a high-intensity UV maximum at 240 to 242 mμ. Table 2-1 shows the shifts produced in the position of
this maximum by introducing substituents at position 6. Suggest an explanation
for these observations.

Table 2-1

X	α-substituent, mμ	β-substituent, mμ
$-F$	-4 to -5	-5 to -8
$-Cl$	-4 to -5	0 to -1
$-Br$	-3 to -4	$+6$ to $+8$
$-I$	——	$+11$ to $+13$

ANSWER 16.   [H. J. Ringold and A. Bowers, *Experientia*, **17**, 65 (1961).]
    The high-intensity band of $\alpha\beta$-unsaturated ketones is a $\pi \rightarrow \pi^*$ (V ← N)
transition[1] which may be represented roughly as

A

The energy required for this excitation will be affected by the introduction of electron-donating or electron-withdrawing groups which can interact with the strong
dipole of A.
    The first effect which might be expected from halogen substitution on 6 is an
inductive one: The electronegative substituent would produce a partial positive
charge on C-6 and destabilize A. As a result there would be a shift to shorter
wavelengths (hypsochromic).

[1]A. I. Scott, *Interpretation of the Ultraviolet Spectra of Natural Products*, Macmillan,
New York, 1964, Chap. 2.

This effect appears to be operative for fluorine, both 6α and 6β, and for chlorine and bromine as 6α substituents. It is clear, though, that some other interaction is taking over for Cl, Br, and I in the 6β orientation, since the shifts are increasingly to longer wavelengths (bathochromic).

It is suggested that in these cases the halogen can stabilize the positive dipole by direct electron donation. This may occur by the formation of a bridged

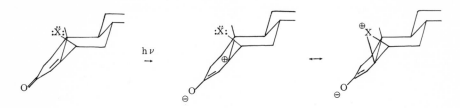

intermediate similar to those proposed for halogenation of alkenes[2] (but note that according to the Franck-Condon principle[3] the halogen cannot move from its normal position during the excitation; so the geometry is likely to be quite different). Regardless of the exact mechanism, the importance of the effect increases, as would be expected, with the size of the halogen, its polarizability, and its ability to accept a positive charge.

The difference between the β and α orientations arises from the geometry of the system. In the former it is possible to get overlap between the halogen and the π system, but in the latter it is not (cf. the preferential axial addition of halogens in cyclic systems).

Similar distinctions between axial and equatorial halogen substitution can be seen in the n → π^* transitions of both saturated and unsaturated ketones.[4]

PROBLEM 17.   Suggest an explanation for the fact that the cis compound shown below dissolves in strong acids to give a deep yellow solution ($\lambda_{max}^{60\% H_2 SO_4}$ 386, 427 mμ), whereas the trans fused isomer shows no strong absorption beyond 300 mμ in 60% $H_2 SO_4$.

[2] Gould, pp. 520–527.
[3] See H. H. Jaffe and M. Orchin, *Theory and Applications of Ultraviolet Spectroscopy,* Wiley, New York, 1962, pp. 134–144.
[4] See A. I. Scott, op. cit., pp. 35, 73–74.

ANSWER 17.   [G. Leal and R. Pettit, *J. Am. Chem. Soc.*, **81**, 3160 (1959).]
    On being dissolved in strong acids, the cis compound forms a nonclassical carbonium ion (A), which exhibits its characteristic UV absorption spectrum. For the trans compound, formation of such a nonclassical ion is impossible. Since the distribution of charge produced by the nonclassical interaction is a stabilizing effect, the cis ion forms under conditions too mild to produce the trans ion.

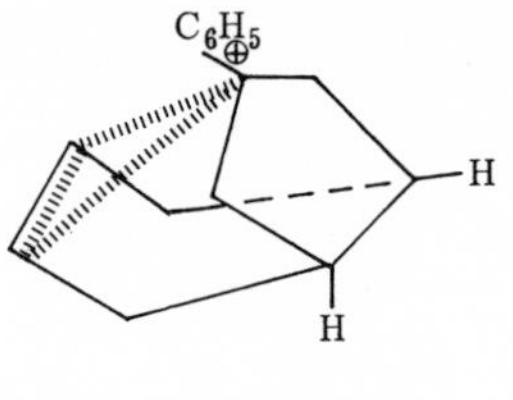

A

PROBLEM 18.   How can infrared spectroscopy be used to distinguish between the structures shown in each of the following pairs?

(18.1)

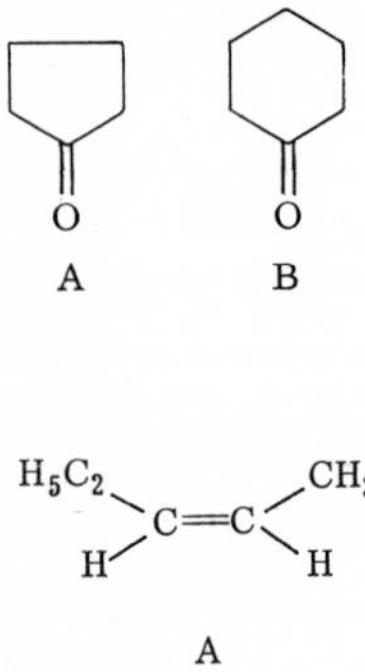

A   B

(18.2)

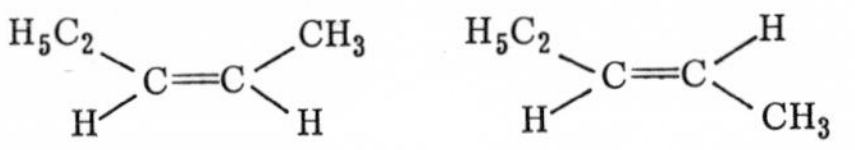

A   B

(18.3)

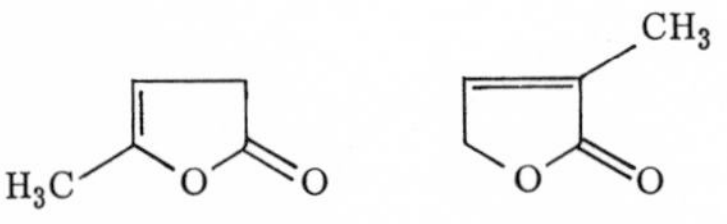

A   B

(18.4)

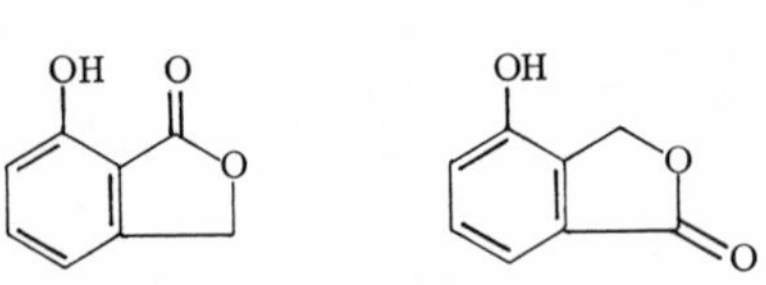

A   B

(18.5)

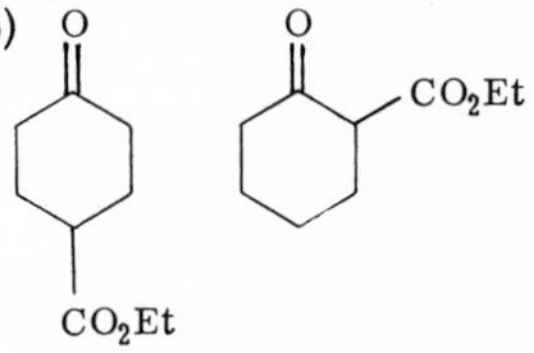

A   B

(18.6)

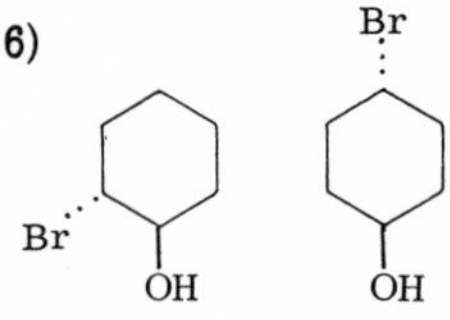

A   B

(18.7)

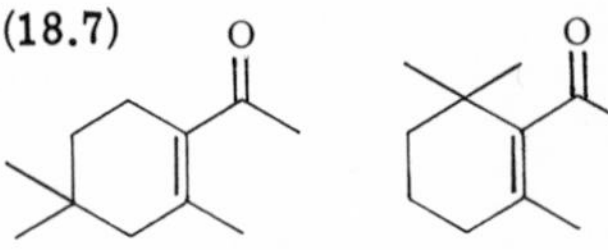

A   B

ANSWER 18.

(18.1)   [Nakanishi, p. 42; Bellamy pp. 147–149.]
Cyclopentanones absorb at a higher frequency than do cyclohexanones.

$$\nu_{C=O}: \text{ (A) 1745 cm}^{-1}; \text{ (B) 1715 cm}^{-1}$$

(18.2)   [Nakanishi, pp. 24–25; Bellamy, pp. 45–49.]
There are fairly characteristic C—H bending bands for cis and trans disubstituted alkenes.

	$\nu_{C=C}$	$\delta_{=C-H}$ (in-plane bending)	$\delta_{=C-H}$ (out-of-plane bending)
(A)	1660 (M)	1415 (W)	730–675 (M)
(B)	1675 (W)		965 (S)

(S = strong, M = medium, W = weak).

The $>\!C\!=\!C\!<$ stretching band is usually weaker in trans olefins than in cis isomers, but its intensity depends more fundamentally on symmetry of the double-bond substitution; i.e., the greater the approach to symmetry, the weaker the band. Thus

$$H_2C\!=\!CH_2 \quad \text{no IR absorption for } \nu_{C=C};$$

$$CH_2\!=\!CH\!-\!OCH_3 \quad \text{very strong absorption}$$

(18.3)   [Bellamy, pp. 186–187; R. N. Jones, C. L. Angell, T. Ito, and R. J. D. Smith, *Can. J. Chem.*, **37**, 2007 (1959).]
The $\nu_{C=O}$ for a saturated γ-lactone is 1770 cm^{-1}. If an $\alpha\beta$-double bond is present (B), there is electron release to the carbonyl group, increasing its single-bond character, and the frequency decreases to ca. 1750 cm^{-1}.

1770 cm^{-1}

1780–1800 cm^{-1}

1750–1760 cm^{-1}

On the other hand, esters of enols and phenols (e.g., the $\beta\gamma$-unsaturated lactone A) have $\nu_{C=O}$ shifted to higher frequency because the interaction of the unshared electrons on the ester oxygen with the double bond reduces their interaction with the carbonyl group.

The intensity of the double-bond stretching band ($\nu_{C=C}$) in A is likely to be greater than that of B.

In practice an extra, intense band is often found in $\alpha\beta$-unsaturated γ-lactones at ca. 1785 cm^{-1}.

(18.4)   [L. A. Duncanson, J. F. Grove, and J. Zealley, *J. Chem. Soc.*, **1953**, 1331.]
The effect of hydrogen bonding to the carbonyl oxygen in A is to shift the absorption to lower frequency by increasing the importance of the charge-separated resonance form. Thus

$$\nu_{C=O}^{CHCl_3}: \text{ (A) 1738 cm}^{-1}; \text{ (B) 1760 cm}^{-1}$$

(18.5)   [Bellamy, pp. 184–185; N. J. Leonard, H. S. Gutowsky, W. J. Middleton, and E. M. Petersen, *J. Am. Chem. Soc.*, **74**, 4070 (1952).]
Whereas A exists as the normal ketoester and shows bands at 1736 (ester) and 1718 (ketone) cm^{-1}, B is a mixture of ketoester (1744, 1718 cm^{-1}) and enol ester C; so four bands can be seen.

C

(18.6)   [See A. Nickon, *J. Am. Chem. Soc.*, **79**, 243 (1957).]
In A a weak hydrogen bond is possible between the Br and the OH. This causes a small shift to lower frequency for ν_{O-H} and to a higher one for ν_{C-O}.

	ν_{O-H}	ν_{C-O}	
(A)	3586	1078 cm^{-1}	
(B)	3615	1051	(cyclohexanol model)

(18.7)   [See H. B. Henbest and G. Woods, *J. Chem. Soc.*, **1952**, 1150; E. A. Braude and C. J. Temmons, *J. Chem. Soc.*, **1955**, 3766.]
In B the steric interaction between the methyl ketone and the ring methyl

substituents tends to rotate it out of the plane of the double bond. This reduces the conjugation and shifts $\nu_{C=O}$ to higher frequencies.

$$\nu_{C=O}$$

(A)   1686 cm^{-1} (model compound)
(B)   1693 cm^{-1}

PROBLEM 19.   Explain for each of the following pairs of isomers why the positions of the carbonyl stretching bands are different.

(19.1)

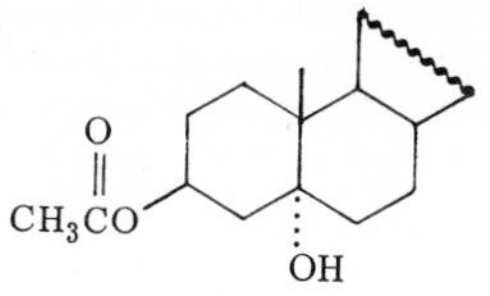

A   1731 cm^{-1} 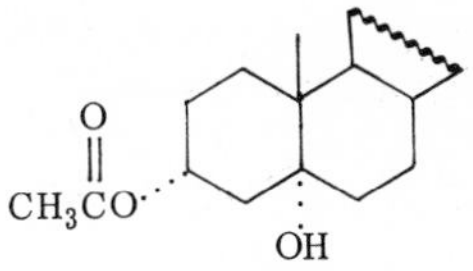   B   1744 cm^{-1}

(19.2)

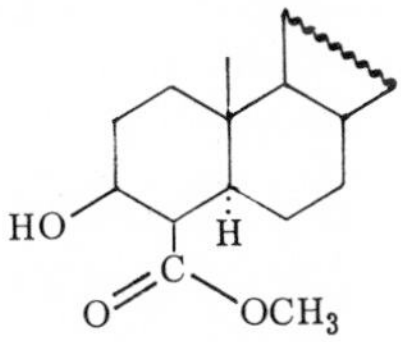

A   1709 cm^{-1} 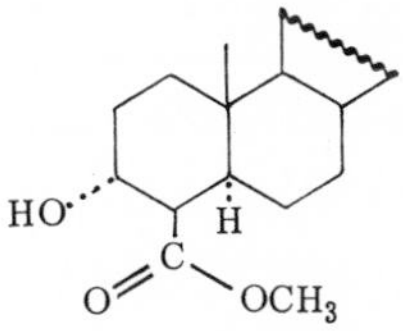   B   1723 cm^{-1}

(19.3)

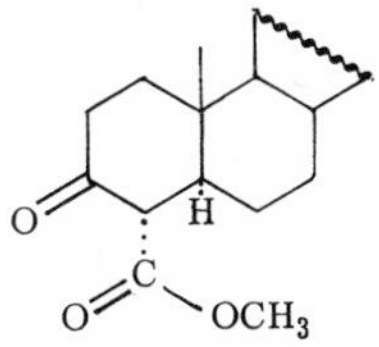

A 1733 cm^{-1}
   1718 cm^{-1} 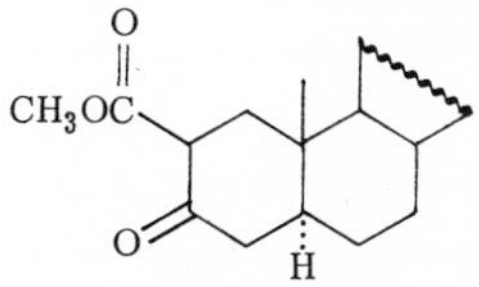   B 1658 cm^{-1}

ANSWER 19.   The position of the carbonyl stretching band of an ester reflects the amount of double-bond character in the C=O group. This result from the balance among the three contributing resonance forms **1**, **2**, and **3**.

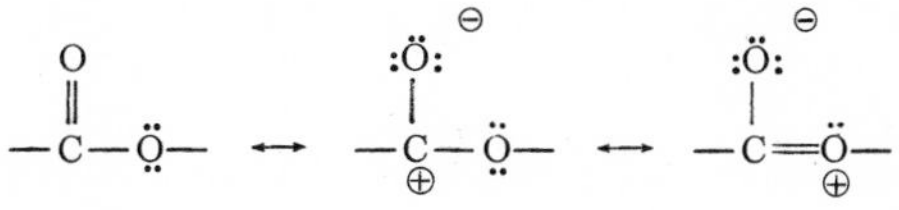

     1   2   3

Of these, **2** is relatively less favored because of the inductive electron-withdraw-ing effect of the ester oxygen. Groups which can contribute electrons by resonance increase the stability of **2**, however, when they are attached to the carbonyl group. Hydrogen bonding to the carbonyl oxygen stabilizes its negative charge in **2** and **3** and favors these forms. Hydrogen bonding to the ester oxygen or the possibility of the involvement of its electrons in another resonance system (e.g., enol esters), on the other hand, reduces the contribution of **3** to the ester resonance.

The greater the contributions of **2** and **3** to the ester, the greater the single-bond character of the carbonyl group and the lower its stretching frequency. Con-versely, substitutions which disfavor **2** and **3** raise the stretching frequency.

(19.1)   [H. B. Henbest and B. J. Lovell, *J. Chem. Soc.*, **1957**, 1965.]
Compound A shows an approximately normal carbonyl band at 1731 cm^{-1}; B, however, exists in the hydrogen-bonded form

This diminishes the contribution of resonance form **3** by tying up the electrons which would be shared with the carbonyl, and results in a shift to higher fre-quencies.

(19.2)   [A. R. H. Cole and G. T. A. Muller, *J. Chem. Soc.*, **1959**, 1224.]
This case also shows the effect of hydrogen bonding, but acting on the car-bonyl rather than the ester oxygen.

A   B

Hydrogen bonding to the carbonyl, favoring forms **2** and **3** and thus lowering the $>C=O$ frequency, can occur in A, but is impossible in B because of the trans-diaxial arrangement.

(19.3)   [E. Wenkert and B. G. Jackson, *J. Am. Chem. Soc.*, **81**, 5601 (1959).]
The difference between these two compounds arises because they actually exist as different tautomeric forms, A as the β-keto ester and B as the enol.

The ester band in B is shifted very strongly to lower frequencies by the combination of conjugation and hydrogen bonding. The ketone band is, of course, lost.

It is suggested that the enol form of A, which would normally be expected, does not occur because it is destabilized by the steric hindrance which would arise between the 6 α-H (equatorial) and the methoxyl group (A′).

PROBLEM 20.   Deduce structures for the acyloin condensation products A_1 through A_4 (see Table 2-2).

Table 2-2

| Compound | R | IR (cm^{-1}) | | pK$_a'$ | |
		CCl$_4$	perchlorate salt in Nujol	66% DMF	H$_2$O
A_1	$-CH_3$	1661, 3410	3440	10.6	9.2
A_2	$-C_2H_5$	1671, 3428	3425	10.2	9.2
A_3	$-CH(CH_3)_2$	1691, 3465	3435	6.9	8.1
A_4	$-C(CH_3)_3$	1698, 3480	1706, 3335	6.4	7.6

ANSWER 20.   [N. J. Leonard and M. Oki, *J. Am. Chem. Soc.*, **76**, 3463 (1954).]
The general structure of the products A is

A   B

Compounds of this type have been found to show transannular interaction, as indicated in B, between the unshared electrons on nitrogen and the CO group.[1]

It was expected that increasing the size of the R group would cause unfavorable steric interactions between R and the groups across the ring ("F strain"[2]), reducing the N···CO interaction.

The increasing CO frequency as R goes Me— → t-Bu— is in agreement with increasing double-bond character of the carbonyl, i.e., decreasing importance of transannular electron donation. Later work shows that the two bands corresponding to the A and B types of molecules can be resolved, and the proportion of B decreases with increasing size of R.[3]

In contrast to the mere transannular interaction of the neutral compounds, the solid perchlorates of A_1, A_2, and A_3 show no carbonyl absorption at all and must have the bicyclic structure C. On the other hand, $A_4 \cdot HClO_4$ has a CO band and corresponds to D, at least in part.

C   D

The decrease in pK_a on going from an organic solvent (66% DMF) to water is characteristic of proton loss from —OH (enols, carboxylic acids),[4] whereas an

increase is observed for proton loss from —$\overset{\oplus}{N}$H.[5] Thus it appears that in *solution* the perchlorates of A_1 and A_2 exist as C, whereas those of A_3 and A_4 occur as D. This has been confirmed by the observation that in D_2O, the salts of A_3 and A_4 show carbonyl bands, whereas those of A_1 and A_2 do not.[3]

---

[1] For a review, see N. J. Leonard, *Rec. Chem. Progr.*, **17**, 243 (1956).
[2] H. C. Brown, H. Bartholomay, Jr., and M. D. Taylor, *J. Am. Chem. Soc.*, **66**, 435 (1944).
[3] N. J. Leonard, M. Oki, J. Brader, and H. Boaz, *J. Am. Chem. Soc.*, **77**, 6237 (1955).
[4] L. Michaelis and M. Mitzutani, *Z. Physik. Chem.* (Leipzig), **116**, 135 (1925); J. C. Speakman, *J. Chem. Soc.*, **1943**, 270.
[5] M. Mitzutani, *Z. Physik. Chem.* (Leipzig), **116**, 350 (1925).

PROBLEM 21.

(21.1) Deduce structures for the following products:

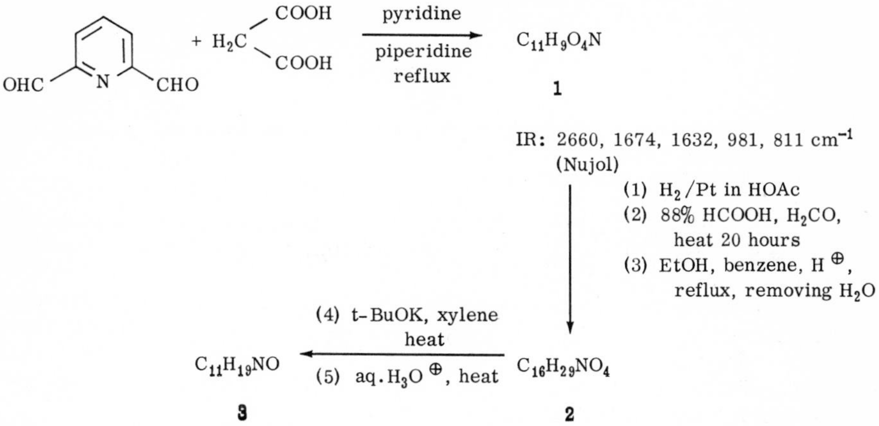

OHC
N
CHO
+ H_2C
COOH
COOH
pyridine
piperidine
reflux
$C_{11}H_9O_4N$
1
IR: 2660, 1674, 1632, 981, 811 cm^{-1}
(Nujol)
(1) H_2/Pt in HOAc
(2) 88% HCOOH, H_2CO, heat 20 hours
(3) EtOH, benzene, $H^{\oplus}$, reflux, removing H_2O
(4) t-BuOK, xylene heat
(5) aq. $H_3O^{\oplus}$, heat
$C_{16}H_{29}NO_4$
2
$C_{11}H_{19}NO$
3

IR: 1664 cm^{-1} (CCl_4)
UV: 221 mμ (6000)

(21.2) Deduce the conformation of **3** with reference to the following dipole moments:

3	4.87 D
cyclohexanone	3.07
1-methylpiperidine	0.8
1-ethyl-4-piperidone	2.95

ANSWER 21. [N. J. Leonard, D. F. Morrow, and M. T. Rogers, *J. Am. Chem. Soc.*, **79**, 5476 (1957).]

(21.1)

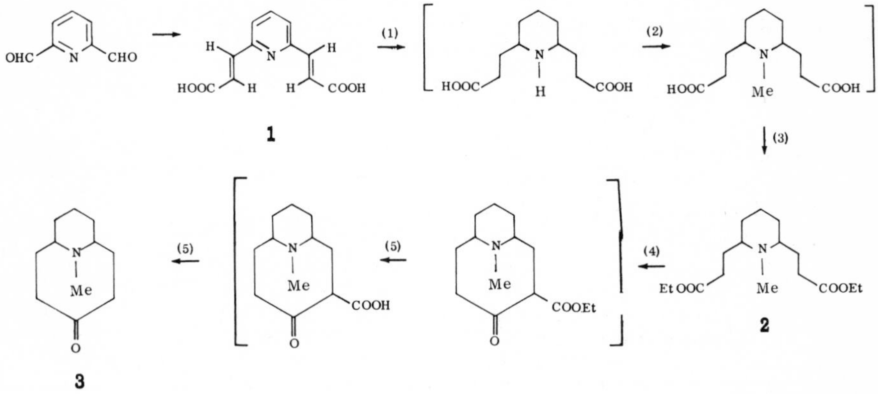

OHC
N
CHO
H
H
HOOC
COOH
1
(1)
(2)
HOOC
N
H
COOH
HOOC
Me
COOH
(3)
(4)
EtOOC
COOEt
2
(5)
COOH
COOEt
O
Me
3

1   IR: 2660, 1674: $\alpha\beta$-unsaturated acid, —OH, and $-\overset{\overset{\displaystyle O}{\|}}{C}-$ [1a]

1632: $-C=C-$ [1b]

981: $\overset{H}{\underset{}{\diagdown}}C=C\overset{\diagup}{\underset{\diagdown H}{}}$ trans-alkene, CH out-of-plane bending[1b]

811: 3 adjacent hydrogens on an aromatic ring[1c]

1 → 2   reaction (2) above is the Leuckart methylation[2]

3   The extremely low frequency of the carbonyl band is attributed to transannular interaction of the carbonyl group with the lone-pair electrons of the nitrogen. The UV absorption, which is surprising for a saturated compound, apparently arises from the same source.[3]

(21.2)   The dipole moments of cyclohexanone and 1-methylpiperidine are considered to be oriented as shown.

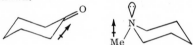

The simplest approximation for 1-ethyl-4-piperidone is

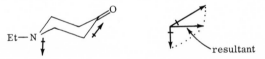

which leads to the suggestion that the resultant moment should be less than that of cyclohexanone (calculated for chair form 2.7 D).

The moment for **3**, however, is greater than the maximum of 3.9 D that would be permitted if the two dipoles were completely aligned but independent, i.e., were additive. This can occur only if there is an interaction which causes a greater separation of charge than is present in the separate dipoles alone. Thus the preferred conformation is

Me   Me
| |
N   ⊕N
                        O   O⊖

⟷

A   B

[1] Nakanishi (a) p. 43, (b) p. 24, (c) p. 27.
[2] M. L. Moore, *Organic Reactions*, Vol. 5, Wiley, New York, 1949, p. 301.
[3] N. J. Leonard and M. Oki, *J. Am. Chem. Soc.*, **77**, 6239 (1955).

in accord with the IR spectrum. The dipole moment of **3** has been taken as implying ca. 10% charge separation, but it is difficult to interpret this in terms of the contribution of B to the resonance hybrid.

PROBLEM 22.   Deduce structures for the following products:

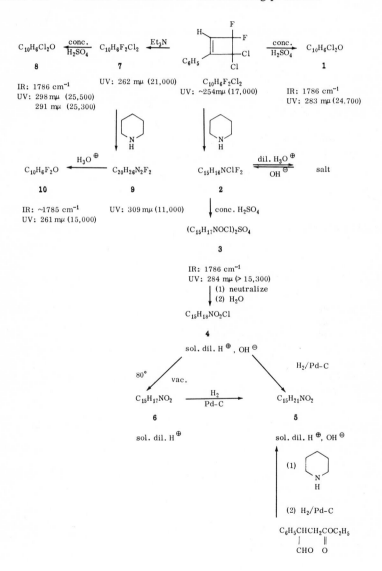

ANSWER 22.   [E. F. Jenny and J. Druey, *J. Am. Chem. Soc.*, **82**, 311 (1960).]

The extremely high frequency of the $\diagdown$C=O stretch[1] in **1** suggests that it is a cyclobutanone. The reaction A → **1** is characteristic of gem-difluorides in this series.

Reaction A → **2** is an S_N2' displacement[2] leading to a product containing a stable vinyl halide. Other possible structures such as

---

[1] Nakanishi, p. 42.

[2] (a) M. C. Caserio, H. E. Simmons, Jr., A. E. Johnson, and J. D. Roberts, *J. Am. Chem. Soc.*, **82**, 3102 (1960), (b) Y. Kitahara, M. C. Caserio, F. Scardiglia, and J. D. Roberts, *J. Am. Chem. Soc.*, **82**, 3106 (1960).

may be eliminated, the first because it would be expected to have an extremely reactive chlorine, and the second because the interaction of the nitrogen lone-pair electrons with the styrene system should shift the UV maximum markedly to the red[3] (see 9).

The ring opening **3** → **4** has been suggested to go through the ketene which is isomeric with the neutral form of **3**.

The reduction **6** → **5** presumably depends on the hydrogenolysis of the allyl ester either prior to or simultaneously with the hydrogenation of the double bond.

The reaction A → **7** is an isomerization which has also been observed in similar systems in the presence of halide ions.[2a] It might be suggested to proceed in this case by

The UV spectral changes between A and **7**, and **1** and **8**, reflect the effect of substituting a halogen for a proton on the absorbing system.

---

[3] H. H. Jaffe and M. Orchin, *Theory and Applications of Ultraviolet Spectroscopy*, Wiley, New York, 1962, pp. 175ff.

The conversion **7** → **9** apparently involves two consecutive $S_N 2'$ changes. The structure given is supported by the UV spectrum, which shows the shift expected for a β-aminostyrene [cf. ϕCH=CH—NC_5H_{10}, 305 mμ (14,700)]. The alternative

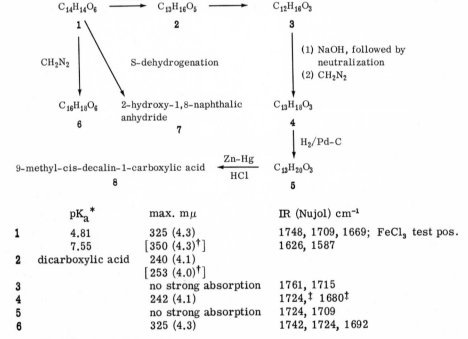

should resemble A in its spectrum.

Note the difference in UV spectra of the cross-conjugated **10** and the linearly conjugated **1** and **3**.

PROBLEM 23.   Deduce structures for the compounds (**1**) to (**6**).

$$C_{14}H_{14}O_6 \xrightarrow{\text{NaOH}} C_{13}H_{16}O_5 \xrightarrow{\text{heat}} C_{12}H_{16}O_3$$

1   2   3

CH$_2$N$_2$ ↓   S-dehydrogenation

3 →
(1) NaOH, followed by
    neutralization
(2) CH$_2$N$_2$

$C_{16}H_{18}O_6$ 2-hydroxy-1,8-naphthalic $C_{13}H_{18}O_3$

6   anhydride   4

7

$\downarrow$ H$_2$/Pd-C

9-methyl-cis-decalin-1-carboxylic acid $\xleftarrow[\text{HCl}]{\text{Zn-Hg}}$ $C_{13}H_{20}O_3$

8   5

	pK$_a$*	max. mμ	IR (Nujol) cm^{-1}
1	4.81	325 (4.3)	1748, 1709, 1669; FeCl$_3$ test pos.
	7.55	[350 (4.3)†]	1626, 1587
2	dicarboxylic acid	240 (4.1)	
		[253 (4.0)†]	
3		no strong absorption	1761, 1715
4		242 (4.1)	1724,‡ 1680‡
5		no strong absorption	1724, 1709
6		325 (4.3)	1742, 1724, 1692

*In 80% methyl Cellosolve.
†In 0.01 N NaOH.
‡In chloroform.

ANSWER 23.   [F. Gautochi, O. Jeger, V. Prelog, and R. B. Woodward, *Helv. Chim. Acta,* **37,** 2280 (1954).]

decevinic acid

The reaction **1** → **7** suggests the skeletal structure of **1,** and merely leaves the location of the methyl and —COOH groups to be found.

Reaction **5** → **8** is obviously the Clemmensen reduction of a carbonyl group.[1] This group may reasonably be equated with the —OH of **7,** thus placing it at 2, 3, 6, or 7. The change in UV between **4** and **5,** as well as the shift in CO frequency (1680 → 1709), indicates that **4** is an $\alpha\beta$-unsaturated ketone.[2a] This unsaturation is generated in **3** → **4** by the β elimination (cf. aldol dehydration in base) of some group.[3] The 1761-cm^{-1} band in **3** suggests that the carboxyl group is present as a γ-lactone,[2b] which could serve as the eliminated group. Two structures are thus possible:

---

[1] E. L. Martin, *Organic Reactions,* Vol. 1, Wiley, New York, 1942, p. 155.
[2] Nakanishi (a) p. 42, (b) p. 44, (c) p. 44, (d) p. 52.
[3] E. R. Alexander, *Principles of Ionic Organic Reactions,* Wiley, New York, 1950, p. 180.

A   B

Of these A will give structure A' for **4** and B will give B'.

UV calc:
    215 + 2(12) + 5 = 244 mμ

A'

UV calc:
    215 + 12 = 227 mμ

B'

A' gives much better agreement between the calculated[4] and observed UV spectra for **4,** and is preferred. On this basis it is clear that the carboxyl function of **4** cannot be one of those appearing in **7**; so the skeleton of **1** can be expanded to C.

1 double bond

C

The long wavelength of the UV absorption, the positive $FeCl_3$ test, and the titration as a dibasic acid point to the enolized glutaconic anhydride structure for **1**. The IR spectrum is probably interpretable as shown.[2 a,c,d] The location of the —COOH group as shown is not determined by the evidence given, the other peri-position remaining a possibility, but is based on other work.[5]

The structure of **2**, which results from hydrolysis and decarboxylation of the resulting β-keto acid, follows from the similarity of the UV spectra of **2** and **4**.

---

[4] L. F. Fieser and M. Fieser, *Steroids*, Reinhold, New York, 1959, pp. 15ff.
[5] See pp. 47ff. in K. J. Morgan and J. A. Barltrop, *Quart. Rev.*, **12**, 35 (1958).

PROBLEM 24. Deduce structures for the following reaction products:

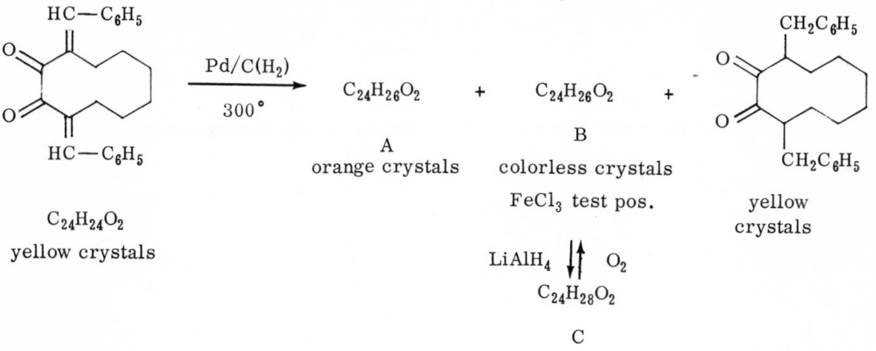

HC—C6H5
HC—C6H5
C24H24O2
yellow crystals
Pd/C(H2)
300°
C24H26O2
A
orange crystals
C24H26O2
B
colorless crystals
FeCl3 test pos.
LiAlH4
O2
C24H28O2
C
CH2C6H5
CH2C6H5
yellow
crystals

IR:
A (Nujol) 1738 (shoulder at 1755), 1605, 1400, 760, 699 cm^{-1}
B (Nujol) 3300, 1697, 1657, 1605, 1587, 1502, 758, 700 cm^{-1}
C ($CHCl_3$) 3510, 1745, 1606, 1500, 703 cm^{-1}

ANSWER 24. [N. J. Leonard and J. C. Little, *J. Am. Chem. Soc.*, **80**, 4111 (1958).]

HC
C6H5
HC
C6H5
C6H5
C6H5
A
1697
C6H5
H
3300
1657
C6H5
B
3510
HO
C6H5
1745
C6H5
C

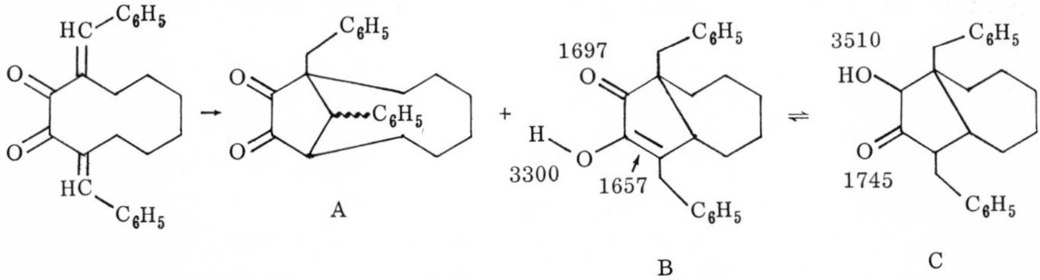

The presence of bands at ca. 760 and 700 cm^{-1} in both A and B suggests the presence of at least one monosubstituted phenyl group, but does not rule out the possibility that the other ring is o-disubstituted.[1a]

The color of A suggests a chromophore more strongly colored than the original compound, despite the uptake of H_2. Thus it appears likely that the un-enolized α-diketone system of the starting material has been maintained, and that the carbonyl groups have been brought more nearly coplanar, providing better conjugation and deeper color. Since enolization normally occurs to a large extent in α-diketones which have their carbonyl groups parallel (e.g., in five- and six-membered rings), it must be blocked in this case. This might arise either from the absence of α-hydrogens or because the molecule contains a bridged bicyclic ring system and enolization would lead to the formation of a forbidden

[1] Nakanishi (a) p. 27, (b) p. 42.

bridgehead double bond (Bredt's rule).[2] It is difficult to design a structure which has no α-H, but that given for A is proposed as satisfying the second condition.

A possible alternative structure, which does not appear to be eliminated by the evidence, is D. The IR spectrum, although consistent with the α-diketone system,[1b] does not distinguish reliably between these possibilities. The bridges in D are of such size that enolization might occur, although it would probably still be attended by strain.

In B the properties expected for the enolized diketo system are shown. The reduction to C gives a product showing the absorption of a saturated cyclopentanone, leading to the proposal of C and thence to B.

The reduction of enolized α-diketones to ketols with LiAlH$_4$ has been observed elsewhere,[3] and presumably occurs because one carbonyl group is blocked as the salt of the enolate anion.

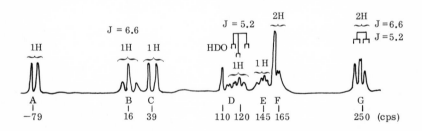

PROBLEM 25.   2'-Deoxyuridine (**1**) exhibits the following 60-Mc NMR spectrum. Assign each of the signals to the protons in the nucleoside.

(D$_2$O solution; benzene as an external reference, ca. 436 cps downfield from TMS)

---

[2] F. S. Fawcett, *Chem. Rev.*, **47**, 219 (1950).
[3] L. W. Trevoy and W. G. Brown, *J. Am. Chem. Soc.*, **71**, 1675 (1949).

(*cont.*)

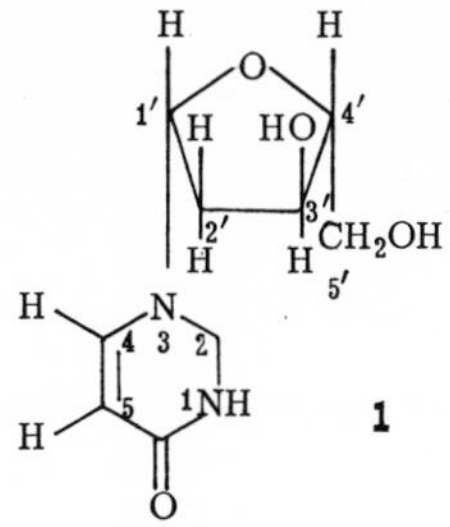

ANSWER 25.   [C. D. Jardetzky, *J. Am. Chem. Soc.*, **83**, 2919 (1961).]
A and C are assigned to the two protons of the double bond in the uracil
moiety. That G is vicinal to B and to D is evident from the coupling constants. Assignments are as follows:

A 4	E 4'
B 1'	F 5'
C 5	G 2'
D 3'	

PROBLEM 26.   Deduce structures for the products A and B.

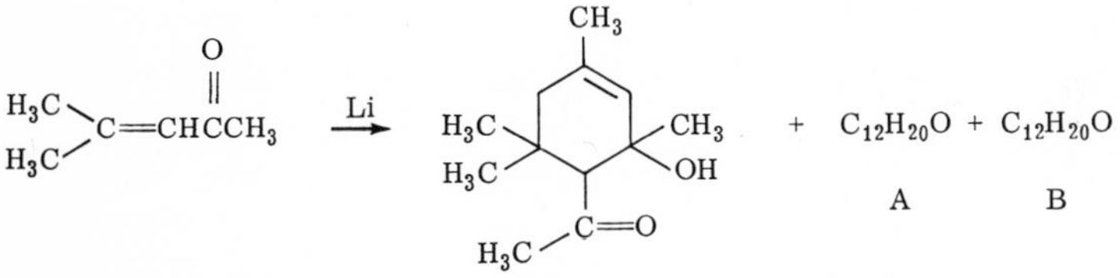

NMR spectra (τ values in CCl_4):

A: 9.11 (3H) singlet
     9.00 (3H) singlet
     8.80 (3H) singlet
     8.30 (3H) singlet*
     8.28 (3H) singlet*
     8.19 (3H) singlet*
     5.71 (1H) singlet*
     4.91 (1H) singlet*

B: 9.12 (6H) singlet
     9.04 (6H) singlet
     8.08 (3H) singlet*
     7.85 (2H) singlet*
     7.80 (3H) singlet

     (singlets with asterisk exhibit fine
     splitting)

ANSWER 26.   [N. Bacon, S. Brewis, G. E. Usher, and E. S. Waight, *J. Chem. Soc.,* **1961**, 2255.]

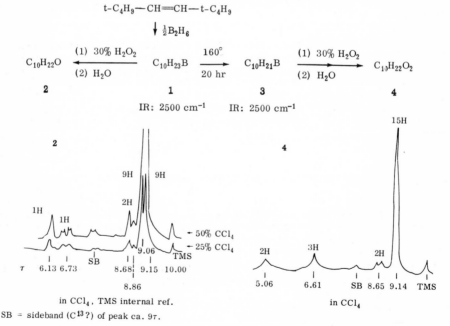

The NMR assignments are those of the original authors, and the pairing of groups and signals may not be correct in all cases. In particular, the system

$$\begin{array}{c} H_3C \\ H_3C \end{array} C=C \begin{array}{c} H \\ C- \end{array}$$

often shows methyl signals at about 8.30τ and 8.19τ and the vinyl proton at about 4.75τ[1]; so the assignments in A are open to some question. The fine splitting by some peaks is presumably caused by long-range coupling, particularly to vinyl protons.

PROBLEM 27.   Deduce structures for the following products:

$$t\text{-}C_4H_9\text{---}CH\text{=}CH\text{---}t\text{-}C_4H_9$$

$$\downarrow \tfrac{1}{2}B_2H_6$$

$$C_{10}H_{22}O \xleftarrow[\text{(2) } H_2O]{\text{(1) 30\% } H_2O_2} C_{10}H_{23}B \xrightarrow[\text{20 hr}]{160°} C_{10}H_{21}B \xrightarrow[\text{(2) } H_2O]{\text{(1) 30\% } H_2O_2} C_{10}H_{22}O_2$$

2   **1**   **3**   **4**

IR: 2500 cm⁻¹   IR: 2500 cm⁻¹

in CCl₄, TMS internal ref.
SB = sideband (C¹³?) of peak ca. 9τ.

---

[1] See, e.g., E. D. Burling, A. Jefferson, and F. Scheinmann, *Tetrahedron,* **21**, 2653, (1965).

ANSWER 27.   [T. J. Logan and T. J. Flautt, *J. Am. Chem. Soc.*, **82**, 3446 (1960).]

Product **1** represents the simple addition of BH_3 to an olefin and is abnormal only in that the steric hindrance present causes the monoalkyl rather than the di- or trialkyl borane to be formed. The subsequent oxidation and hydrolysis then give the alcohol **2**.[1] The NMR is consistent with the formula shown, i.e.,

The two sets of methyl protons can be seen to be nonequivalent, presumably because one set is closer to the oxygen than the other. The assignment of the 9.15τ peak to the closer set is by analogy with the spectrum of **4** (see below). The appearance of the quartet at 6.73τ suggests that the two methylene protons are nonequivalent, either because of hindered rotation about the central C-C bond, or because of the asymmetry of the adjacent carbon atom.[2]

---

[1] For an extensive review of this reaction, see H. C. Brown, *Hydroboration*, Benjamin, New York, 1962.

[2] See Jackman, pp. 99ff.

The intermediate **3**, which was not actually isolated in pure form, is suggested to arise by a dehydrogenative attack of the borane on one of the saturated carbon atoms.[3] Compound **4** then results from oxidative hydrolysis. Alternative structures which might be suggested for **4** are

$$
\underset{\text{A}}{
\begin{array}{c}
 \quad \underset{\displaystyle CH_3}{|} \qquad\qquad \underset{\displaystyle CH_3}{|} \\
H_3C-\overset{\displaystyle CH_3}{\underset{\displaystyle CH_3}{\overset{|}{\underset{|}{C}}}}-CH_2CH-\overset{\displaystyle CH_3}{\underset{\displaystyle CH_3}{\overset{|}{\underset{|}{C}}}}-CH_2OH
\end{array}}
\qquad
\underset{\text{B}}{
\begin{array}{c}
H_3C\,C-CH-CH-CH-CH_2OH
\end{array}}
$$

and analogous rearranged structures, or the vic-diol

$$
\underset{\text{C}}{
H_3C-\overset{CH_3}{\underset{CH_3}{\overset{|}{\underset{|}{C}}}}-\overset{}{\underset{OH}{\overset{|}{CH}}}-\overset{}{\underset{OH}{\overset{|}{CH}}}---\overset{CH_3}{\underset{CH_3}{\overset{|}{\underset{|}{C}}}}-CH_3
}
$$

Possibilities B and C may be eliminated by the NMR spectrum of **4**, which can be interpreted as

9.14τ: $-CH_3$	not split, as would be expected for B
8.65τ: $-CH_2-CH$ with OH	group not present in C, splitting not correct for B
6.61τ: $-CH-$, $-CH_2OH$ with OH	3 protons, not 2 as for C
5.06τ: $-OH$	

The selection of **4** over A is based on the argument that the single signal at 9.14τ suggests equivalent or nearly equivalent methyl groups (the spectrum was taken at 40 Mc, so small separations might not be resolved). In **4**, all the $-CH_3$ are substituted β to one OH and are to this extent the same. In A, however, two methyls are β to two OH's and three are γ to only one, so the splitting observed in **2** might be expected to be accentuated. In the absence of more extensive analogies, though, the structure assigned is better regarded as "more probable" than as "certain."

A further argument in favor of **4** is the probable preference in the reaction **1 → 3** for the formation of a five-membered ring as shown, over the four-membered one which would be required to yield A.

---

[3] P. F. Winternitz, *A.C.S. Abstracts of Papers*, **135**, 19M (1959).

PROBLEM 28.   Which compound, A or B, in each of the following pairs, might be expected to give rise to the mass spectrum indicated? The relative intensities of the peaks in (3) are given in parentheses. Portions of the spectra marked ×50 have been magnified fiftyfold.

(28.1)

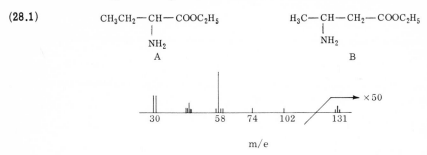

$CH_3CH_2-CH-COOC_2H_5$
$\qquad\qquad\quad |$
$\qquad\qquad\quad NH_2$
$\qquad\qquad\quad$ A

$H_3C-CH-CH_2-COOC_2H_5$
$\qquad\quad |$
$\qquad\quad NH_2$
$\qquad\quad$ B

30   58   74   102   131   ×50

m/e

(28.2) $CH_3CH_2-CH_2-CH_2-CH-COOC_2H_5$
$\qquad\qquad\qquad\qquad\qquad\quad |$
$\qquad\qquad\qquad\qquad\qquad\quad NH_2$
$\qquad\qquad\qquad\qquad\qquad$ A

H_3C
$\qquad\rangle CH-CH_2-CH-COOC_2H_5$
H_3C
$\qquad\qquad\qquad\qquad |$
$\qquad\qquad\qquad\qquad NH_2$
$\qquad\qquad\qquad\qquad$ B

30   44   74 86   102   116   127   144   159   ×50

m/e

(28.3)

H_3C — [cyclohexane ring] — CH_3, CH_3, i-C_3H_7

[cyclohexane ring] — CH_3, C_2H_5, i-C_3H_7

A   B

m/e: 168 (4.4), 139 (38), 125 (14), 97 (18)

ANSWER 28.

(28.1)   [K. Biemann, J. Seibl, and F. Gapp, *J. Am. Chem. Soc.,* **83,** 3795 (1961).]
The principal fragmentation of amino compounds often tends to occur by cleavage of bonds α to the nitrogen and the formation of a stabilized ion.

$$\left[-C\!\!-\!\!C- \right]^{\oplus} \rightarrow \quad -C \quad + \quad \cdot C- $$
$$\qquad \cdot NH_2 \qquad\qquad\qquad \overset{\|}{\underset{\oplus\,NH_2}{}}$$

Thus one might expect

$$CH_3CH_2{-}CH{-}COOC_2H_5 \qquad\qquad H_3C{-}CH{-}CH_2COOC_2H_5$$
$$\qquad\quad | \qquad\qquad\qquad\qquad\qquad\qquad\quad |$$
$$\qquad\quad NH_2 \qquad\qquad\qquad\qquad\qquad\qquad NH_2$$
$$\quad\;102\;\;58 \qquad\qquad\qquad\qquad\qquad\;116\quad 44$$

A   B

It is clear that the former agrees with the data and the latter does not. The rest of the spectrum may be accounted for as

$$102 \qquad\qquad\qquad\qquad\qquad\qquad 74$$

(28.2)   [Biemann et al., loc. cit.]
   In this case the principal cleavages, leading to peaks at 86 and 102, will be the same for both compounds. The distinction must be made on the basis of the different fragmentation expected for the side chains. Thus one might expect

$$H_3C{-}CH_2{-}CH_2{-}CH_2{-}CHCOOC_2H_5 \qquad\qquad H_3C{-}CH{-}CH_2{-}CHCOOC_2H_5$$
$$\;144\;\;130\;\;116\;\;102\;\;NH_2 \qquad\qquad\qquad\qquad 144\;\;116\;\;102\;\;NH_2$$

A   B

The absence of a peak at 130 (127 is due to a totally different process) suggests that loss of an ethyl group cannot occur, and favors B. Support may be drawn from the relatively intense M-15 peak at 144. Methyl groups are less easily lost than higher alkyl homologs unless they are attached to a particularly favorable site for cleavage, such as a highly branched carbon. The actual spectrum of A, for example, shows a significant peak at 130 but none at 144.

(28.3) [A. J. Birch, J. Grimshaw, A. R. Penfold, N. Sheppard, and R. N. Speake,
        J. Chem. Soc., **1961**, 2286.]
        This problem resembles the previous one. Reasonable predictions would be

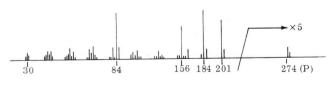

A   B

   In fact, there are peaks corresponding to the loss of ethyl and isopropyl
groups, but none for methyl, so B is favored. The fragment of m/e 97 corresponds to a rearrangement process leading to the loss of ethylene (28) from 125
or propylene (42) from 139, and confirms the presence of both C_2 and C_3 side
chains.

PROBLEM 29.   A natural product was synthesized as shown below. Deduce
the structures of the products **1** and **2** and show how the indicated major peaks of
the mass spectrum of **2** may be explained.

N — ε — carbobenzoxylysine

              + $\xrightarrow[\text{heat}]{\text{Ba(OH)}_2}$ $\xrightarrow{\text{HBr}}$ $\xrightarrow{\text{neut.}}$ $C_9H_{18}N_2O_4$ $\xrightarrow[\text{HCl}]{C_2H_5OH}$ $C_{13}H_{26}N_2O_4$

α-bromopropionic acid

                                                              1   **2**

Mass spectrum of **2**:

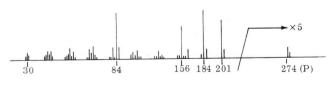

m/e

ANSWER 29.   [K. Biemann, C. Lioret, J. Asselineau, E. Lederer, and J.
Polonsky, *Bull. Soc. Chim. Biol.*, **42**, 979 (1960).]

$$
\underset{\text{H}}{\text{C}_6\text{H}_5\text{CH}_2\text{O}\overset{\text{O}}{\overset{\|}{\text{C}}}-\text{N}}-\text{CH}_2\text{CH}_2\text{CH}_2\text{CH}_2\underset{\underset{\text{NH}_2}{|}}{\text{CH}}\text{COOH} \quad + \quad \text{CH}_3\underset{\overset{|}{\text{Br}}}{\text{CH}}\text{COOH}
$$

$$\downarrow \text{OH}^\ominus$$

$$
\underset{\text{H}}{\text{C}_6\text{H}_5\text{CH}_2\text{O}\overset{\text{O}}{\overset{\|}{\text{C}}}-\text{N}}-\text{CH}_2\text{CH}_2\text{CH}_2\text{CH}_2\underset{\underset{\text{CH}_3\text{CHCOOH}}{\overset{|}{\text{NH}}}}{\text{CH}}\text{COOH}
$$

$$\downarrow \text{HBr}$$
$$\downarrow \text{neut.}$$

$$
\underset{\underset{\text{CH}_3\text{CHCOOH}}{\overset{|}{\text{NH}}}}{\text{H}_2\text{NCH}_2\text{CH}_2\text{CH}_2\text{CH}_2\text{CH}}\text{COOH} \qquad \underset{\underset{\text{CH}_3\text{CHCOOC}_2\text{H}_5}{\overset{|}{\text{NH}}}}{\text{H}_2\text{NCH}_2\text{CH}_2\text{CH}_2\text{CH}_2\text{CH}}\text{COOC}_2\text{H}_5
$$

1   **2**

Mass spectroscopy has proved a valuable tool for the study of small quantities of amino acids, usually in the form of their ethyl esters.[1] The decomposition patterns are reasonably well-defined and predictable, so information can be obtained about compounds of unknown as well as known structure. In this case it is suggested that

---

[1] K: Biemann, *Mass Spectrometry*, McGraw-Hill, New York, 1962, Chap. 7; H. Budzikiewicz, C. Djerassi, and D. H. Williams, *Structure Elucidation of Natural Products by Mass Spectrometry*, Vol. II, Holden-Day, San Francisco, 1964, Chap. 26.

$H_2NCH_2CH_2CH_2CH_2CHCO_2C_2H_5$

|
•NH $^\oplus$
|
$CH_3CHCO_2C_2H_5$

m/e 274

$-•CO_2C_2H_5 \longrightarrow$

H
|
$H_2NCH_2CH_2CH_2CH_2C$
‖
$^\oplus$ NH
|
$CH_3CHCO_2C_2H_5$

201

$\left[\begin{array}{c} H_2N \quad \overset{\oplus}{N}H \\ | \\ CH_3\overset{|}{C}HCO_2C_2H_5 \end{array} \right]$

201

$\leftarrow$

$\left[\begin{array}{c} H_2\overset{\oplus}{N}\!=\!CHCH_2CH_2CH_2CH_2 \\ | \\ NH \\ | \\ CH_3CHCO_2C_2H_5 \end{array} \right]$

201

$\left[\begin{array}{c} \overset{\oplus}{N} \quad NH \\ H \quad H \quad | \\ CHCO_2C_2H_5 \\ | \end{array} \right]$

201   CH_3

$\downarrow$ − NH_3

$\downarrow$ rearr.

$\overset{\oplus}{H_2N}\!=\!CH_2$

30

$\downarrow$ − $NH_2CHCO_2C_2H_5$

|
CH_3

$CH_3CH\!-\!C\overset{O}{\underset{O-CH_2}{\diagdown}}\overset{H}{\underset{CH_2}{\diagup}}$

184

$\downarrow$ − $CH_2\!=\!CH_2$

$^\oplus$N
|
H
84

$CH_3CHCOOH$

156

Most of these fragmentation steps find analogies in the mass spectrum of lysine itself.

PROBLEM 30.

(30.1)   Can the following pair of compounds be distinguished by application of the octant rule?

Me   Me

O   O

H   H

(30.2)

The following bromo ketone shows a negative Cotton effect curve. Which of the rotamers, A or B, is preferred?

(cont.)

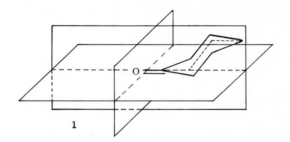

A   B

ANSWER 30.

(30.1)   The sign of the Cotton effect curve[1] of optically active cyclohexanone derivatives can often be predicted by the application of the octant rule.[2] This states (in a somewhat simplified form; for details see Ref. 2) that if a cyclohexanone derivative is oriented so that it may be viewed as in **1**, substituents may be regarded as being in one of the eight octants cut off by the three planes shown.

1

In the usual case, no substituents extend further to the left than the carbonyl oxygen, and the picture can be simplified by viewing the four significant octants down the O → C axis and using a rather stylized representation of the ring. Thus

According to the rule, substituents in the various octants cause the Cotton effect to have the sign indicated, whereas those on the dividing planes are without effect.

---

[1] See C. Djerassi, *Optical Rotatory Dispersion,* McGraw-Hill, New York, 1960, Chap. 2.

[2] C. Djerassi, op. cit., Chap. 13; W. Moffitt, R. B. Woodward, A. Moscowitz, W. Klyne, and C. Djerassi, *J. Am. Chem. Soc.,* **83**, 4013 (1961).

If there are substituents implying opposite signs, the net effect depends on the number in each octant, their nature, and their distance from the carbonyl group, and thus it may not be possible to make firm predictions.

For the problem in question,

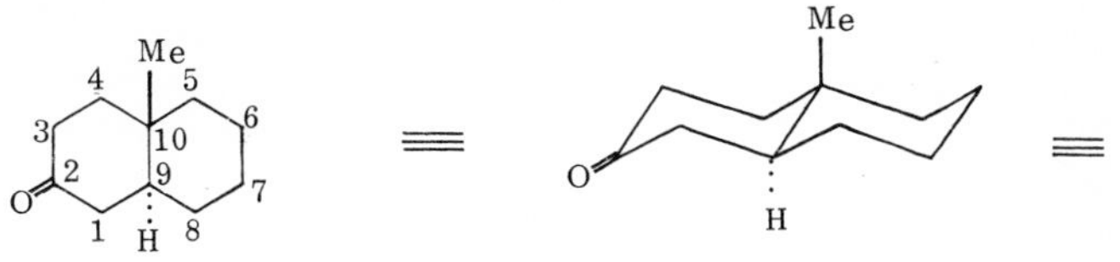

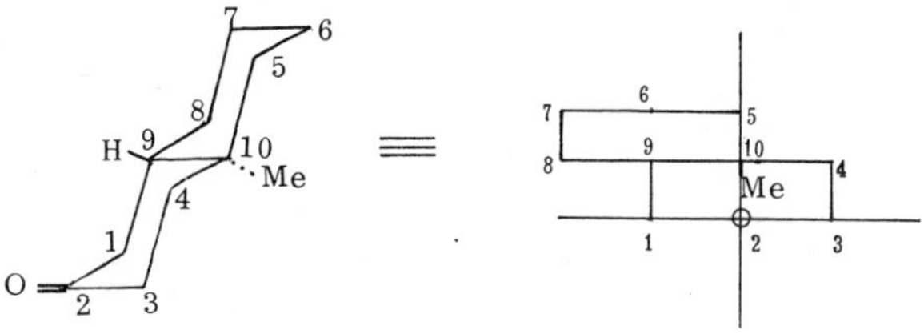

It is clear that 4 can be balanced against 9, and that the remaining "substituents" (6, 7, and 8) all indicate a positive Cotton effect. On the other hand, for the cis isomer two possible conformations exist. One of these (A) is like that in the A/B cis fused steroids[3] and the octant rule indicates a negative Cotton

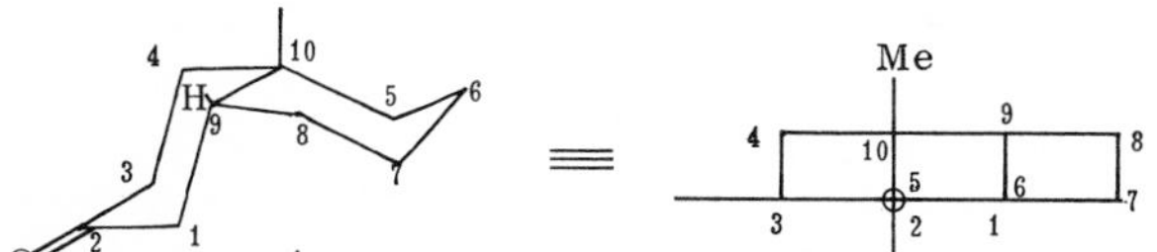

approximately

effect.[4] The other conformation, however, is

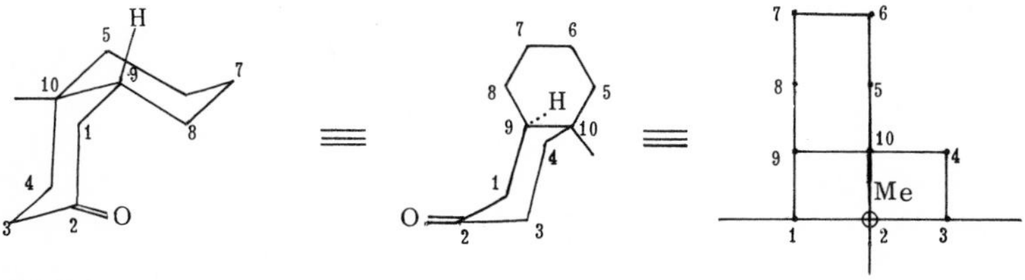

---

[1]L. F. Fieser and M. Fieser, *Steroids*, Reinhold, New York, 1959, pp. 7ff.
[2]But see Ref. 2b, footnote 21.

and would be predicted to have a strongly positive Cotton effect.

Experimentally, it is found that cis decalones of this absolute configuration usually have weakly negative Cotton effect,[5] in agreement with the steroid-like conformation.

(30.2)   [C. Djerassi, op. cit., p. 128.]

The two possible rotamers can be simplified by regarding them as

A   B

The bromine atom, because of its large electron cloud and its closeness to the carbonyl group, can be expected to determine the sign of the Cotton effect, allowing the carbon atoms of the ring to be ignored. Thus, using the octant rule, a negative Cotton effect would be predicted for A and a positive one for B. A negative effect is observed, so A is considered to be favored. The argument is a rather tenuous one, however, and may be regarded more in the light of a suggestion than a proof.

PROBLEM 31.   Suggest an explanation for the fact that the Cotton effect curve of the following compound is markedly changed, as shown, by the addition of a trace of hydrochloric acid:

ANSWER 31.   [D. Herbst and C. Djerassi, *J. Am. Chem. Soc.*, **82**, 4337 (1960).]

The Cotton effects predicted for the two keto groups in this molecule can be obtained by applying the octant rule.[1] The 6-keto group has 4 C and 1 O in a

---

[5] C. Djerassi, op. cit., p. 75.

[1] (a) C. Djerassi, *Optical Rotatory Dispersion*, McGraw-Hill, New York, 1960, Chap. 13, (b) W. Moffitt, R. B. Woodward, A. Moscowitz, W. Klyne, and C. Djerassi, *J. Am. Chem. Soc.*, **83**, 4013 (1961).

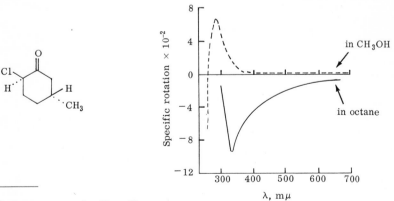

+ octant and 1 C in a − octant; the 2-keto group has 5 C and 1 O, all in a − octant. Thus the 2-keto system would be expected to have a large negative Cotton
effect, whereas the 6-keto one would have a less pronounced positive effect. The
net result, if both groups are in the same molecule, should be a rather weak
negative effect. This is what is observed.

    In $HCl—CH_3OH$, the possibility exists of converting the ketone groups par-
tially or completely into ketals, which do not show Cotton effects.[2] In this case,
it would be predicted that the less hindered 6-keto group should undergo ketaliza-
tion to a greater extent than the 2-keto one. As a result, the ORD curve comes
to resemble more closely the strongly negative one expected for the 2-keto system alone.

PROBLEM 32.   Deduce favorable conformations for the following compound:

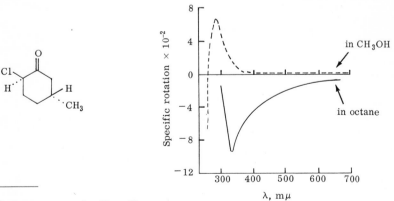

---

[2] C. Djerassi, op. cit., Chap. 11.

ANSWER 32.   [C. Djerassi, L. E. Geller, and E. J. Eisenbraun, *J. Org. Chem.*, **25**, 1 (1960); C. Djerassi, *Optical Rotatory Dispersion*, McGraw-Hill, New York, 1960, p. 125.]

The two chair conformations, A and B, are possible and more stable than any of the boat conformations:

The Cotton effects predicted for these by the octant rule[1] are

moderate +   large −

Thus conformer A would appear to be favored in methanol solution and B in octane. Similar effects have been found by other methods in similar α-halo ketones,[2,3] and have been explained on the basis that there exists a repulsion between the C–O and C–Cl(Br) dipoles which causes the axial orientation to be favored in nonpolar solvents. In polar solvents the improved solvation of the dipoles reduces their repulsion and allows an increase in the amount of the sterically favored equatorial form in the equilibrium mixture.

Despite the change in the ORD curves, it should not be assumed, however, that B necessarily predominates even in octane. The corresponding trans-2-bromo-5-methylcyclohexanone shows a similar effect, although the Cotton effect curve never actually becomes positive. Nevertheless, independent measurements by a number of techniques[4] have shown that the concentration of the trans diaxial form (B) is only about 40% in heptane, falling to 15% in methanol. Even at this concentration, the molecular rotation of B is so much greater (CH$_3$ and Cl both implying −) than that of A (only CH$_3$ implying +) that rather small proportions of B dominate the ORD curve. On the other hand, when the curve goes positive, as it does in the case shown, it appears safe to assume that A is markedly predominant.

---

[1] C. Djerassi, *Optical Rotatory Dispersion*, McGraw-Hill, New York, 1960, Chap. 13; W. Moffitt, R. B. Woodward, A. Moscowitz, W. Klyne, and C. Djerassi, *J. Am. Chem. Soc.*, **83**, 4013 (1961).

[2] E. J. Corey, *J. Am. Chem. Soc.*, **75**, 2301 (1953).

[3] N. L. Allinger and J. Allinger, *J. Am. Chem. Soc.*, **80**, 5476 (1958).

[4] N. L. Allinger, J. Allinger, L. E. Geller, and C. Djerassi, *J. Org. Chem.*, **25**, 6 (1960).

CHAPTER 3

SUBSTITUTION REACTIONS

As one of the most investigated areas of physical organic chemistry, these reactions are described in mechanistic detail in advanced texts. The following are more specialized reviews.

1. A. Streitwieser, Jr., *Solvolytic Displacement Reactions*, McGraw-Hill, New York, 1962; *Chem. Rev.*, **56**, 571 (1956). A classic review of displacements on saturated carbons.
2. C. A. Bunton, *Nucleophilic Substitution at a Saturated Carbon Atom*, Elsevier, Amsterdam, 1963. A less extensive discussion, similar to that in Gould.
3. E. R. Thornton, *Solvolysis Mechanisms*, Ronald Press, New York, 1964. Contains more modern work and a discussion of theory.
4. B. Capon, *Quart. Rev.*, **18**, 45 (1964). A review of neighboring group effects.

PROBLEM 33.

(**33.1**)   Suggest an explanation for the fact that the compound in which R = H reacts 35 times as fast as the one in which R = CH$_3$:

(**33.2**)   When the following compounds were treated with KHCO$_3$ in benzene-methanol-water at 20° for 65 hours, hydrolysis occurred to the extent of 18% with **1** and 70% with **2**. Explain the difference in reactivity.

(cont.)   65

1   2

ANSWER 33.

(33.1)   [W. C. Spitzer and G. W. Wheland, *J. Am. Chem. Soc.*, **62**, 2995 (1940); see G. S. Hammond and M. F. Hawthorne in *Steric Effects in Organic Chemistry* (M. S. Newman, ed.), Wiley, New York, 1956, pp. 184ff.]

The reaction is a nucleophilic displacement[1] involving the intermediate A, a resonance hybrid to which A_1 is the principal contributor. When R = CH_3, however, the steric hindrance between the methyl groups and the $-NO_2$ keep the latter from being in the plane of the benzene ring and reduce the contribution of A_1 in stabilizing the intermediate and the closely related transition state.

Even with this steric hindrance, however, the displacement is much easier than in bromobenzene itself. This may be accounted for in two ways, both of which probably apply. First, the interaction between the π orbitals in the benzene ring and those in the nitro group, required for A_1 to contribute, is not greatly affected by small rotations (up to ca. 40°) about the intervening bond. Thus it is often possible to have considerable relief of strain without losing much resonance stabilization. Second, the NO_2 group is capable of stabilizing the canonical form A_2 by an *inductive* effect operating through the σ electrons in the bond joining it to the ring. This effect is independent of orientation about the bond.

A_2 A_1

(33.2)   [H. B. Henbest and B. J. Lovell, *J. Chem. Soc.*, **1957**, 1965.]

As a general rule,[2] equatorial esters are more easily hydrolyzed than axial ones. This case represents a specific exception because of the presence of the 5α-hydroxyl group.

The conformations[2] of 1 and 2 are considered to be

---

[1]Gould, pp. 452ff.

[2]D. H. R. Barton, *Experientia*, **6**, 316 (1950); D. H. R. Barton and R. C. Cookson, *Quart. Revs.*, **10**, 44 (1956).

In **1** there is no interaction between the 5-OH and the acetate, so the hydrolysis of the ester would be expected to proceed at the usual equatorial rate. (This is apparently an oversimplification, as there seems to be a small rate enhancement in this case, too. Similar results have been observed in other molecules in which direct interaction between the group requires major conformational changes.[3]) In 2, however, the 5-OH is hydrogen-bonded to the ester oxygen as shown. The effect of this bond is to reduce the donation of the unshared oxygen electrons to the carbonyl group (form B). This reduces the stabilization of the carbonyl group in the ground state and increases the ease of attack by base (cf. acid anhydrides,

in which the contribution of form B to one carbonyl group is diminished by the need for an equivalent interaction with the others).[4,5]

Evidence supporting this view is given by the IR spectra of the esters with and without the 5α-OH. The effect of adding the —OH group is to increase the frequency of the C=O stretching band ($1733 \rightarrow 1744$ cm^{-1}) and to lower that of the ester —C—O— stretch ($1237 \rightarrow 1224$ cm^{-1}). These results imply an increased double-bond character for the carbonyl group and a lessened one for the —C—O—.[6] This is what would be predicted on the basis of an increased contribution of A (or lessened one of B) to the ground state of the ester.

---

[3] See C. Djerassi and A. E. Lippman, *J. Am. Chem. Soc.*, **77**, 1825 (1955); C. Djerassi and J. S. Mills, *J. Am. Chem. Soc.*, **80**, 1236 (1958).

[4] Note that the slow step in ester hydrolysis is the addition of base to the carbonyl group, so destabilization of the ground state will be reflected in an increased rate. See Gould, pp. 315ff.

[5] An alternative view, based on thermodynamic measurements on some model compounds, has been expressed by T. C. Bruice and T. H. Fife, *Tetrahedron Letters*, **1961**, 263.

[6] See R. N. Jones and C. Sandorfy in *Chemical Applications of Spectroscopy*, Vol. IX of *Techniques of Organic Chemistry* (A. Weissberger, ed.), Wiley-Interscience, New York, 1956, pp. 472ff.

PROBLEM 34.   Suggest an explanation for the fact that in the following reaction the rate of solvolysis (S_N1) decreases in the order: n = 5 ~ 7 > 6 > 4.

ANSWER 34.   [H. C. Brown and M. Barkowski, *J. Am. Chem. Soc.*, **74**, 1894 (1952); cf. A. Streitwieser, Jr., *Chem. Rev.*, **56**, 666 (1956).]

The slow step in these solvolyses is the ionization of the halide to the intermediate carbonium ion. The structure of the activated complex in this step is not known, but it is assumed to resemble the ion rather closely. Thus a discussion of the probable effect of structural changes on the stability of the ion should apply to the preceding transition state as well.

It is suggested that the effect of ring size on the stability of the ion arises from varying amounts of internal strain (I strain)[1] in the different systems. This strain can arise either from the deformation of the ring bond angles from their stable values, or from repulsions between neighboring hydrogens. Thus in the cyclobutane case, ionization requires converting a tetrahedral carbon (sp^3 bond angle 109°) to a trigonal one (sp^2 — 120°) in a ring whose angles are constrained near 90°. The increased strain in the ion inhibits its formation and reduces the rate of solvolysis.

It should be noted that additional effects come into play with secondary cyclobutyl halides, in which the first-order solvolysis rate may actually be faster than for the corresponding cyclopentane derivatives.[2] These effects appear to involve nonclassical delocalization of the charge from the highly unstable secondary ion, but do not occur with the more stable tertiary species.

In the five-, six-, and seven-membered cases the angle strain produced by ionization is relatively small and can be accommodated by flexing the ring. The systems differ significantly in their hydrogen-hydrogen interactions, however. This results in less stable ground states for the five- and seven-membered rings (as is shown by their heats of combustion per CH_2 group)[3] compared with the cyclohexane system. Some of the unstable eclipsed interactions are relieved with the conversion of one carbon to the flattened, trigonal form, and so the transition state is made relatively more stable compared to the ground state.

---

[1]H. C. Brown, R. S. Fletcher, and R. B. Johannesen, *J. Am. Chem. Soc.*, **73**, 212 (1951).
[2]J. D. Roberts and V. C. Chambers, *J. Am. Chem. Soc.*, **73**, 5037 (1951).
[3]E. L. Eliel, *Stereochemistry of Carbon Compounds*, McGraw-Hill, New York, 1962, pp. 188ff.

PROBLEM 35. Predict the product of each of the following reactions:

(35.1)

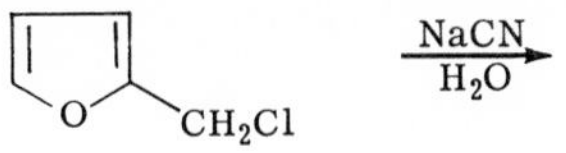

$$\xrightarrow[\text{H}_2\text{O}]{\text{NaCN}}$$

(35.2)

$$C_6H_5-\overset{\overset{\displaystyle H}{|}}{\underset{\underset{\displaystyle CH_3}{|}}{C}}-OH \qquad \xrightarrow{\text{SOCl}_2}$$

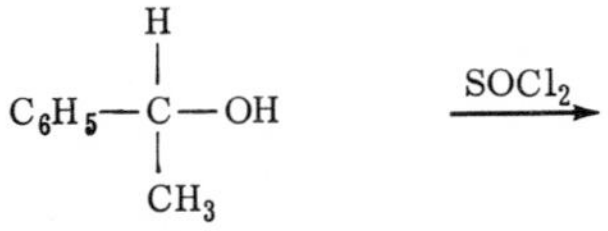

Optically
active

(35.3)

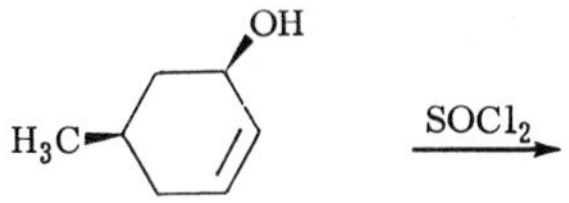

$$\xrightarrow{\text{SOCl}_2}$$

(35.4)

$$\xrightarrow[\text{H}_2\text{SO}_4]{\text{HNO}_3} \quad C_8H_8N_2O_5$$

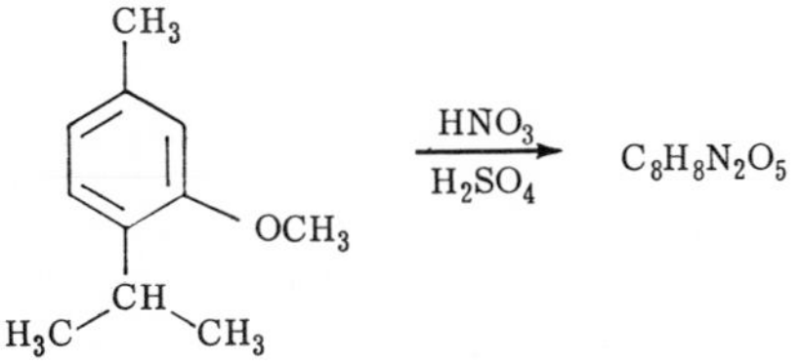

ANSWER 35.

(35.1)   [M. M. Runde, E. W. Scott, and J. R. Johnson, *J. Am. Chem. Soc.*, **52**, 1284 (1930).]

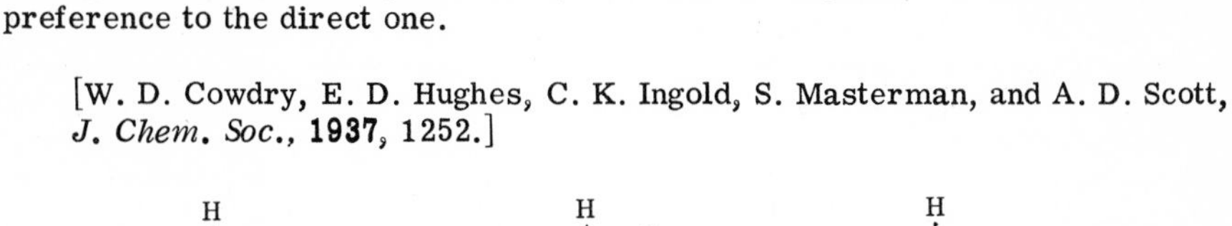

The reaction may be either S_N2', as shown, or S_N1', involving the ion A. No explanation has been given of why the indirect displacement occurs in preference to the direct one.

(35.2)   [W. D. Cowdry, E. D. Hughes, C. K. Ingold, S. Masterman, and A. D. Scott, *J. Chem. Soc.*, **1937**, 1252.]

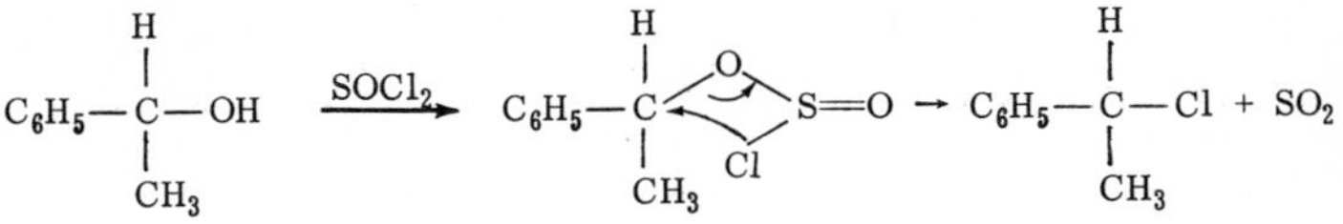

This is the classic $S_N i$ reaction[1] and proceeds with retention of both optical activity and configuration.

(35.3)   [H. L. Goering, T. D. Nevitt, and E. F. Silversmith, *J. Am. Chem. Soc.*, **77**, 4042 (1955).]

This is an $S_N i'$ reaction.[2] Note that the C-Cl bond being formed is cis to the C-O bond being cleaved.

(35.4)   [M. Guia, *Gazz. Chim. Ital.*, **49**, (II), 158 (1919). For discussion and references see P. B. D. de la Mare and J. H. Ridd, *Aromatic Substitution*, Butterworth, London, 1959, pp. 210ff.]

Simple nitration to the products **1** or **4** might be expected, but neither of these corresponds to the formula of the observed product. Instead, **1** is formed and undergoes further reaction, not at the hindered 2-position (to give **4**), but by attack of nitronium ion at the less hindered and equally activated 4-position to give the intermediate **2**. This ion can either revert to **1** or lose the isopropyl group (as propylene?) to give **3**.

---

[1] Gould, pp. 294ff.

[2] Gould, p. 296.

Similar substitution reactions are shown by

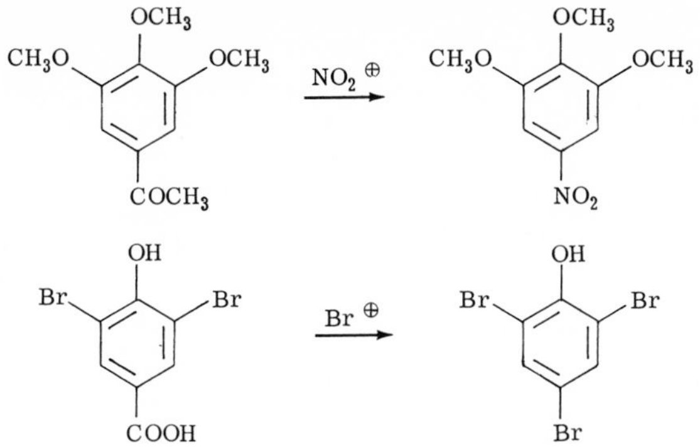

OCH₃ aromatic structure with CH₃O, OCH₃ substituents and COCH₃ group, reacting with NO₂⁺ to give nitro-substituted product (NO₂)

OH phenol with Br substituents and COOH group, reacting with Br⁺ to give tribromophenol product (Br)

PROBLEM 36.

(36.1)   Which of the isomers, A or B, is converted more readily into C?

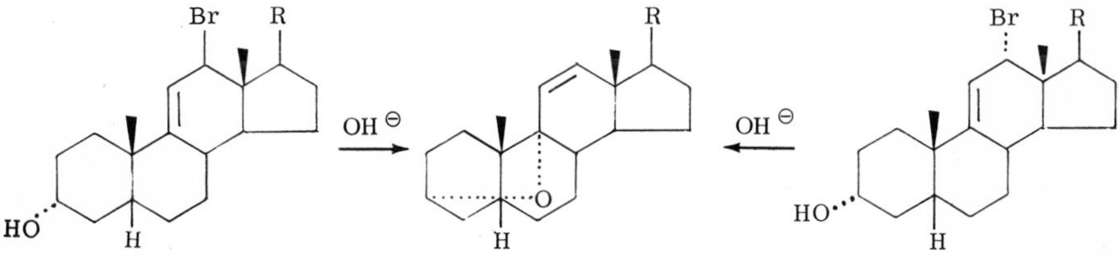

Steroid structure A (with Br, R, HO, H) →[OH⁻]→ epoxide steroid C ←[OH⁻]← steroid structure B (with Br, R, HO, H)

        A   C   B

(36.2)   Deduce the configurations of the acetyl groups in the following reaction products.

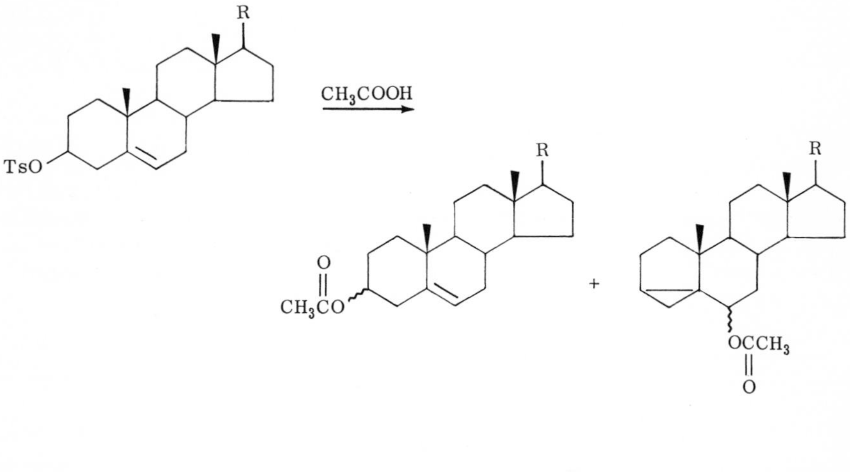

Steroid structure with R and TsO group →[CH₃COOH]→ acetate product (CH₃CO–O) + cyclopropane-fused steroid product (OCCH₃)

ANSWER 36.

(36.1)   (L. F. Fieser and M. Fieser, *Steroids,* Reinhold, New York, 1959,
           pp. 641–643.)

This reaction represents an $S_N 2'$ displacement,[1] and as such proceeds
most readily when the entering and leaving groups are cis. A convenient, if
grossly oversimplified, picture of these reactions is as two concerted back-
side displacements: The first, by the incoming group, displaces the electron
pair of the olefin to the opposite side of the molecule, and the second, by this
electron pair, ejects the halide.

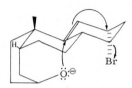

(36.2)   [Fieser and Fieser, op. cit., pp. 314–318; S. Winstein and R. Adams, *J. Am.
           Chem. Soc.,* **70**, 838 (1948).]

The reaction has been shown to be a unimolecular one in which the loss of
the tosyl group is accelerated by participation of the π-electrons of the 5,6-
double bond. An intermediate, A, is formed which then undergoes attack at
either the 3- or the 6-positions to give the products.[2]

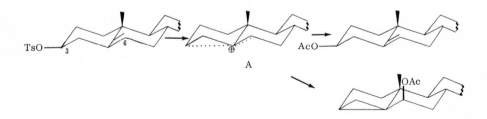

Both substituents approach from the upper side of the molecule, leading to the
products shown. The addition at 3 can be justified as resembling an $S_N 2$ displacement in which the leaving group is the partial bond between C-3 and C-5,
while the reaction at 6 resembles the normal preference for axial addition to
cyclic alkenes.

<hr>

[1]Gould, pp. 290–291.
[2]See G. H. Whitman, *Proc. Chem. Soc.,* **1961**, 422; S. Winstein and E. M. Kosower, *J. Am.
Chem. Soc.,* **81**, 4399 (1959).

PROBLEM 37.   Suggest a mechanism for the following reaction:

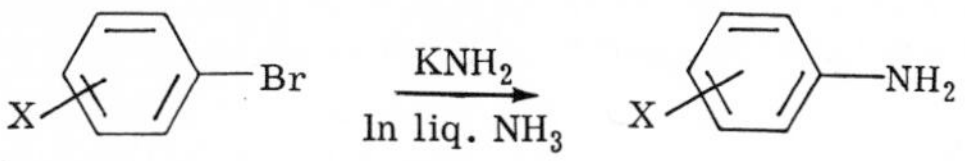

X = o- or m-OCH$_3$ m-OCH$_3$
X = p-OCH$_3$ m-OCH$_3$ (49%), p-OCH$_3$ (51%)
X = m-CH$_3$ o-CH$_3$ (22%), m-CH$_3$ (56%), p-CH$_3$ (22%)

ANSWER 37.   [J. D. Roberts, C. W. Vaughan, L. A. Carlsmith, and D. A. Semenow, J. *Am. Chem. Soc.*, **78**, 611 (1956).]

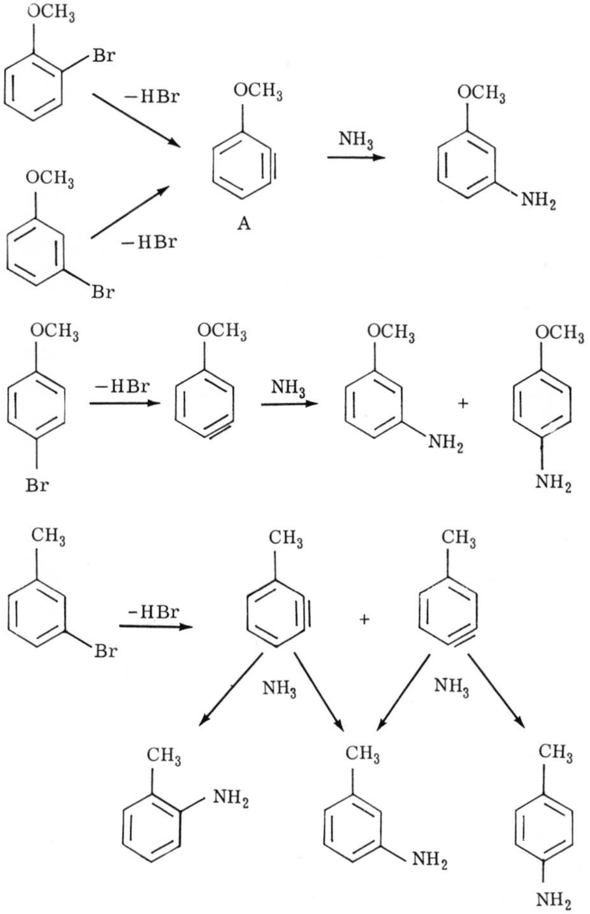

These reactions are known to occur by mechanisms involving benzyne[1] inter-mediates, formed by elimination of HX. The existence of the sort of intermediate shown has been proved by Roberts et al.[2] with the demonstration that

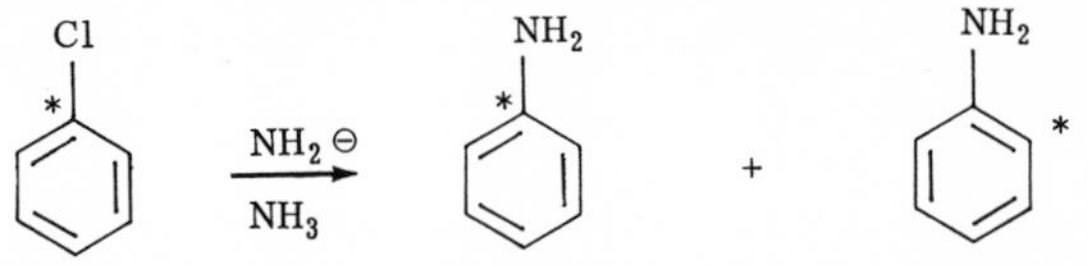

It is suggested that the differences in the product ratios can be explained in terms of the acidities of the various aromatic protons, which control the direction of elimination, and of the stabilities of the anions formed by the addition of $NH_2^{\ominus}$ to the benzyne.

The acidity of the aromatic protons (actually controlled by the stability of the resulting anion) is determined by the *inductive* effect of the substituents. Thus inductively electron-withdrawing groups such as $-OCH_3$ tend to favor anions at o > m > p, whereas for inductively electron-releasing groups such as CH_3—(weak effect) the order is reversed. The results obtained are roughly consistent with this view. Elimination from m-bromoanisole occurs selectively from the 2-position to give the 2,3-benzyne A. The addition of $NH_2^{\ominus}$ to this preferentially forms the o anion rather than the m one, and leads to m-amino-anisole.

Only one benzyne can be formed from p-bromoanisole and addition to this gives the two observed products. By the above argument, the p-product should be favored, but this is not found to be the case to any significant extent.

In the case of m-bromotoluene, the inductive effects are small, and both benzynes are formed. The 3,4-product apparently predominates and shows preferential m > p addition, but the results are not clean-cut, and other effects are obviously entering the picture.

PROBLEM 38.   Suggest mechanisms for the following reactions:

(38.1) $(CH_3)_2SO + BrCH_2COOEt \xrightarrow{70°} (CH_3)_2S + OHCCOOEt + HBr$

(38.2)

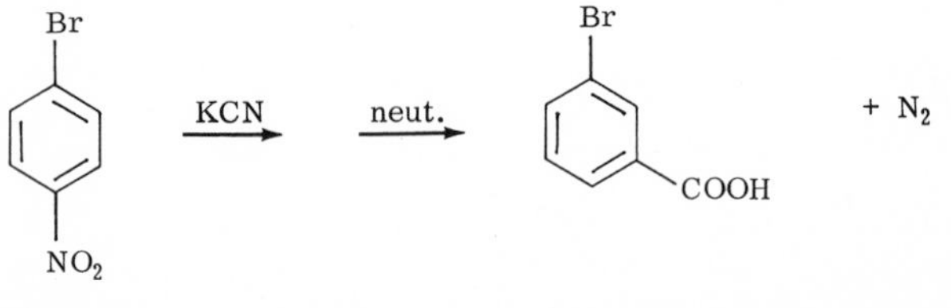

---

[1]For a brief survey of benzyne chemistry see J. D. Roberts, *Chem. Soc. (London) Spec. Publ.*, **12**, 115 (1958), and for an extensive review see R. Huisgen in *Organometallic Chemistry* (H. Zeiss, ed.), Reinhold, New York, 1961, pp. 36–87; also H. Heaney, *Chem. Rev.*, **62**, 81 (1962).

[2]J. D. Roberts, D. A. Semenow, H. E. Simmons, Jr., and L. A. Carlsmith, *J. Am. Chem. Soc.*, **78**, 601 (1956).

(*cont.*)

(38.3)

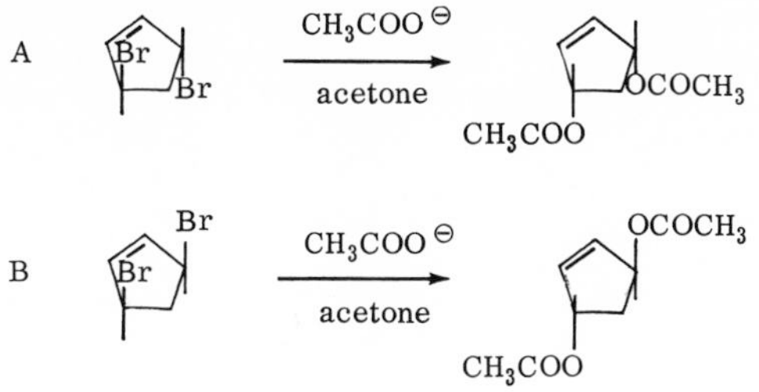

A ... $\xrightarrow[\text{acetone}]{\text{CH}_3\text{COO}^{\ominus}}$ ...

B ... $\xrightarrow[\text{acetone}]{\text{CH}_3\text{COO}^{\ominus}}$ ...

ANSWER 38.

(38.1)   [I. M. Hunsberger and J. M. Tien, *Chem. Ind. (London)*, **1959**, 88.]

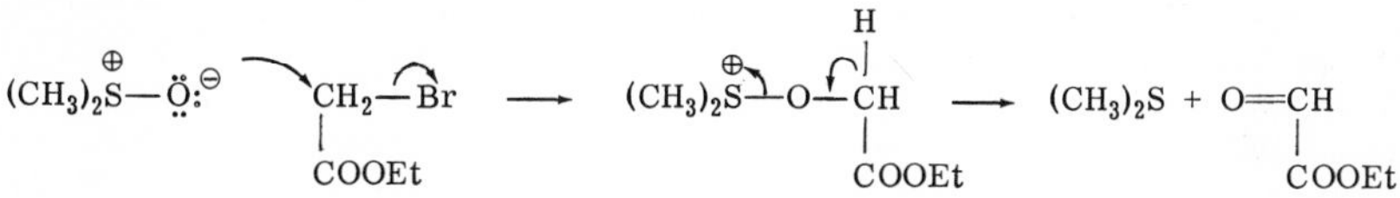

This has proved to be a useful synthetic method for the preparation of aldehydes. Analogous reactions occur with tosylates in place of halides, allowing the selective oxidation of primary alcohols to aldehydes.[1]

(38.2)   [M. Rosenblum, *J. Am. Chem. Soc.*, **82**, 3796 (1960).]

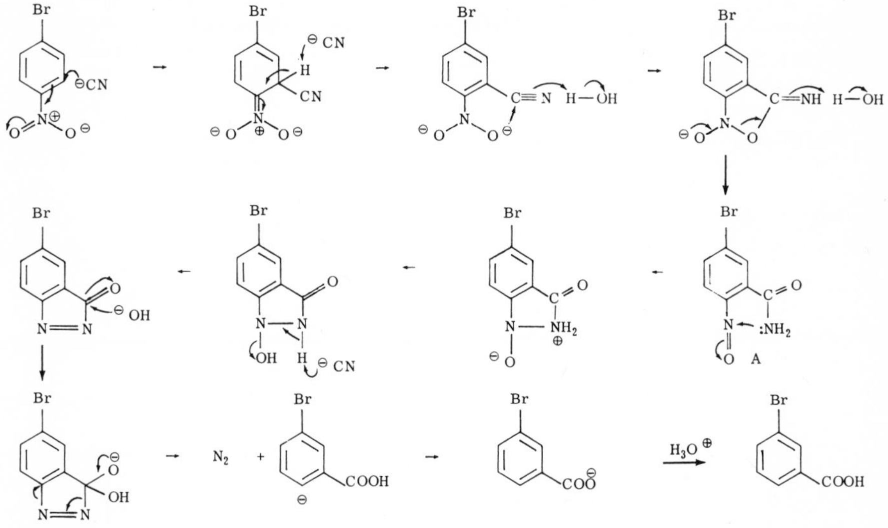

[1]N. Kornblum, W. J. Jones, and G. J. Anderson, *J. Am. Chem. Soc.*, **81**, 4113 (1959).

This is the von Richter reaction. A large number of mechanisms have been proposed, including ones based on benzyne intermediates. These are not consistent, however, with the observations that the nitrogen atoms are eliminated as N_2 (not derived from the oxidation of NH_3) and one oxygen atom is transferred from the nitro group to the carboxyl.[1] A model of the proposed intermediate A has been synthesized and shown to undergo the expected reaction in base.[2]

(38.3)   [K. A. Saegebarth, *J. Org. Chem.*, **25**, 2212 (1960).]

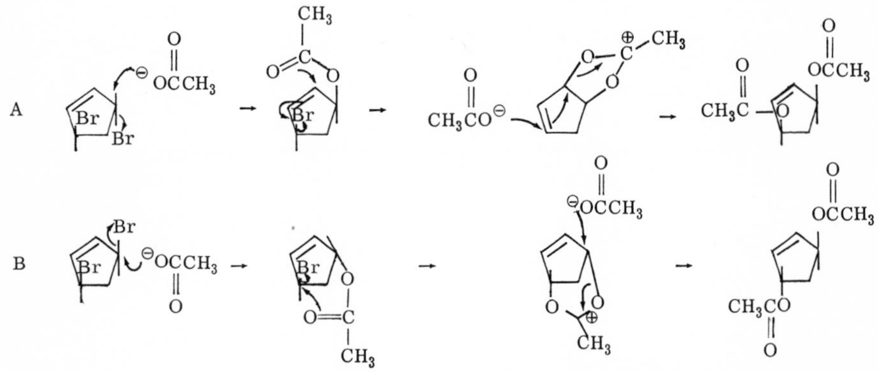

The conditions used are normally favorable to S_N2 displacements in allylic systems, and the first bromine is replaced in this way. The loss of the second Br^- involves a neighboring group effect and either a S_N2' reaction (A) or the more common S_N2 (B).[3] The choice is presumably determined by the stereochemistry of the intermediate bromoacetate, since the S_N2' reaction requires the entering and leaving groups to be on the same side of the molecular plane,[4] whereas the S_N2 requires them to be on opposite sides.

PROBLEM 39.   Suggest a mechanism for the following reaction:

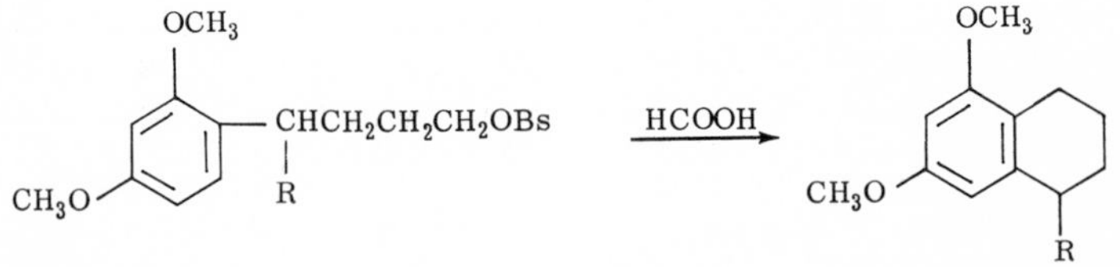

91% yield

---

[1] D. Samuel, *J. Chem. Soc.*, **1960**, 1318.
[2] K. M. Ibne-Rasa and E. Koubek, *J. Org. Chem.*, **28**, 3240 (1963).
[3] Gould, p. 291.
[4] G. Stork and W. N. White, *J. Am. Chem. Soc.*, **75**, 4119 (1953); **78**, 4607 (1956).

ANSWER 39.   [See R. Heck and S. Winstein, *J. Am. Chem. Soc.*, **79**, 3105 (1957).]

The displacement of the —OBs group in compounds such as A can proceed either by direct attack by solvent, leading to the normal products of solvolysis, or by attack by the benzene ring, leading to intermediates such as B. These can re-arrange to C, the secondary carbon being expected to be more mobile than the primary one, and then lose a proton to give the observed product.

The importance of this aryl-assisted displacement depends on the size of the ring formed and on the effect of the aromatic substituents (e.g., —OCH_3) in stabilizing the intermediate B. Thus the yields of tetralin vary as follows:

Aromatic substituent	Tetralin yield
2,4-di-OMe	91%
4-OMe	55%
unsubstituted	20%

Considering the effect of chain length in the series

$$Ar - (CH_2)_n - OBs$$

the relationship between chain length and aryl participation is

n	Participation
2	very important
3	vanishingly small
4	some to considerable
5	vanishingly small

When n = 2, the system is that of the ordinary "neighboring group effect"[1] and the participation is accompanied by a great increase in the rate of $^\ominus$OBs liberation. The intermediate in this case is presumably D, which is opened by attack of solvent to give the normal solvolysis product.

---

[1] For a review, see B. Capon, *Quart. Rev.*, **18**, 45 (1964).

PROBLEM 40.   Deduce the structures of the products in the following reactions, where (A) means that the substance is treated first with 2,4,6-tri-
ethylbenzoyl chloride and then with potassium t-butoxide.

(40.1)

$$\text{LiAlD}_4 \longrightarrow \qquad \text{(A)} \longrightarrow$$

(40.2)

$$\text{LiAlD}_4 \longrightarrow \qquad \text{(A)} \longrightarrow$$

ANSWER 40.   [D. Y. Curtin and D. B. Kellom, *J. Am. Chem. Soc.*, **75**, 6011
(1953).]

The reductive opening of epoxide rings with metal hydrides can be regarded
as an $S_N 2$ reaction involving a hydride ion. Thus the trans compound (1) gives
the erythro product by a deuteride attack from the side opposite the C-O bond,
and the cis compound (2), in a similar manner, gives the threo alcohol.

Base-catalyzed elimination reactions normally require that the two groups
lost (in this case a hydrogen or deuterium and the esterified hydroxyl function)
be trans.[1] Each of the reduction products has two conformations (cf. A, B) in
which this arrangement appears. Elimination from one of the conformers will
give the cis alkene and from the other the trans. In the transition state leading
to the trans product, however, it is possible for both phenyl groups to be in the
plane of the developing double bond and to add resonance stabilization. The cis
transition state, on the other bond, is destabilized by hindrance between the
bulky phenyl groups. For this reason the trans product is favored, and the elimination occurs from the conformer which will give it. As a result, the alchohol
from (1) loses D, whereas that from (2) reacts in the form B and loses H.

---

[1]Gould, p. 489.

PROBLEM 41.   Suggest a mechanism for the following reaction.

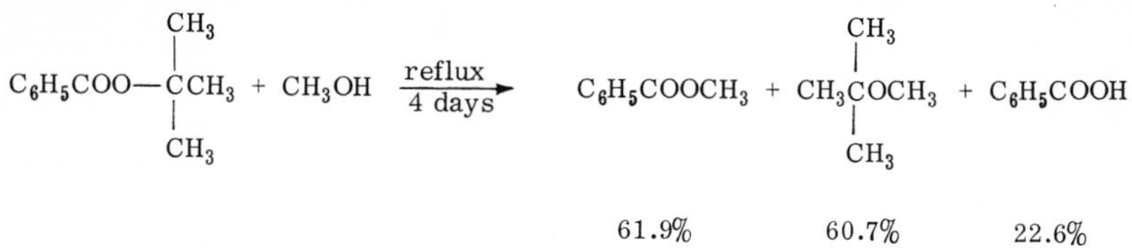

$$C_6H_5COO-\overset{\overset{\displaystyle CH_3}{|}}{\underset{\underset{\displaystyle CH_3}{|}}{C}}CH_3 + CH_3OH \xrightarrow[\text{4 days}]{\text{reflux}} C_6H_5COOCH_3 + CH_3\overset{\overset{\displaystyle CH_3}{|}}{\underset{\underset{\displaystyle CH_3}{|}}{C}}OCH_3 + C_6H_5COOH$$

| | 61.9% | 60.7% | 22.6% |

$$\text{N.B.} \quad C_6H_5COOH + CH_3\overset{\overset{\displaystyle CH_3}{|}}{\underset{\underset{\displaystyle CH_3}{|}}{C}}OH + CH_3OH \xrightarrow[\text{7 days}]{\text{reflux}} \quad \text{no} \quad CH_3\overset{\overset{\displaystyle CH_3}{|}}{\underset{\underset{\displaystyle CH_3}{|}}{C}}OCH_3$$

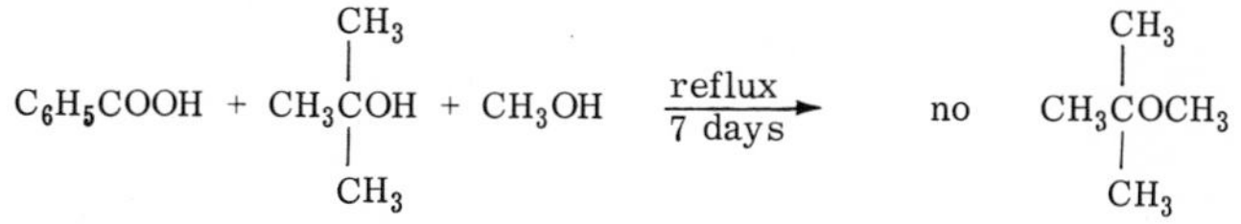

ANSWER 41.   [S. G. Cohen and A. Schneider, *J. Am. Chem. Soc.,* **63**, 3382 (1941).]

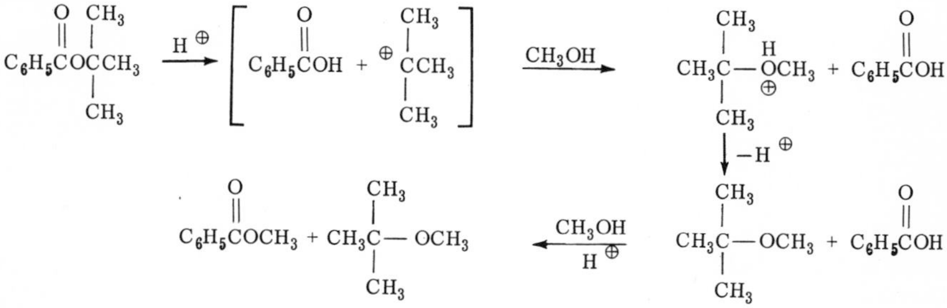

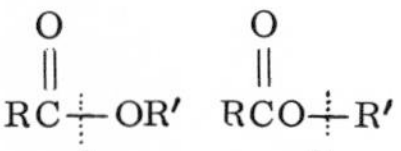

$$\underset{\underset{\displaystyle CH_3}{|}}{\overset{\overset{\displaystyle O \quad CH_3}{\| \quad |}}{C_6H_5COCCH_3}} \xrightarrow{H^{\oplus}} \left[\overset{\overset{\displaystyle O}{\|}}{C_6H_5COH} + \overset{\oplus}{\underset{\underset{\displaystyle CH_3}{|}}{\overset{\overset{\displaystyle CH_3}{|}}{C}}}CH_3 \right] \xrightarrow{CH_3OH} \underset{\underset{\displaystyle CH_3}{|}}{\overset{\overset{\displaystyle CH_3}{|}}{CH_3C}}\overset{\overset{\displaystyle H}{|}}{\underset{\oplus}{-OCH_3}} + \overset{\overset{\displaystyle O}{\|}}{C_6H_5COH}$$

$$\Big\downarrow -H^{\oplus}$$

$$\overset{\overset{\displaystyle O}{\|}}{C_6H_5COCH_3} + CH_3\overset{\overset{\displaystyle CH_3}{|}}{\underset{\underset{\displaystyle CH_3}{|}}{C}}-OCH_3 \xleftarrow[H^{\oplus}]{CH_3OH} \underset{\underset{\displaystyle CH_3}{|}}{\overset{\overset{\displaystyle CH_3}{|}}{CH_3C}}-OCH_3 + \overset{\overset{\displaystyle O}{\|}}{C_6H_5COH}$$

$$\underset{1}{\overset{\overset{\displaystyle O}{\|}}{RC\!+\!OR'}} \quad \underset{2}{\overset{\overset{\displaystyle O}{\|}}{RCO\!+\!R'}}$$

Two fundamentally different modes of cleavage are possible for the alcoholysis or hydrolysis of esters. These involve (**1**) cleavage of the acyl-oxygen bond (A_{AC} and B_{AC} mechanisms)[1] or (**2**) alkyl-oxygen cleavage (A_{AL} and B_{AL} mechanisms).[1] The majority of ester hydrolyses proceed by acyl-oxygen cleaveage, but the case shown does not.

The normal transesterification mechanism would give

---

[1]C. K. Ingold, *Structure and Mechanism in Organic Chemistry*, Cornell University Press, Ithaca, 1953, pp. 752–783; Hine, Chap. 12.

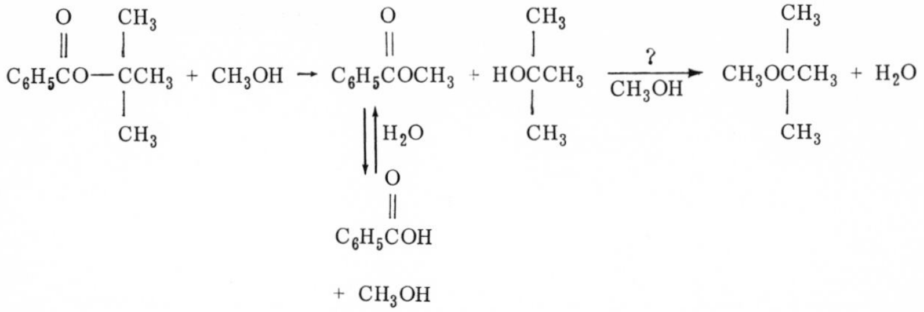

which would explain the results, except that the second experiment shows that there is no reaction between methanol and t-butyl alcohol under the conditions used. Thus the methyl ether must be formed directly from the initial ester.

The reactions of tertiary esters of this kind appear to be acid catalyzed even in neutral solution,[2] and would appear to involve the formation of an ionic intermediate. On the other hand, similar optically active esters have been shown to solvolyze with considerable net inversion,[3] so it is unclear whether the reaction is unimolecular or bimolecular.

PROBLEM 42.   Suggest mechanisms for the following reactions:

(42.1)

(42.2)

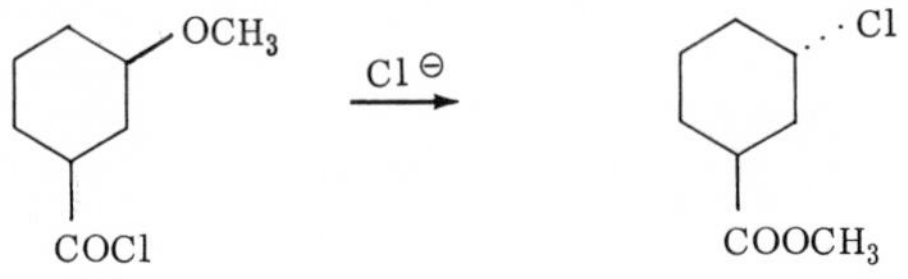

(42.3)

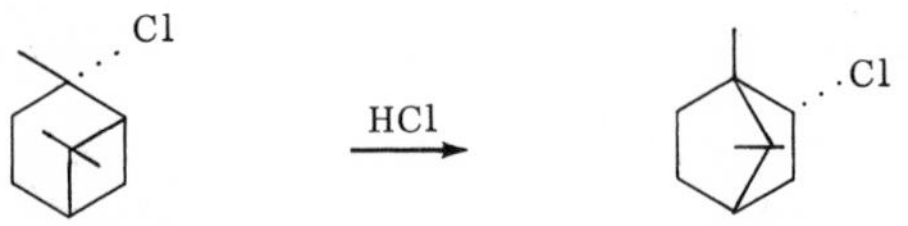

(42.4)

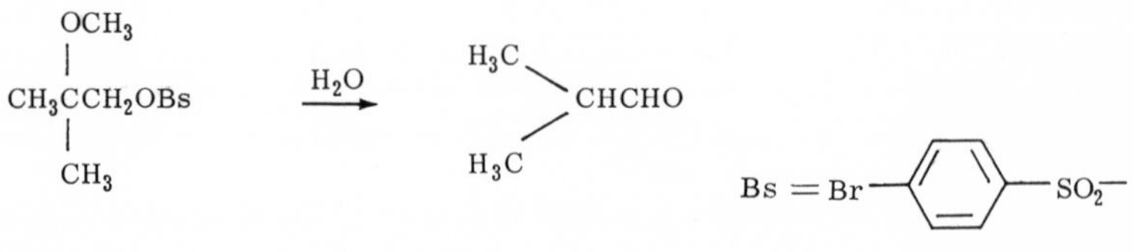

---

[2] See A. G. Davies and J. Kenyon, *Quart. Rev.*, **9**, 203 (1955).

[3] W. von E. Doering and H. N. Zeiss, *J. Am. Chem. Soc.*, **65**, 4733 (1953).

ANSWER 42.   [For a general review of neighboring group effects see B.
Capon, *Quart. Rev.*, **18**, 45 (1964).]

(42.1)   [S. Winstein, H. V. Hess, and R. E. Buckles, *J. Am. Chem. Soc.*, **64**, 2796
(1942); S. Winstein and R. E. Buckles, J. Am. Chem. Soc., **65**, 613 (1943).]

(42.2)   [D. S. Noyce and H. I. Weingarten, *J. Am. Chem. Soc.*, **79**, 3093 (1957).]

(42.3)   [See J. Berson in *Molecular Rearrangements*, Vol. I (P. de Mayo, ed.),
Wiley-Interscience, New York, 1963, p. 185.]

(42.4)   [S. Winstein, C. R. Lindegren, and L. L. Ingraham, *J. Am. Chem. Soc.*, **75**,
155 (1953).]

Loss of a proton from the intermediate **1** to give a vinyl ether followed by hydrolysis would be a reasonable alternative route, but it was shown that in fact the ether **2** is stable under the reaction conditions.

PROBLEM 43.   Predict which will be solvolyzed faster, the cis or trans isomer having the structure A. Predict any change in the rates of these solvolyses when a nitro group is introduced into the para position of the phenyl group.

ANSWER 43.   [H. L. Goering and K. L. House, *J. Am. Chem. Soc.*, **79**, 6542 (1957).]

These are examples of two apparently similar reactions, one of which because of its geometry involves neighboring group participation,[1] and one of which does not. In the case of the 1,2-trans compound, unshared electrons on the sulfur atom can interact with the developing positive center in the transition state B and accelerate the elimination of the chloride ion. In the cis case the lack of planarity of the C—Cl and C—S bonds prevents this interaction, and the rate of hydrolysis is actually less than that of cyclohexyl chloride.

B

The electron-withdrawing effect of the nitro group in the p position lessens the availability of the unshared electrons on the sulfur atom for participation in the displacement reaction. Thus the reaction rate of the trans compound is decreased by introduction of a p-nitro group, although it is still much greater than that of the unassisted cis compound. The retardation effect of a nitro group in the cis compound is very small, since its effects all occur at a considerable distance from the site of reaction.

---

[1]See B. Capon, *Quart. Rev.*, **18**, 45 (1964).

PROBLEM 44.   Suggest an explanation for the fact that the acidic and alkaline hydrolyses of the following chloroamine derivative afford isomeric alcohols.

$$(C_6H_5CH_2)_2NCH_2CHCH_3 \xrightarrow[\text{acidic conditions}]{\text{basic conditions}} \begin{array}{c} (C_6H_5CH_2)_2NCHCH_2OH \\ | \\ CH_3 \end{array}$$

$$\underset{Cl}{|}$$

$$(C_6H_5CH_2)_2NCH_2CHCH_3$$
$$\underset{OH}{|}$$

ANSWER 44.   Under strongly acidic conditions, the protonation of the basic nitrogen is complete, and its normally unshared electrons are not available to participate in the hydrolysis of the halide. Thus the reaction occurs as a normal, unassisted displacement (A).

If the amine is not tied up as the salt, however, the first stage of the hydrolysis is an internal displacement leading to the ethylenimmonium ion B_1.[1] In the presence of strong base (OH^-), this undergoes S_N2 ring opening at the more reactive primary carbon to give the rearranged product.[2]

Matters are complicated, however, by the observation[3] that an intermediate corresponding to B_1 has been found to give unrearranged product in approximately neutral solution (HCO_3^-). The explanation has been advanced[4] that the transition state in the attack by neutral water has more positive charge on the carbon than does that formed during attack by OH^-, and that consequently reaction at the secondary carbon is favored.

A

$$\underset{H_2\ddot{O}}{\overset{\oplus}{R_2NH-CH_2}\overset{Cl}{\underset{|}{C}}HCH_3} \rightarrow \overset{\oplus}{R_2NH-CH_2CHCH_3} \xrightarrow{H_2O} \overset{\oplus}{R_2NHCH_2CHCH_3} + H_3O^{\oplus}$$
$$\overset{}{\underset{\oplus OH_2}{}} \qquad \underset{OH}{|}$$

---

[1]See Gould, pp. 570ff.

[2]See S. D. Ross, *J. Am. Chem. Soc.*, **69**, 2982 (1947).

[3]See J. F. Kerwin, G. E. Ullyot, R. C. Fuson, and C. L. Zirkle, *J. Am. Chem. Soc.*, **69**, 2961 (1947).

[4]A. Streitwieser, Jr., *Chem. Rev.*, **56**, 680 (1956).

B

$R_2N:$ — CH_2CHCH_3 — Cl → R R \ ⊕ / N / \ CH_2——$CHCH_3$ $\xrightarrow{OH \ominus}$ $:NR_2$ | $HOCH_2$—$CHCH_3$

B_1 $\xrightarrow[-H \oplus]{H_2O}$ $R_2N:$ | CH_2—$CHCH_3$ | OH

PROBLEM 45.   Suggest an explanation for the difference in the ratio of the products given by the following two reactions:

		Ratio of products	
		Nitro compound	Nitrite ester
n–$C_7H_{15}I$	$\dfrac{AgNO_2}{\text{in ether}} \longrightarrow$	8 :	1
	$\dfrac{AgNO_2}{\text{in acetonitrile}} \longrightarrow$	5 :	2

ANSWER 45.   [N. Kornblum, R. A. Smiley, R. K. Blackwood, and D. C. Iffland, *J. Am. Chem. Soc.*, **77**, 6269 (1955).]

The reaction of nitrite ion (an "ambident" anion, capable of reacting at two sites, N or O) with alkyl halides proceeds via transition states which may have either S_N1 or S_N2 character, or both. In the presence of silver ion, which helps remove the halide ion, there is a tendency for the C—X bond breaking to be farther advanced than the C $\cdots$ NO_2 bond forming. The result is a transition state in which the carbon atom involved has partial carbonium ion character, i.e., a partial positive charge. The greater this charge, the greater the tendency for the orientation of the incoming nitrite ion to be determined by the electrostatic attraction between the positive carbon and the most negatively charged atom of the incoming group (this is usually the most electronegative atom in the conjugated charged system). In the present case, such orientation leads to the formation of nitrite esters by attack by the nitrite oxygen.

It is suggested that in the absence of such electrostatic effects, attack at the least charged atom predominates, since fewer molecules of solvent must be displaced to bring the reactants together. Whether or not the interpretation is correct, the results are consistent with this view. Under conditions which would be expected to reduce the ionic character of the transition state, attack at the least electronegative atom increases (formation of nitro compounds in this case).

For the examples cited, the transition state in acetonitrile should have more carbonium ion character than that in ether, for the former solvent is more polar. This increase in carbonium ion character increases the yield of nitrite ester.

As would be expected from the above discussion, the proportions of nitrite and nitro compounds vary with the structure of the halide; tertiary halides give more nitrite ester than do secondary halides, and these in turn give more than primary ones. Likewise, a charge from silver nitrite to sodium nitrite, in which the sodium ion does *not* help remove the halide ion, decreases the fraction of nitrite ester formed.

PROBLEM 46.   Suggest mechanisms for the following reactions:

(46.1)

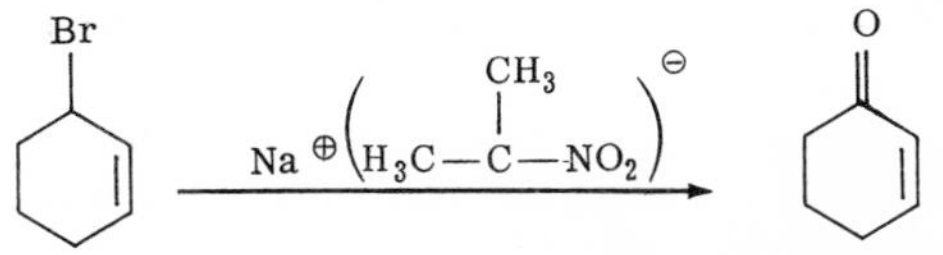

(46.2)

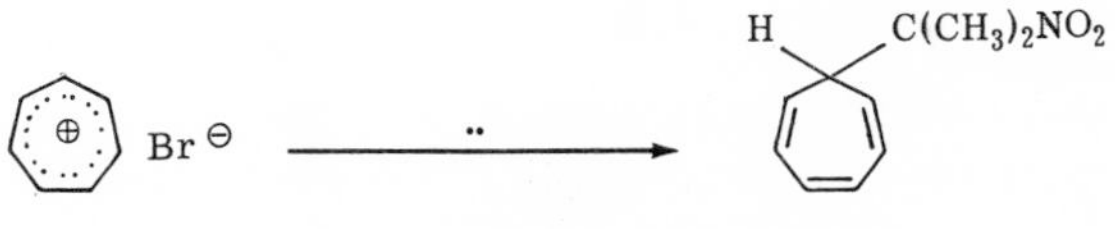

ANSWER 46.   [M. Bersohn, *J. Am. Chem. Soc.,* **83**, 2136 (1961).]

(46.1)

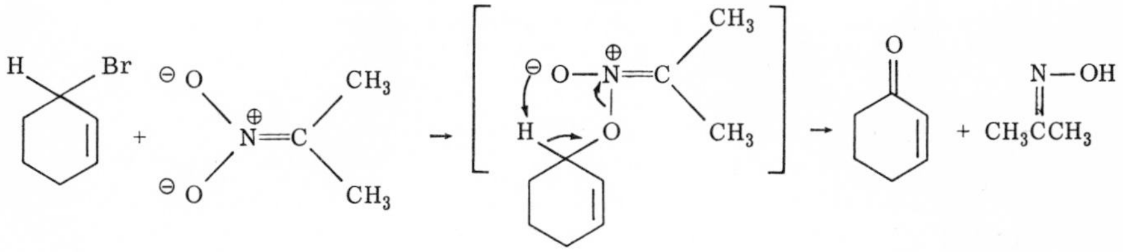

(46.2)

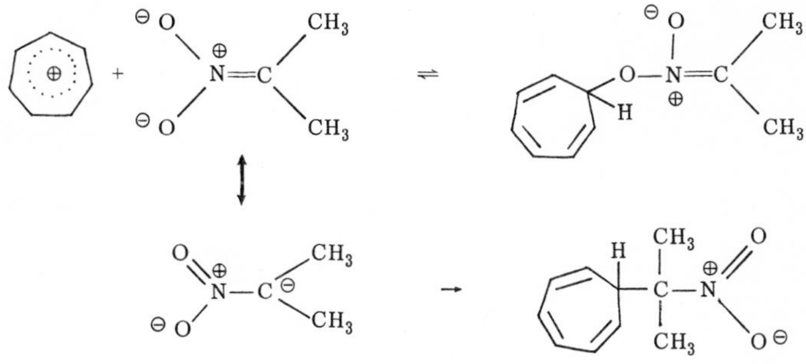

The alkylation of ambident anions (those capable of reacting at two sites) has been found to yield different products, depending on the exact reaction conditions. It has been suggested by Kornblum[1] that these reactions represent a graded series between pure $S_N 1$ and $S_N 2$.[2] In this series there is more or less positive charge on the carbon on which displacement occurs, depending on whether the halide begins to leave first ($S_N 1$ as the limiting case) or the incoming group has to force it out ($S_N 2$ limiting). The experimental results are consistent with the idea that in reactions with a large $S_N 1$ character, the electrostatic attraction between the developing positive center and the most negatively charged atom in the anion (usually the most electronegative) determine the direction of attack. On the other hand, for reactions with a predominately $S_N 2$ character, attack tends to occur on the least electronegative atom of the ambident system.

The direction of ambident alkylation can also be greatly affected by the solvent[3] and the physical state of the anion.[4]

In the present case, the reaction with an allyl halide is expected to have a large $S_N 1$ component; i.e., the carbon is partially charged before the transition state, even though the kinetics are probably second-order. Consequently, the reaction with the 2-nitropropane anion leads to O-alkylation. The intermediate product, a nitrous ester, is unstable[5] and rearranges to give the observed products.

If the reaction proceeds as described for the partially charged allyl bromide system, the reactants would be expected to be even more strongly oriented in the case of the stable tropenium cation. The observation that only C-alkylated products are found is explained by suggesting that because of the stability of the cation, the rapidly formed O-alkylation product is in equilibrium with the starting materials and that the more stable C-alkylated product accumulates (thermodynamic versus kinetic control).

---

[1]N. Kornblum, R. A. Smiley, R. K. Blackwood, and D. C. Iffland, *J. Am. Chem. Soc.*, **77**, 6269 (1955).

[2]See Gould, Chap. 8, for a discussion of these terms.

[3]N. Kornblum, P. J. Berrigan, and W. J. leNoble, *J. Am. Chem. Soc.*, **85**, 1141 (1963); N. Kornblum, R. Seltzer, and P. Haberfield, *J. Am. Chem. Soc.*, **85**, 1148 (1963).

[4]N. Kornblum and A. P. Lurie, *J. Am. Chem. Soc.*, **81**, 2705 (1959).

[5]M. Montavon, H. Lindlar, R. Marbet, R. Ruegg, G. Ryser, G. Sancy, P. Zellar, and O. Isler, *Helv. Chim. Acta.*, **40**, 1250 (1957).

CHAPTER 4

ADDITION AND
ELIMINATION REACTIONS

In addition to advanced texts, the following references are useful.

1. J. F. Bunnett, *Angew. Chem. Intern. Ed. Engl.*, **1**, 225 (1962). A short but excellent study of the mechanisms of bimolecular eliminations.
2. D. V. Banthorpe, *Elimination Reactions,* Elsevier, Amsterdam, 1963. A general survey of olefin-forming reactions and their mechanisms.
3. *The Chemistry of Alkenes,* Vol. 1 of *The Chemistry of Functional Groups* (S. Patai, ed.), Wiley-Interscience, New York, 1965. An extensive collection of contributions on various phases of alkene chemistry.

PROBLEM 47.   The dehydrobromination of $CH_3 CH_2 CBr(CH_3)_2$ with bases affords a mixture of isomeric 1- and 2-olefins. Explain why the proportion of 1-olefin increases with the following series of basic reagents:

Reagents	Proportions of 1-olefin
pyridine	25%
2-picoline	30%
2,6-lutidine	45%

ANSWER 47.   [H. C. Brown and M. Nakagawa, *J. Am. Chem. Soc.*, **78**, 2196 (1956).]
    The factors determining the direction of elimination by bimolecular processes are complex, and there is no full agreement of the relative importance

of the various factors involved.[1] It is clear, however, that steric interaction between the various components in the possible transition states can have a major effect on their relative stabilities and thus on the products observed.

Bimolecular dehydrohalogenations usually proceed so as to yield the most highly substituted, i.e., the most stable, olefin (Saytzeff rule).[1a] Thus the expected product in this case is the 2-olefin (A). As methyl groups are added around the basic nitrogen, however, their steric interaction with the groups surrounding the secondary proton to be removed (F strain)[2] makes the transition state leading to A less favorable. As a consequence, the alternative elimination leading to the 1-olefin B (Hofmann elimination)[1a] can play a greater role. This elimination, although less favored on electronic grounds, is less sensitive to steric factors, since it involves removal of a primary proton, and becomes relatively more important as the formation of A is suppressed.

PROBLEM 48.   Suggest an explanation for the fact that the proportion of the 1,4-addition product B found increases as the reaction temperature is raised.

$$CH_2{=}CH{-}CH{=}CH_2 \xrightarrow{Br_2} \underset{Br}{\underset{|}{CH_2}}{-}\underset{Br}{\underset{|}{CH}}{-}CH{=}CH_2 \ + \ \underset{Br}{\underset{|}{CH_2}}{-}CH{=}CH{-}\underset{Br}{\underset{|}{CH_2}}$$

$$\qquad\qquad\qquad\qquad\qquad A \qquad\qquad\qquad\qquad B$$

Reaction temperature	Proportions
Room temperature	A > B
100°	B > A

Note: The predominant formation of B is also observed when the reaction mixture obtained at room temperature is heated to 100° or merely allowed to stand for several days.

---

[1] (a) See Gould, Chap. 12. (b) For expositions of the two major schools of thought, see M. L. Dhar, E. D. Hughes, C. K. Ingold, A. M. M. Mandour, and G. A. Marv, *J. Chem. Soc.*, **1948**, 2093; H. C. Brown and I. Moritani, *J. Am. Chem. Soc.*, **78**, 2203 (1956).

[2] For a brief review and leading references, see H. C. Brown, *Record Chem Progr. Kresge-Hooker Sci. Lib.*, **14**, 83 (1953).

ANSWER 48.   [E. H. Farmer, C. D. Lawrence, and J. F. Thorpe, *J. Chem.*
Soc., **1928**, 729; L. F. Hatch, P. D. Gardner, and R. E. Gilbert,
J. Am. Chem. Soc., **81**, 5943 (1959): see Gould, pp. 530ff.]

This example represents a well-defined case of kinetic versus equilibrium
control in determining the products of a reaction. That the 1,4-dibromide (B) is
more stable than the 1,2-isomer (A) both at room temperature and at 100° is
shown by its predominance in the equilibrium mixtures. On the other hand, A is
formed more rapidly, at least at room temperature. From the data given, it is
not possible to tell whether the reaction at 100° leads directly to B, or first to
A, followed by a rapid isomerization to B.

The greater stability of B is generally ascribed to the fact that it possesses
a more substituted and therefore more stable double bond than does A. The more
rapid formation of A, however, indicates that the transition state leading to it is
more stable than that leading to B. The routes may be suggested to be

and various arguments have been presented to account for the preferred formation of A. Since the details of the structures of the activated complexes are not
known, none of them can be regarded as proved.

PROBLEM 49.   Predict the structure of the chief unsaturated product in each
of the following elimination reactions:

(49.1)

(49.2)

(cont.)

(49.3)

$$\xrightarrow[\text{acetone}]{\text{Zn}}$$

(49.4)

$$-CHBrCH_2Br \xrightarrow[\text{NaNH}_2]{\text{excess}} \xrightarrow{} H_3O^{\oplus}$$

ANSWER 49.   [For extensive discussion of the effects controlling the direction of elimination under various conditions, see Gould, Chap. 12, and W. H. Saunders, Jr., in *The Chemistry of Alkenes*, Vol. 1 of *The Chemistry of Functional Groups* (S. Patai, ed.), Wiley-Interscience, New York, 1965, pp. 149-201.]

(49.1)   The acid-catalyzed dehydration of tertiary alcohols proceeds much more rapidly than that of primary ones, and gives the most substituted double bond (Saytzeff rule). Thus in this case the preferred product is A.

A

(49.2)   Base-catalyzed dehydrohalogenations also follow the Saytzeff rule, at least when conducted with bases of low steric requirements.

$$CH_3CH_2CH = CCH_3$$
$$\overset{|}{C}H_3$$

(49.3)   Dehalogenations of this sort require, or at least are greatly facilitated by having, the halogen bonds coplanar and antiparallel. Thus

$$\xrightarrow{\hspace{2cm}}$$

$+$ $ZnBr_2$

cis −2− butene

(49.4)

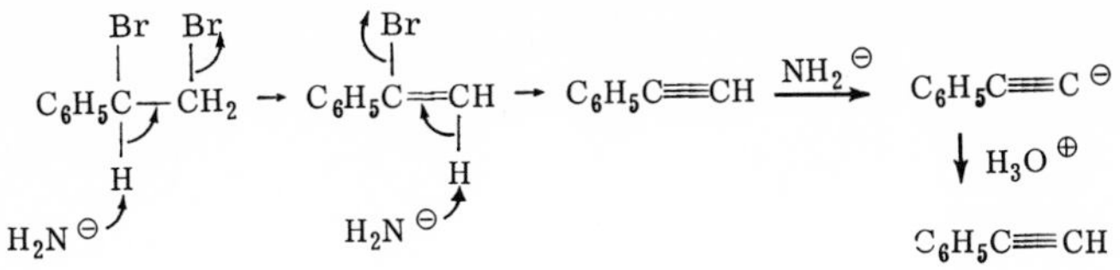

      Since the $-C\equiv CH$ group has an acidic proton and forms a sodium salt under the reaction conditions, acidification is necessary to isolate the final product.

PROBLEM 50.   The following shows the proportions of isomeric olefins produced in each of the elimination reactions. Suggest explanations for these observations.

(50.1)

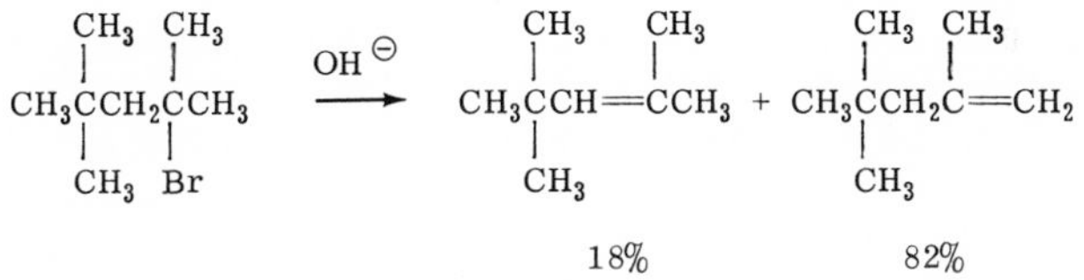

(50.2)

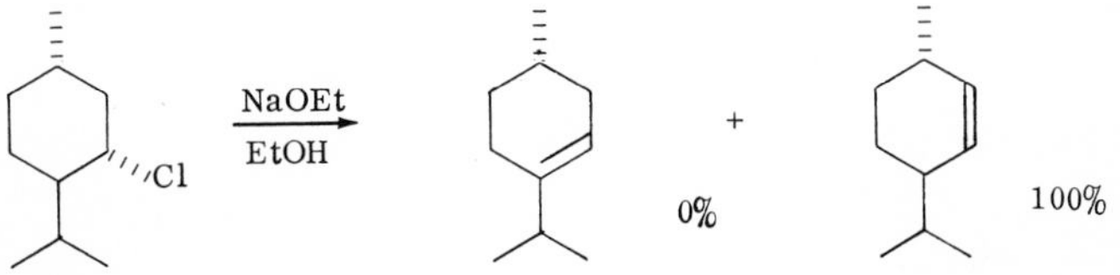

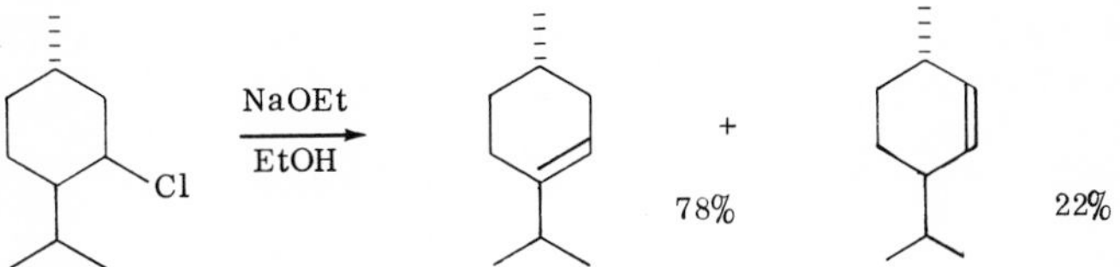

(50.3)

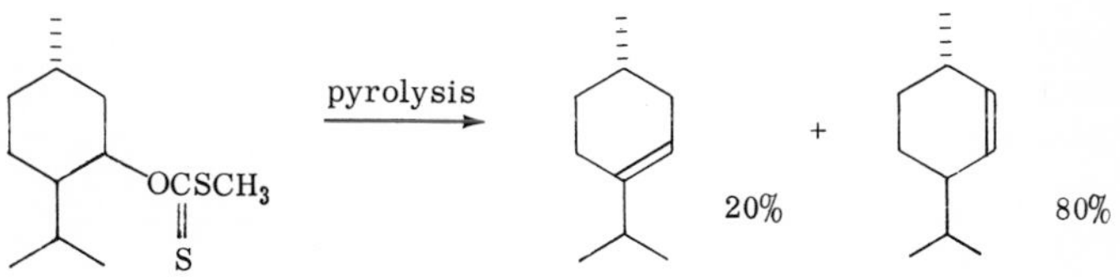

(cont.)

ANSWER 50.   [For discussions of elimination reactions, see Gould, Chap. 12, and W. H. Saunders, Jr., in *The Chemistry of Alkenes*, Vol. 1 of *The Chemistry of Functional Groups* (S. Patai, ed.), Wiley-Interscience, New York, 1965, pp. 149-201.]

(50.1)   [H. C. Brown and I. Moritani, *J. Am. Chem. Soc.*, **77**, 3607 (1955), and following papers.]

This is one of the rare cases of an elimination proceeding by the E1 mechanism which does not give a product distribution following the Saytzeff rule (more substituted alkene preferred). In this case, however, the olefin B contains a methyl group cis to a t-butyl and is badly strained. This strain appears as well in the transition state leading to B and raises its energy to the point at which formation of A becomes favored.

(50.2)   [E. D. Hughes, C. K. Ingold, and J. B. Rose, *J. Chem. Soc.*, **1953**, 3839.]

These reactions have been shown to be second-order E2 eliminations. Such eliminations favor strongly the loss of groups which are trans-diaxial. In case A, only the hydrogen shown can be brought into the required orientation with respect to the chlorine, and elimination gives exclusively 2-menthene. Because of the extra instability of the transition state caused by the two axial substituents, the activation energy is larger than that for elimination from cyclohexyl chloride, and the reaction proceeds at ca. 0.01 the rate.

In the second case, the chlorine is already axial and trans to two hydrogen atoms. The ratio of the two products is about that often found for reactions whose direction of elimination is determined by the Saytzeff rule. In this example there is no extra hindrance in the transition state, and the rate resembles that of cyclohexyl chloride.

(50.3)   [W. Hückel, W. Tappe, and G. Legutke, *Ann.*, **543**, 191 (1940); Gould, pp. 500-507.]

The pyrolytic elimination of xanthates (Chugaev reaction)[1] normally gives as the main product alkene(s) resulting from cis elimination. In A, the only hydrogen available for such elimination is on carbon 2, and so the major product is 2-menthene. B, on the other hand, has two possible hydrogen, on 2 and 4. In this case the usual preference for transition states leading to the most highly substituted double bond[2] comes into play, and elimination from C-4 is favored over that from C-2.

------

[1] See C. H. DePuy and R. W. King, Chem. Rev., **60**, 431 (1960); H. R. Nace in *Organic Reactions*, Vol. 12, Wiley, New York, 1962, p. 57.

[2] It is sometimes suggested that the Chugaev and related pyrolyses follow the Hofmann elimination rule (least substituted alkene formed), but an examination of the actual results[1] indicates that conformational effects and the stability of the product olefin interact to complicate the question so that a single "rule" cannot be applied.

Whereas in case B the 2-menthene which appears as a minor product can be accounted for as the result of an alternative cis elimination, this is not true for the 3-menthene from A. Such trans eliminations usually occur as side reactions during the pyrolyses, and it has been suggested[3] that they arise from heterolytic cleavage into an ion pair in which there is enough relative motion of the two ions that the anion can find its way to the trans hydrogen which must be removed.

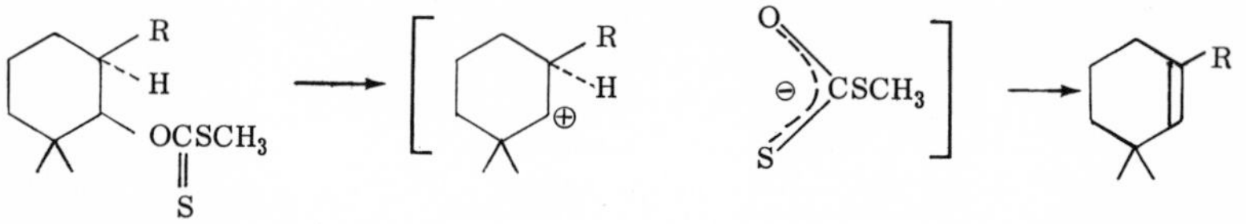

PROBLEM 51.   Suggest an explanation for the difference between the following reactions.

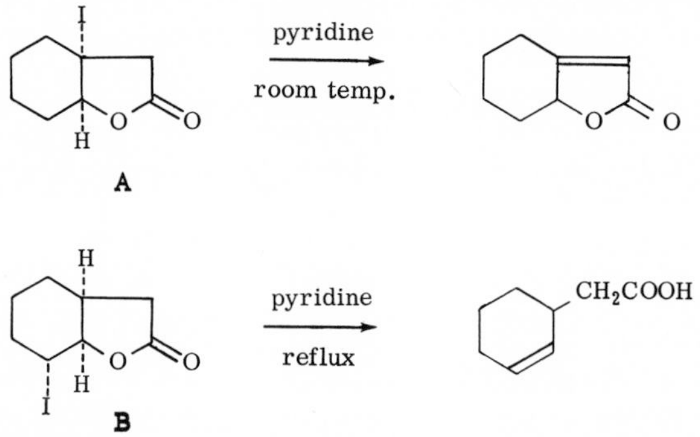

A

B

ANSWER 51.   [J. Klein, *J. Am. Chem. Soc.*, **81**, 3611 (1959).]

The reaction of A represents the usual trans elimination reaction resulting in the loss of HI.[1] Its relative ease arises from the fact that the proton to be removed is α to a carbonyl group and so is more readily lost to the base (compare the slower formation of C, p. 95).

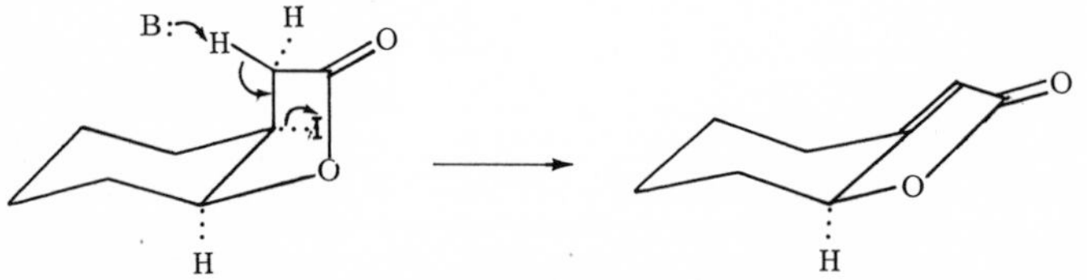

It is suggested that the second reaction involves base attack on the iodine, with concerted displacement of the acid anion. Thus

---

[3]See Gould, pp. 502–507.
[1]Gould, pp. 489ff.

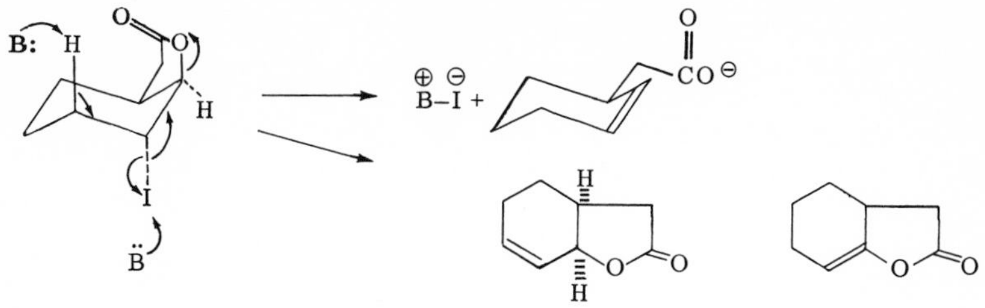

The product shown is actually a minor one (22%), the major one (36%) being C, which arises from a normal dehydrohalogenation. The alternative product, D, is not formed, because the required proton is cis to the iodine and the elimination is thus too slow to compete.

A few analogies are known for reaction B, but it still appears somewhat un-usual. In particular, the fate of the iodine (removed in the formal state of $I^{\oplus}$) is unclear. It would be expected to react with $I^{\ominus}$, produced along with C, to give I_2, but the author reports that I_2 could not be found.

PROBLEM 52.   Predict the structure and configuration of the product of each of the following reactions:

(52.1)

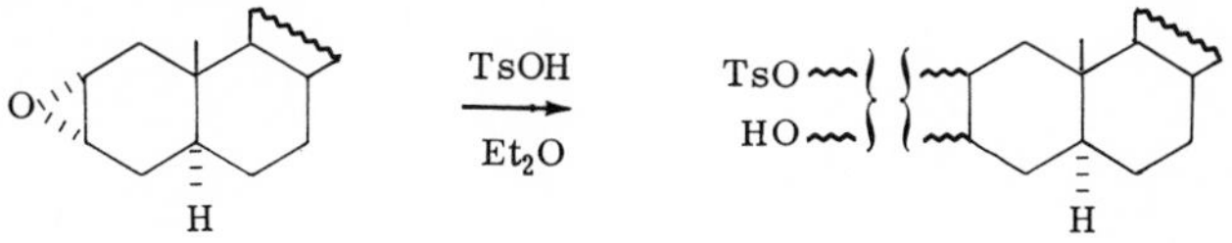

(52.2)

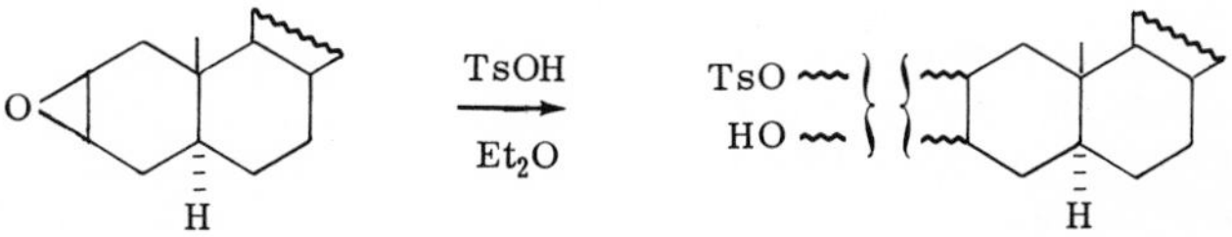

(52.3)

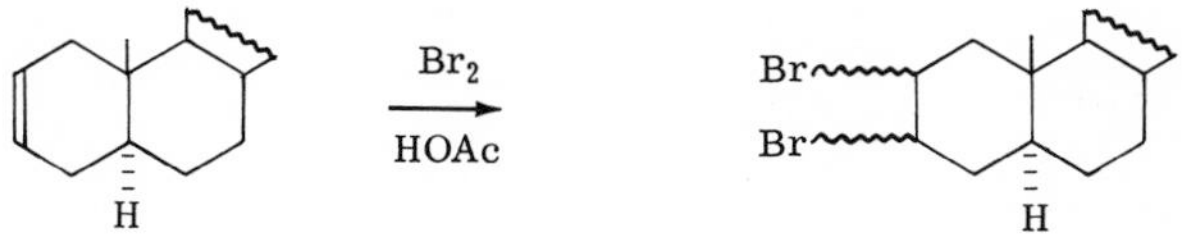

ANSWER 52.   [See E. L. Eliel in *Steric Effects in Organic Chemistry* (M. S. Newman, ed.), Wiley, New York, 1956, pp. 130ff.]

These reactions are examples of the preferred trans-diaxial opening of epoxides and the analogous trans-diaxial addition to double bonds.

(52.1)

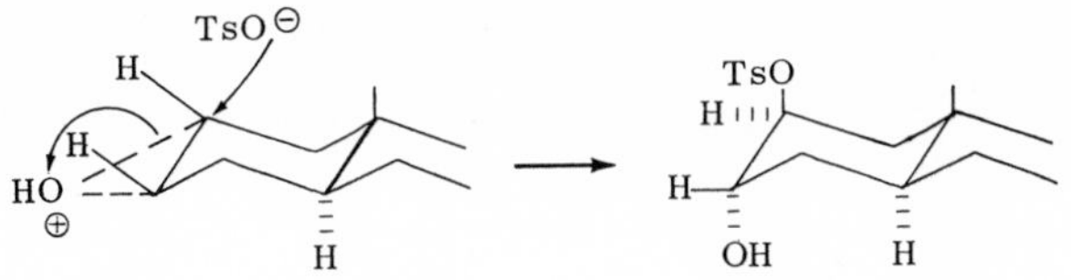

(52.2)

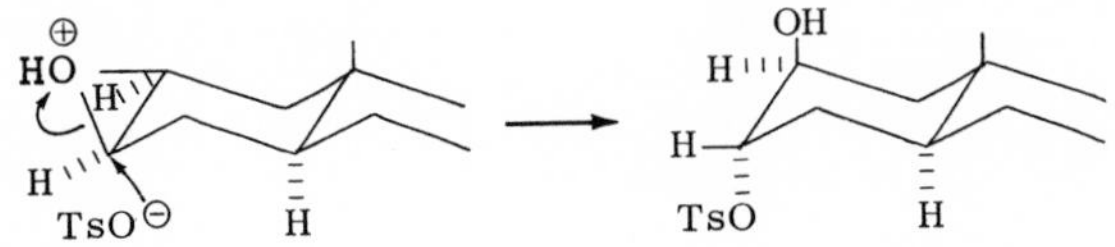

(52.3)

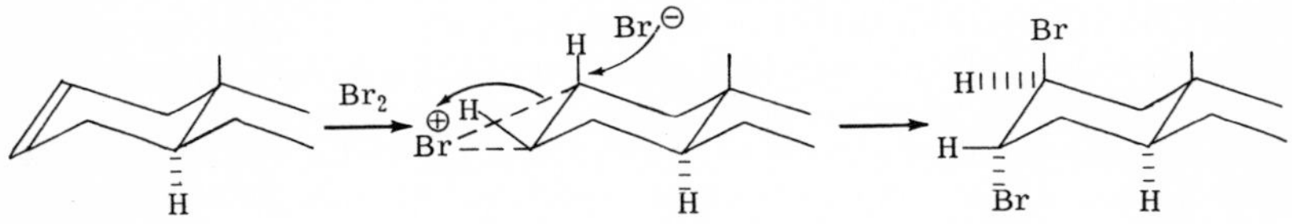

PROBLEM 53.   Suggest a mechanism for each of the following decarboxylation reactions.

(53.1)

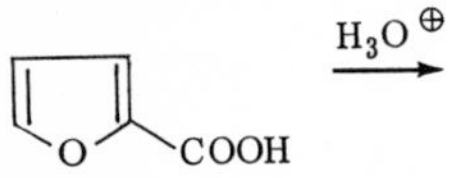

$H_3O^{\oplus}$

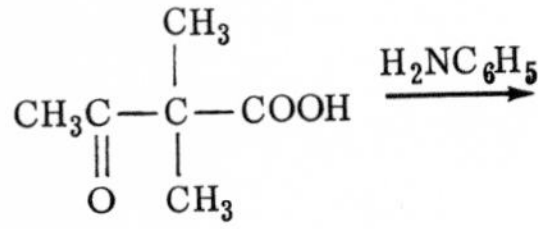

(53.4)

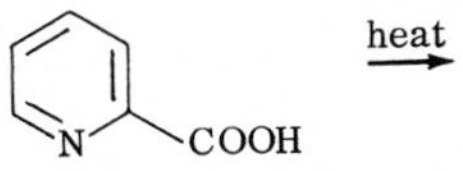

heat

(53.2)

$OH^{\ominus}$

(53.5)

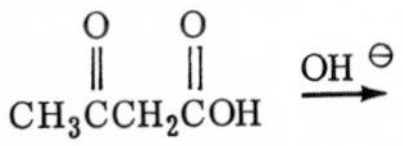

$\dfrac{heat}{H_2O}$

(53.3)

$H_2NC_6H_5$

(53.6)

$H_3O^{\oplus}$

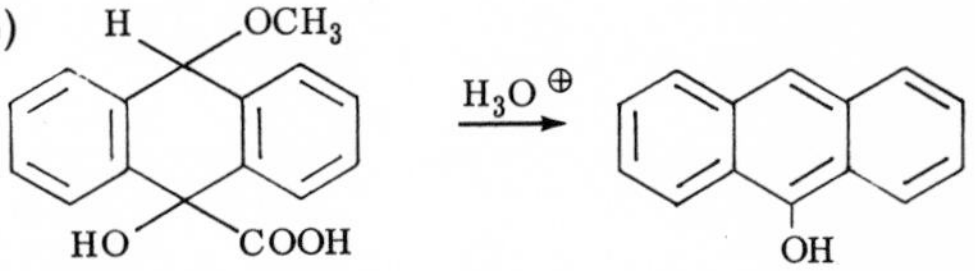

ANSWER 53.   [For a general discussion of decarboxylation mechanisms see
B. R. Brown, *Quart. Rev.*, **5**, 131 (1951); Gould, pp. 346-353.]

(53.1)

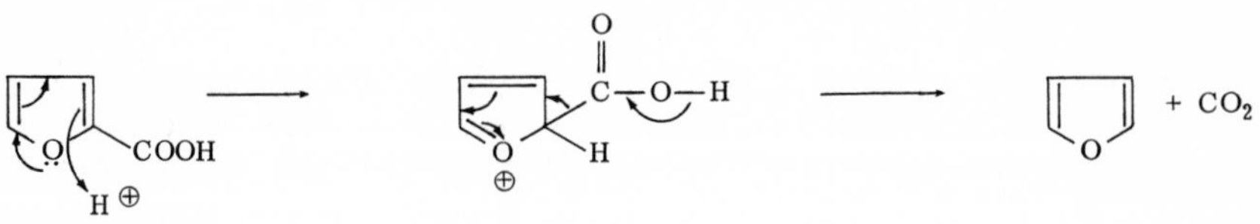

+ CO$_2$

This decarboxylation resembles electrophilic aromatic substitution and involves addition of a proton followed by elimination of the carboxyl group from the intermediate. Similar decarboxylations[1,2] and decarbonylations[3] are known in substituted benzenoid systems.

(53.2)   [Gould, p. 346.]

$$CH_3CCH_2COH \xrightarrow{OH^{\ominus}} CH_3C-CH_2-C-O^{\ominus} \longrightarrow CO_2 + CH_3C=CH_2 \xrightarrow{H_2O} CH_3CCH_3$$

This reaction is likely to be the major mode of decarboxylation only in solutions which are sufficiently basic to keep the acetoacetic acid present as the anion. If any considerable amount of the conjugate acid is present, it can decarboxylate more rapidly by the path

$$ \longrightarrow \quad CH_3C=CH_2 + CO_2 \quad (OH)$$

The relative rates of decomposition of the acid and anion forms of acetoacetic acid are 53:1.

(53.3)

$$CH_3C-C-C\overset{O}{\underset{OH}{}} + H_2NC_6H_5 \rightarrow \quad \longrightarrow \quad CH_3C=C\overset{CH_3}{\underset{CH_3}{}} + CO_2$$

$$\downarrow H_2O$$

$$CH_3CCH(CH_3)_2$$

The rate of decarboxylation of β-keto acids has been found to be markedly enhanced by the presence of primary amines. This cannot be due to their action as bases (see the preceding answer), so the mechanism given above has been proposed to account for the increased decomposition of the acid.

---

[1] W. M. Schubert, *J. Am. Chem. Soc.*, **71**, 2639 (1949).
[2] B. R. Brown, D. L. Hammick, and A. J. B. Scholefield, *J. Chem. Soc.*, **1950**, 778.
[3] H. Burkett, W. M. Schubert, F. Schultz, R. B. Murphy, and R. Talbott, *J. Am. Chem. Soc.*, **81**, 3923 (1959), and references cited there.

(53.4)   [See B. R. Brown and D. L. Hammick, *J. Chem. Soc.*, **1949**, 659.]

It has been shown that the anion of quinaldic acid (B) is stable under conditions which decarboxylate the free acid, whereas the corresponding methylated
compound C decomposes very readily. For this reason it is believed that the
decomposition of picolinic acid occurs through the zwitterion A.

(53.5)   [See W. von E. Doering and V. Z. Pasternak, *J. Am. Chem. Soc.*, **72**, 143
(1950).]

As in the preceding case, this free acid is found to decarboxylate readily,
although the derived salts (acid and base) are stable. The mechanism may involve either the zwitterion B, or a concerted process on the acid A, similar to
the decarboxylation of acetoacetic acid (see part 2).

(53. 6)   [J. Rigaudy and L. Nédélec, *Bull. Soc. Chim. France,* **1959**, 648.]

A

B

Although the compound B also gives anthronol on acid treatment, the conditions required are more vigorous, and B cannot be an intermediate in the decarboxylation of A.

PROBLEM 54.   The following order indicates the ease of decarboxylation in alkaline medium. Suggest an explanation.

$$CBr_3COOH > CCl_3COOH > CF_3COOH$$

ANSWER 54.   [I. Auerbach, F. H. Verhoek, and A. L. Henne, *J. Am. Chem. Soc.,* **72**, 299 (1950); F. H. Verhoek, *J. Am. Chem. Soc.,* **56**, 571 (1934); O. de Groote, *Bull. Soc. Chim. Belges,* **37**, 225 (1928).]

The results cannot be explained in terms of simple inductive stabilization of CX_3^-, since the inductive effect decreases in the order F > Cl > Br. It has been suggested[1] that they reflect the greater ability of bromine and chlorine to distribute the charge of the intermediate ion either by no-bond-resonance (A) or by expansion of the outer shell to accommodate ten electrons (B).

---

[1]R. E. Glick, *Chem. Ind.* (London), **1955**, 716.

$$
\begin{array}{ccc}
\underset{\underset{\displaystyle Br}{|}}{\overset{\overset{\displaystyle Br}{|}}{Br-C:^{\ominus}}} & \longleftrightarrow & \underset{\underset{\displaystyle Br}{|}}{\overset{\overset{\displaystyle :\ddot{Br}:^{\ominus}}{|}}{Br-C:}}
\end{array}
\qquad\qquad
\begin{array}{ccc}
\underset{\underset{\displaystyle Br}{|}}{\overset{\overset{\displaystyle Br}{|}}{Br-C:^{\ominus}}} & \longleftrightarrow & \underset{\underset{\displaystyle Br}{|}}{\overset{\overset{\displaystyle :\ddot{Br}:^{\ominus}}{||}}{Br-C}}
\end{array}
$$

A   B

Of these, the latter concept is more widely accepted.

An alternative argument would relate the enhanced rates to greater steric crowding in the starting acids containing the larger halogens and the relief of strain in going to the more open ion.

PROBLEM 55.   Predict which compounds of the following pairs are more readily decarboxylated under the conditions given.

(55.1)

$$
\underset{\underset{\displaystyle CH_3}{|}}{\overset{\overset{\displaystyle CH_3}{|}}{CH_3CCH{=}CHCOOH}}
\qquad
\underset{\underset{\displaystyle CH_3}{|}}{\overset{\overset{\displaystyle CH_3}{|}}{CH_2{=}CH-C-COOH}}
\qquad
\begin{array}{c}
\underline{\text{conditions}}\\[2pt]
\text{heat } 250\text{--}300°
\end{array}
$$

A   B

(55.2)

$$
\underset{\underset{\displaystyle C_6H_5\ \ COOH}{|\quad\ |}}{\overset{\overset{\displaystyle Br\ \ \ C_6H_5}{|\quad\ |}}{H{-}{-}{-}C{-}{-}C{-}{-}{-}{-}H}}
\qquad
\underset{\underset{\displaystyle C_6H_5\ \ C_6H_5}{|\quad\ |}}{\overset{\overset{\displaystyle Br\ \ \ COOH}{|\quad\ |}}{H{-}{-}{-}C{-}{-}C{-}{-}{-}{-}H}}
\qquad
\text{weak base in EtOH}
$$

A   B

ANSWER 55.   [For reviews of decarboxylation, see Gould, pp. 346-353, and B. R. Brown, *Quart. Rev.*, **5**, 131 (1951).]

(55.1)   [R. T. Arnold, O. C. Elmer, and R. M. Dodson, *J. Am. Chem. Soc.*, **72**, 4359 (1950).]

$\beta\gamma$-Unsaturated carboxylic acids such as B are decarboxylated thermally by a mechanism involving the cyclic transition state **1**. $\alpha\beta$-Unsaturated acids decarboxylate more slowly since they must first rearrange to the $\beta\gamma$-unsaturated isomer. In A this rearrangement is impossible, and decarboxylation is not observed.

$$
\longrightarrow
$$

$+\ CO_2$

1

(55.2) [D. Y. Curtin, *Rec. Chem. Progr. Kresge Hooker Sci. Lib.*, **15**, 111 (1954).]
Decarboxylation of β-halo acids occurs via a concerted trans-elimination
mechanism.[1]

$$Br^{\ominus} \quad + \quad \overset{\cdots}{C}{=}\overset{\cdots}{C} \quad + \quad CO_2$$

In these cases

A   B

The transition state for the elimination from A resembles somewhat the cis-
stilbene product and brings the two bulky phenyl groups closer than in the starting material. Consequently, it is less favorable ("cis effect") than that from B,
and the reaction is slower.

PROBLEM 56.   Give structures for the products.

(56.1)

(1) B$_2$H$_6$
$\longrightarrow$
(2) H$_2$O$_2$

(56.3) $Cl-CH_2CH{=}CH_2$

(1) B$_2$H$_6$
$\longrightarrow$
(2) OH$^{\ominus}$

(56.2)

(1) B$_2$H$_6$
$\longrightarrow$
(2) H$_2$O$_2$

(56.4)

(1) di-sec-isoamylborane
$\longrightarrow$
(2) H$_2$O$_2$

ANSWER 56.   [For an excellent survey of the hydroboration reaction, see H. C.
Brown, *Hydroboration,* Benjamin, New York, 1962.]

(56.1)   [H. C. Brown and G. Zweifel, *J. Am. Chem. Soc.*, **83**, 2544 (1961).]

+ di- and trialkyl products

---

[1] But see E. R. Trumbull, R. T. Finn, K. M. Ibne-Rasa, and C. K. Sauers, *J. Org. Chem.*,
27, 2339 (1962).

The hydroboration-oxidation reaction gives as its product the alcohol re‑sulting from cis anti-Markownikoff hydration; i.e., the preferred products are I° > II° > III°. Furthermore, the carbonium ion rearrangements often observed in acid-catalyzed additions rarely, if ever, occur in hydroborations.

In the case of β-pinene, the cis addition occurs from the less hindered side to give the stereochemistry shown.

(56.2)   [K. A. Sagebarth, *J. Org. Chem.*, **25**, 2212 (1960).]

A

It is suggested that the formation of the cis diol may be due to the formation of the intermediate alkyl borane A.

(56.3)   [M. F. Hawthorne and J. A. Dupont, *J. Am. Chem. Soc.*, **80**, 5830 (1958).]

The reaction appears to be a general one for the formation of cyclopropanes.

(56.4)   [F. Sondheimer and M. Nusseim, *J. Org. Chem.*, **26**, 630 (1961).]

Di-sec-isoamylborane ("disiamylborane") is a sterically much more selective reagent than diborane. Whereas the addition of diborane to 1,2-disubstituted ethylenes usually gives approximately equal amounts of the two possible products, the use of disiamylborane leads to the preferential formation of the less hindered isomer.

PROBLEM 57.   Predict the stereochemistry of the products.

(57.1)

(57.2)

(cont.)

(57.3)

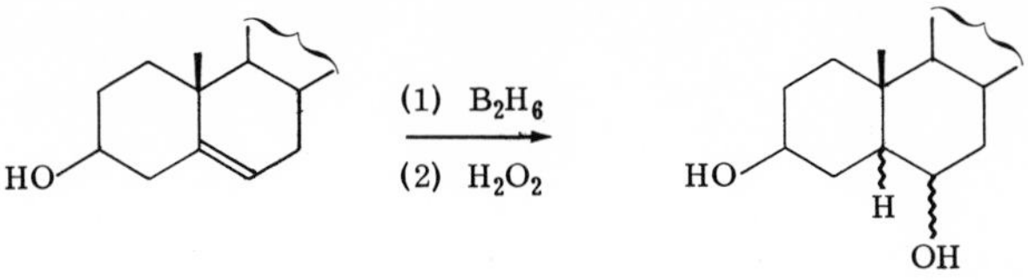

(1) B_2H_6

(2) H_2O_2

ANSWER 57.   [H. C. Brown, *Hydroboration*, Benjamin, New York, 1962, Chap. 8; H. C. Brown and G. Zweifel, *J. Am. Chem. Soc.*, **83**, 2544 (1961).]

(57.1)

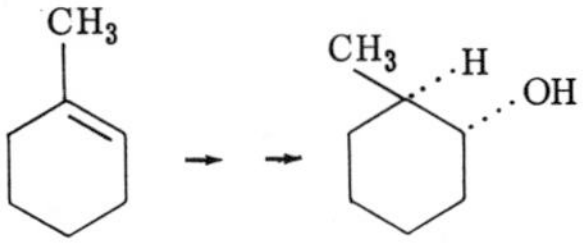

The hydroboration-oxidation reaction proceeds to give cis hydration from the less hindered side of the molecule.

(57.2)

The exo direction (toward the one carbon bridge) is the less hindered side of norbornene.

(57.3)   [W. J. Wechter, *Chem. Ind.* (London), **1959**, 294.]

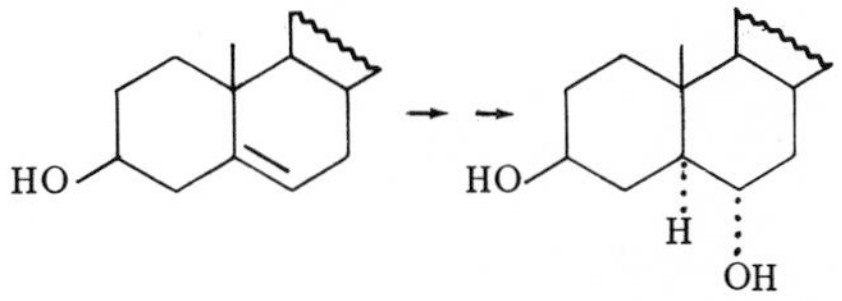

Because of the axial methyl group, which shields the front, attack occurs from the reverse side.

PROBLEM 58.   For each of the following reactions deduce the structure of the product by considering the relative energies of possible transition states.

(58.1)

$$CH_3CH{=}CH_2 \xrightarrow[H_2O]{Cl_2} C_3H_7OCl$$

(58.2)

$$(CH_3)_3\overset{\oplus}{N}{-}CH{=}CH_2 \xrightarrow{HI} [C_5H_{13}NI]^{\oplus}$$

(cont.)

(58.3)

$$ClCH{=}CH_2 \xrightarrow{\text{HBr}} C_2H_4ClBr$$

(58.4)

$$\text{C}_6\text{H}_5\text{—}CH{=}CH_2 \xrightarrow[\text{dil. } H_2SO_4]{CH_2O} C_9H_{12}O_2$$

ANSWER 58.   [For discussions of electrophilic additions to alkenes, see Gould, Chap. 13, and Hine, Chap. 9.]

(58.1)

$$CH_3CH{=}CH_2 \xrightarrow[\text{Cl—Cl}]{A} CH_3{-}\overset{\oplus}{CH}{-}CH_2Cl \xrightarrow[-H^{\oplus}]{H_2O} \overset{\overset{\text{OH}}{|}}{CH_3CHCH_2Cl}$$
$$\hspace{9cm} \textbf{1} \hspace{4cm} \textbf{2}$$

$$\searrow B$$
$$\text{Cl—Cl} \searrow$$

$$H_3C{-}\overset{.\,.\,\overset{\displaystyle \text{Cl}}{}\,.\,.}{\underset{\oplus}{CH}}{-}CH_2 \hspace{2cm} \overset{\overset{\displaystyle\oplus}{}}{\underset{\underset{\text{Cl}}{|}}{CH_3CHCH_2}} \xrightarrow[-H^{\oplus}]{H_2O} \underset{\underset{\text{Cl}}{|}}{CH_3CHCH_2OH}$$
$$\hspace{2cm}\textbf{5} \hspace{6cm}\textbf{3}$$

Two routes are possible. Path A produces a transition state resembling **1**, which is a secondary carbonium ion and is favored over the alternative **3**, a primary carbonium ion.

The problem is less obvious if the reaction is considered to pass through the "chloronium" intermediate **5**, because it is harder to predict how this bridged species might open. The existence of such ions is not definitely proved, however, although the concept is a useful one, and the products of addition correspond to those predicted on the basis of simple ions.

(58.2)

$$(CH_3)_3\overset{\oplus}{N}CH{=}CH_2 \xrightarrow{\text{HI}} (CH_3)_3\overset{\oplus}{N}{-}\overset{\oplus}{CH_2}CH_2 \xrightarrow{I^{\ominus}} (CH_3)_3\overset{\oplus}{N}{-}CH_2CH_2I$$
$$\hspace{5cm}\textbf{1}\hspace{4cm}\textbf{2}$$

$$\searrow \text{HI}$$

$$(CH_3)_3\overset{\oplus}{N}{-}\overset{\oplus}{CH}CH_3 \xrightarrow{I^{\ominus}} (CH_3)_3\overset{\oplus}{N}{-}\underset{\underset{\text{I}}{|}}{CHCH_3}$$
$$\hspace{3cm}\textbf{3}\hspace{4cm}\textbf{4}$$

Although normally secondary carbonium ions such as **3** are more stable than primary ones such as **1**, in this case **3** has two adjacent positive charges and is markedly destabilized with respect to **1**. As a result, the observed product is **2**.

Although the reaction is written above in terms of ionic species, nothing is known of the molecularity of the addition, and it is quite possible that a concerted process occurs, avoiding the formation of a full primary carbonium ion. It has also been suggested that a protonated π-complex may be formed (cf. the chloronium ion above) which is opened by the anion to yield the product.

(58.3)

$$ClCH{=}CH_2 \xrightarrow[HBr]{HBr} \overset{\oplus}{:}\!\!\ddot{C}l{-}CH{-}CH_3 \quad \overset{\ominus}{\xrightarrow{Br}} \quad ClCHCH_3$$

with $\overset{\oplus}{:}\!\ddot{C}l{=}CH{-}CH_3$ above intermediate **1** and Br on **2**

$$ClCH_2{-}\overset{\oplus}{C}H_2 \xrightarrow{Br^{\ominus}} ClCH_2CH_2Br$$

3   **4**

This reaction is quite similar to the preceding one and again the question is one of the preferred ionic intermediate. Experimentally, it is found that the major product is **2**, suggesting that the chlorine provides net stabilization to the intermediate **1** through donation of its unshared electrons.

(58.4)

$$CH_2{=}O + H^{\oplus} \rightarrow CH_2{=}\overset{\oplus}{O}H \leftrightarrow \overset{\oplus}{C}H_2{-}OH$$

Under acidic conditions formaldehyde adds to alkenes (Prins reaction).[1] In this case the benzyl carbonium ion of **1** is greatly favored over the primary ion of **2**, and the reaction proceeds by way of **1**.

An alternative product which might be considered would be **3**, formed by electrophilic aromatic substitution and hydration of the alkene, but the activation energy for substitution on benzene is much greater than that for addition to the styrene double bond.

PROBLEM 59.   Suggest an explanation for the fact that formation of a 3,4-double bond by pyrolysis of A is faster than the corresponding reaction of B.

A   B

ANSWER 59.   [G. L. O'Connor and H. R. Nace, *J. Am. Chem. Soc.*, **74**, 5454 (1952).]

The Chugaev and other similar elimination reactions are usually pictured as involving a cyclic transition state (**1**), at least at low temperatures.

1

In most cases there appears to be partial breaking of both the C—O and C—H bonds in this transition state, although not necessarily to the same extent. As a result, **1** has a partial 3,4-double bond, and in the case of A this is conjugated with the 5,6-double bond already present. This conjugation contributes to the stabilization of the transition state and is reflected in a lessened activation energy.[1]

---

58 [1]E. Arundale and L. A. Mikeska, *Chem. Rev.*, **51**, 505 (1952).

59 [1]The differences in activation energies for A and B are ca. 1 kcal/mole. If it is assumed that the ground states are equivalent and that the difference is due entirely to partial conjugation in the activated complex from A, this is about one fourth the resonance energy of 1,3-butadiene, a fairly reasonable figure.

PROBLEM 60.   It has been found that with OH⁻ in 50% aqueous dioxane

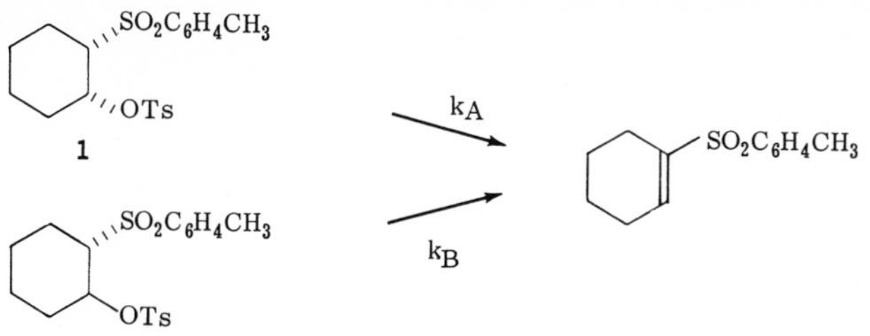

Both reactions are first-order in both OH⁻ and tosylate, and the relative rates are k_A / k_B = 434.

If the OH⁻ is replaced by buffer solutions of $Me_3 N$ and $Me_3 NH^+$, it is observed that the rate of disappearance of **1** or **2** increases with increasing amine concentration, even though the pH of the medium is held constant. This has been shown not to be due to a salt effect.

Provide a mechanistic interpretation of these observations.

ANSWER 60.   [J. Weinstock, R. G. Pearson, and F. G. Bordwell, *J. Am. Chem. Soc.*, **78**, 3468, 3473 (1956).]

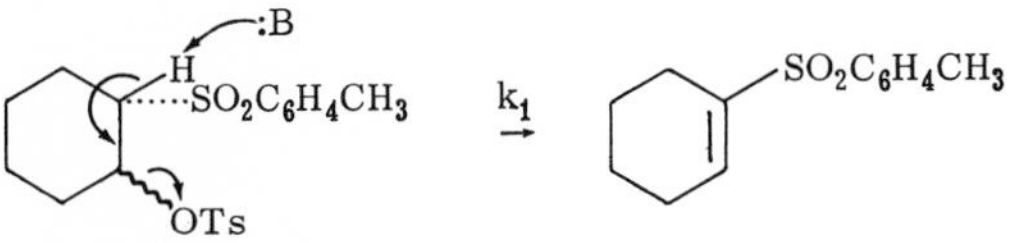

    Two possible mechanisms for elimination reactions are shown above. The first, concerted, one is that normally found for cases in which the trans leaving groups and the carbon atoms connecting them can be placed in one plane.[1] It is presumably applicable in the case of compound **1**.

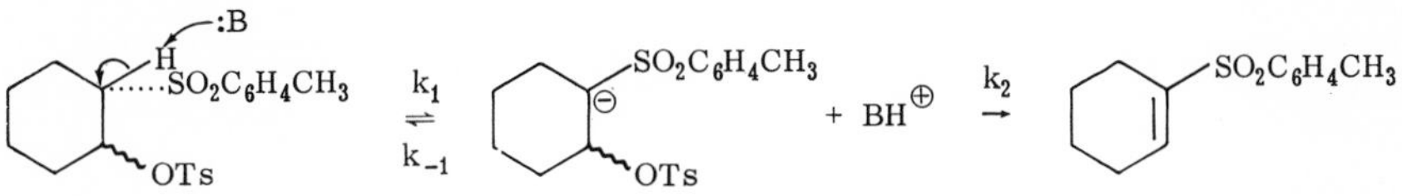

---

[1] Gould, Chap. 12.

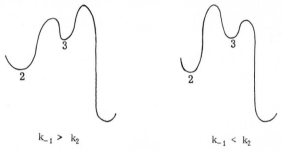

The cis elimination from **2** is the more surprising, since there are hydrogens available for trans elimination as well. It was originally suggested[2] that the electron-withdrawing effect of the sulfonyl group enhanced the acidity of the proton adjacent to it and that the reaction proceeded by the formation of an anion which subsequently lost a tosyl ion (mechanism B). Two cases should be considered with regard to such a mechanism. In the first, $k_{-1} > k_2$ (see the figure), and an equilibrium concentration of the anion is formed. In the second, $k_2 > k_{-1}$, and the anion merely represents a brief way-station after the slow step (k_1) of the reaction is completed. The distinction of this case from that of the concerted mechanism is slight, however (at least experimentally), and they are often lumped together.

$$k_{-1} > k_2 \qquad\qquad k_{-1} < k_2$$

The two cases may be distinguished by the results with amine catalysis. Case 1: The rate of disappearance of **2** is given by

$$v = k_2[3]$$

and since at equilibrium

$$k_{-1}[3][BH^+] = k_1[2][B]$$

$$[3] = \frac{k_1[2][B]}{k_{-1}[BH^+]}$$

$$v = k_2 \frac{k_1[2][B]}{k_{-1}[BH^+]}$$

[2]F. G. Bordwell and R. J. Kern, *J. Am. Chem. Soc.*, **77**, 1141 (1955).

Case 2: $v = k_1[2][B]$

In case 1, the observed rate is determined by the ratio $[B]/[BH^+]$ and not by the concentration of B alone. Since this same ratio determines the pH of the buffer, this behavior is often referred to as specific OH^- catalysis. In case 2, however, there is no return from the anion, and every base in the medium which can help remove a proton contributes its share to the observed rate, regardless of the concentration of its conjugate acid. This is general base catalysis.

The increase in rate with increasing amine concentration observed with **1** is reasonable, since no return is expected for the concerted mechanism. Its observation with **2**, however, indicates either that the elimination is also concerted or that if an anion is formed, it corresponds to case **2**.[3]

Despite the fact that the reaction of **2** does not involve a stable anion, the direction of elimination is probably still determined by the acidity enhancing powers of the sulfonyl group. It is quite possible that the transition state for cis elimination involves more C—H than C—OTs bond-breaking, with the result that there is a partial negative charge to be accommodated on the ring carbon atoms. The sulfonyl group assists this process, and the transition state is thereby stabilized. To explain the results, this stabilization must be enough to overcome the usual energy advantage for the trans process. The greater rate for elimination from **1** shows the increased advantages of having both effects operative.

PROBLEM 61.   Suggest a consistent set of mechanisms which accounts for the following reactions.

A

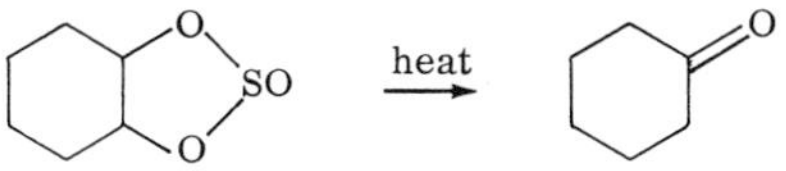

B

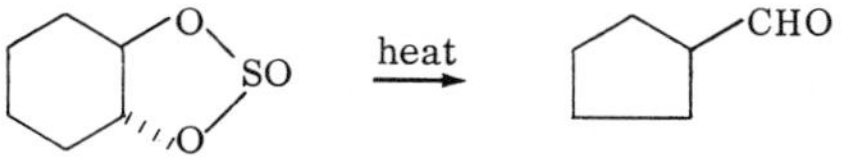

C

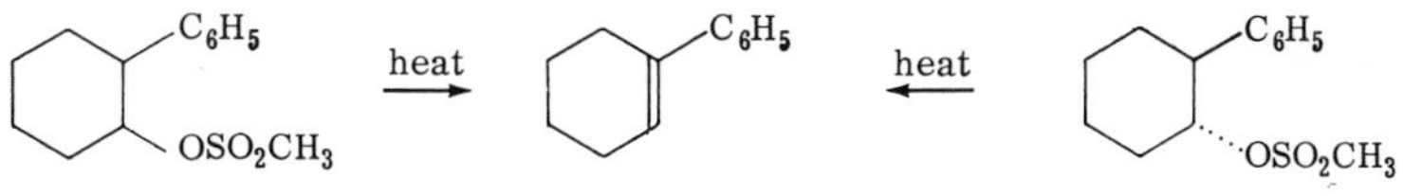

ANSWER 61.   [C. C. Price and G. Berti, *J. Am. Chem. Soc.,* **76**, 1211, (1954); G. Berti, *J. Am. Chem. Soc.,* **76**, 1213 (1954).]

---

[3] For discussions of this question see J. Weinstock, J. L. Bernardi, and R. G. Pearson, *J. Am. Chem. Soc.,* **80**, 4961 (1958); J. Hine and O. B. Ramsey, *J. Am. Chem. Soc.,* **84**, 973 (1962).

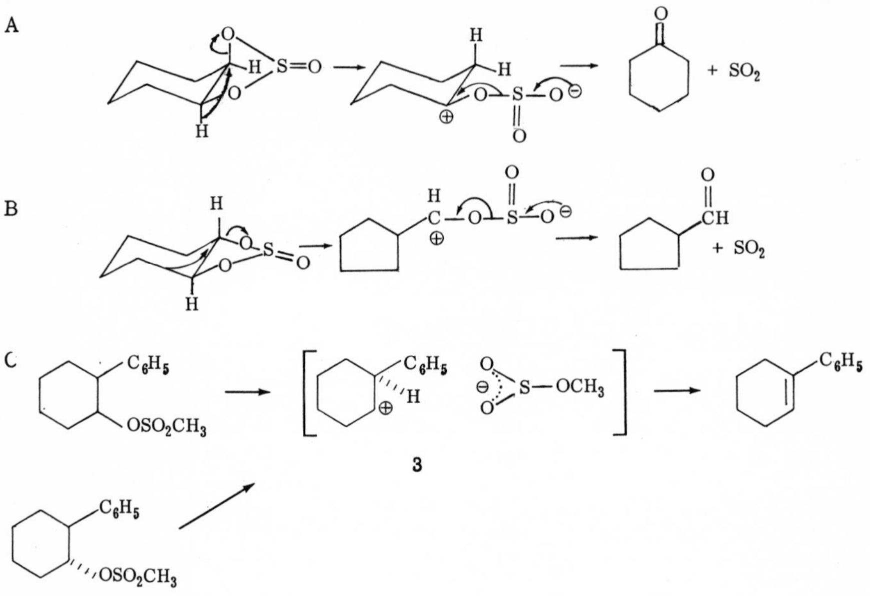

A

B

C

3

The pyrolytic decompositions of alkyl sulfites appear to involve heterolytic C—O bond-breaking and the formation of carbonium ion intermediates. In the case of the cyclic sulfites (A, B) the products resemble those from the pinacol rearrangement of the similarly oriented diols **1** and **2**.[1]

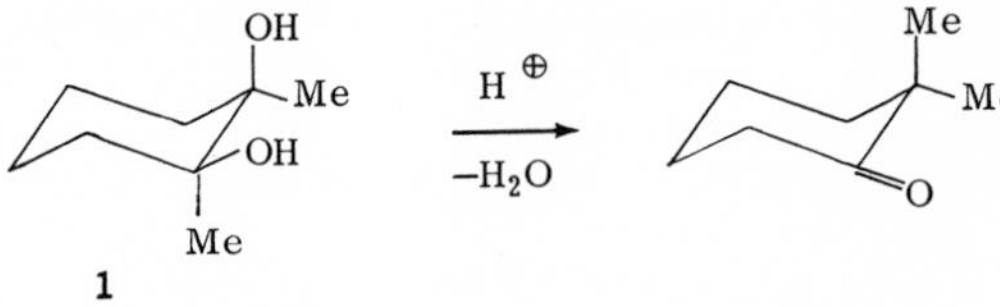

1

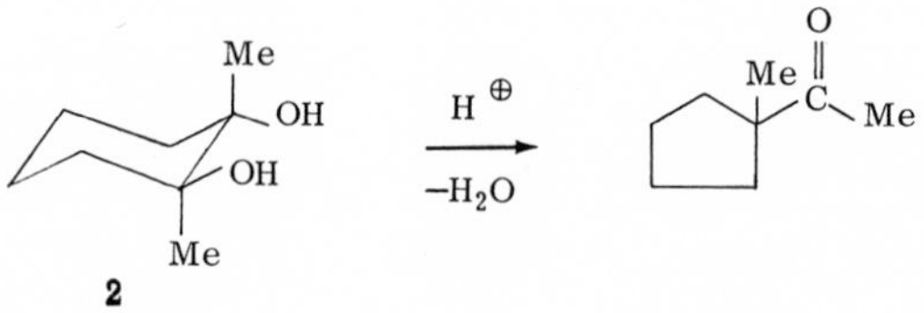

2

---

[1] See Gould, pp. 601–607.

Likewise, the decomposition of the acyclic sulfite ester in C appears to involve ionic intermediates and not, as might be expected, a concerted cis elimination similar to that proposed for xanthates and esters.[2] Thus it is suggested that cleavage occurs to give the ion pair **3**, and the sulfite ion then abstracts that proton which gives the more stable alkene. Similar ionic mechanisms have been proposed to account for the small amounts of trans elimination products which usually occur in other pyrolytic eliminations.

PROBLEM 62.   Suggest an explanation for the fact that, in the following elimination reaction, the ratio of the reaction rates of the cis and trans compounds is decreased when X = H is replaced by X = NO_2:

$$X \text{—} \langle \bigcirc \rangle \text{—} CH{=}CHBr \xrightarrow[\text{i-PrOH}]{\text{NaOH}} X \text{—} \langle \bigcirc \rangle \text{—} C{\equiv}CH$$

		k	k_{cis}/k_{trans}
X = H:	cis	3.00×10^{-3}	210,000
	trans	1.4×10^{-8}	
X = NO_2:	cis	3.71	16,000
	trans	2.36×10^{-4}	

ANSWER 62.   [S. Cristol and W. P. Norris, *J. Am. Chem. Soc.*, **76**, 3005 (1954).]
Two mechanisms have been proposed for bimolecular base-catalyzed eliminations.[1] In the first (A), the removal of a proton is synchronized with the elimination of an anion, and no discrete intermediate is formed. In the second (B), a proton is abstracted to give an intermediate carbanion, which then completes the elimination in a second step.

A

transition state

---

[2] See Gould, pp. 500–507; Hine, 515–518.
[1] Gould, Chap. 12.

B

transition state   intermediate

The first path appears to be generally favored in those cases in which the H and X groups can assume the trans antiparallel arrangement shown. When they cannot, the second route appears, although more vigorous conditions are often required to produce such elimination.

In the present example, the elimination from the cis compound (H and Br trans) can follow the concerted path A′.

A′

The elimination from the trans compounds (H and Br cis) is assumed to follow the path B′ and to involve the formation of the carbanion as the slow step.

B′

In the case of A′, the negative charge in the transition state is spread over several centers, particularly the departing halide. The fraction of the charge distributed into the benzene ring is relatively small. The stabilization which is gained by adding a nitro group to distribute the charge still further, although real (note that the rate increases by ca. 10^3) is less than that obtained in B′. Here the transition state presumably resembles the carbanion (except perhaps in geometry), and there is a much larger charge on the benzyl carbon to be transmitted to the ring. The effect of adding a nitro group is to provide a relatively greater stabilization effect, and consequently, a greater rate increase (ca. 2×10^4). The result is a reduced k_{cis}/k_{trans} ratio.

PROBLEM 63. Suggest mechanisms for the following reactions.

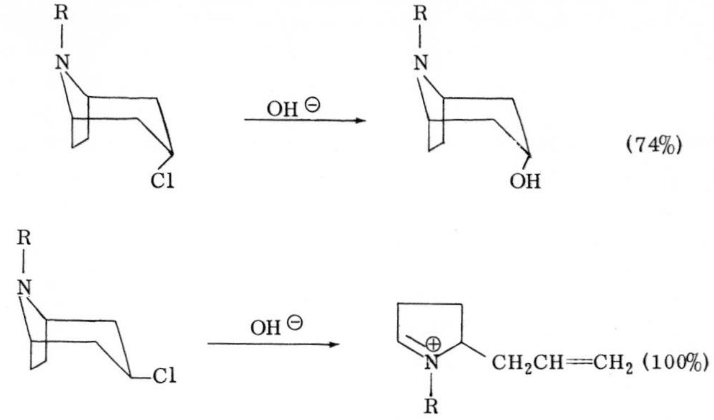

(74%)

$CH_2CH{=}CH_2$ (100%)

ANSWER 63. [C. A. Grob, *Bull. Soc. Chim. France,* **1960**, 1360; S. Archer, T. R. Lewis, and B. Zenitz, *J. Am. Chem. Soc.,* **80,** 958 (1958); S. Archer, M. R. Bell, T. R. Lewis, S. W. Schulenberg, and M. J. Unser, *J. Am. Chem. Soc.,* **80,** 4677 (1958).]

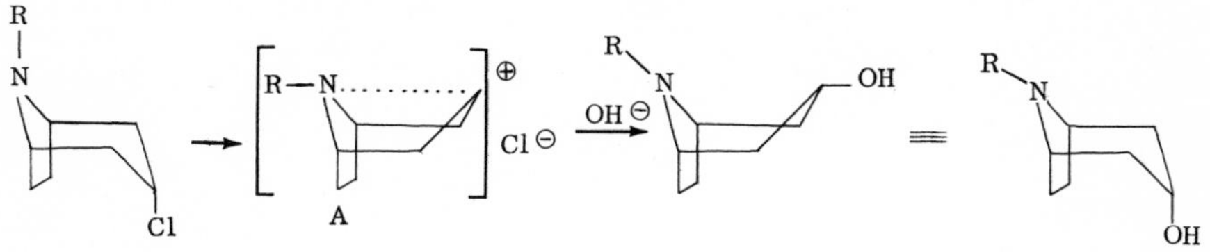

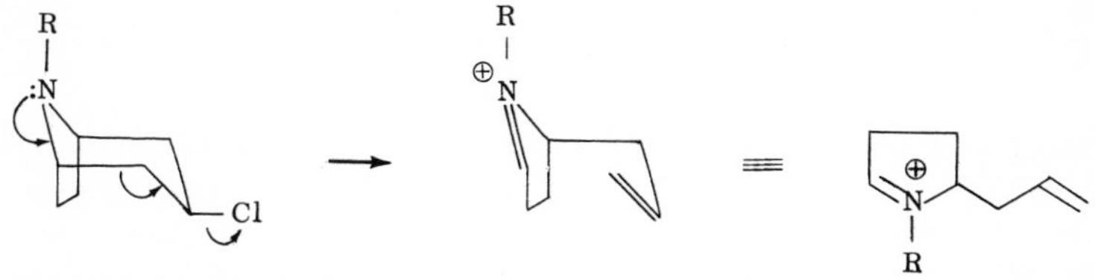

Both of these reactions proceed at rates which are faster by several powers of ten than the corresponding displacement on cyclohexyl chloride, so the effect of the nitrogen is to increase the reactivity of the halide as well as to control the products formed.

The first reaction is presumably unimolecular, internal attack by the nitrogen displacing the halogen and leading to the intermediate A. The extent to which the bridging bond is formed in A is not known, nor is the distribution of plus charge between the nitrogen and carbon. A subsequent attack by OH⁻ displaces the nitrogen and leads to products. Other, similar reactions in this series are known.

In the second reaction, the chlorine is oriented so that its direct displacement cannot be assisted by the nitrogen as above. On the other hand, the geometry is such that the four centers Cl, C_α, C_β, and C_γ are coplanar, as are N, C_γ, and C_β. This arrangement

apparently facilitates electron shifts as shown (cf. the more common trans-diaxial arrangement for eliminations),[1] which result in the loss of Cl⁻ and the fragmentation of the ring system.

PROBLEM 64.   Suggest an explanation for the fact that in an E1 reaction A eliminates the BsO— group 2.5 times faster than B.

A

threo

B

erythro

$$BsO = Br—\langle\!\!\!\bigcirc\!\!\!\rangle—SO_2—O—$$

ANSWER 64.   [S. Winstein, E. Allred, R. Heck, and R. Glick, *Tetrahedron*, **3**, 1 (1958).]

---

[1] See Gould, pp. 489ff.

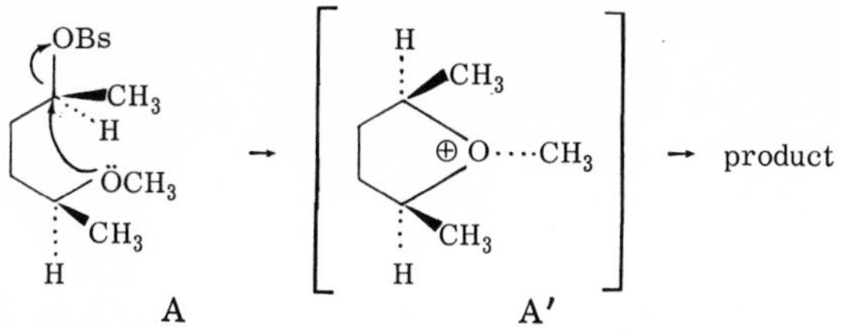

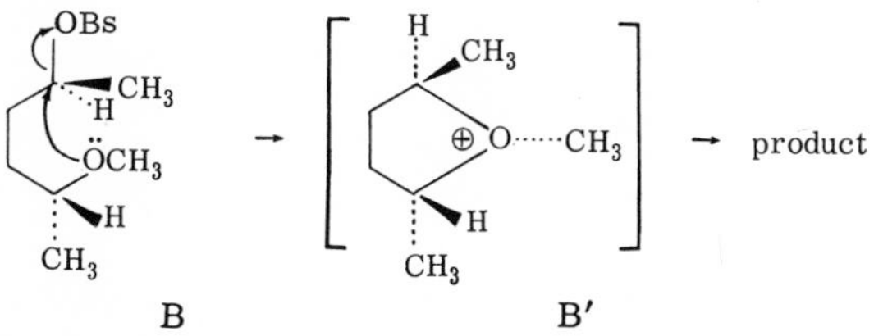

In both cases the rate-determining step in the reaction is the methoxyl-assisted elimination of the brosylate group to yield ion A′ or B′. The transition state leading to ion A′ is considered to be slightly more stable than that going to B′, and therefore to be formed more rapidly, because in it the three methyl groups can be arranged trans-trans. In the B′ arrangement, on the other hand, the O—CH₃ must always be cis to one of the adjacent C—CH₃'s, and it is suggested that the resulting steric interaction provides the small destabilization needed to account for the rate differences.

PROBLEM 65.   Explain why the following reactions give mainly one stereoisomer of the olefin.

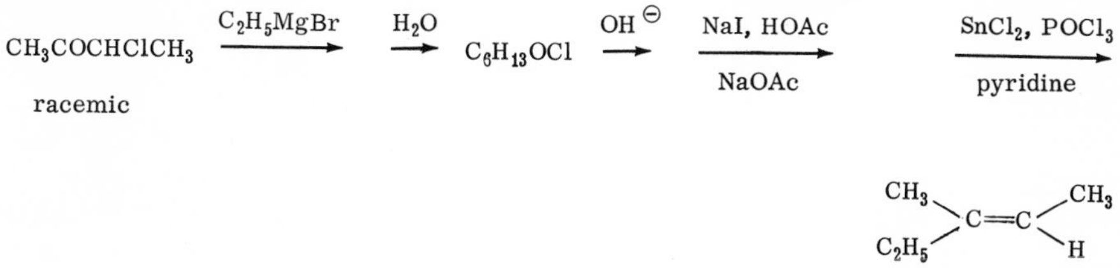

ANSWER 65.   [J. W. Cornforth, R. H. Cornforth, and K. K. Mathew, *J. Chem. Soc.*, 1959, 112.]

The stereochemistry of the product alkene is actually determined by the direction of addition of the Grignard reagent in the first step. All the subsequent reactions require a particular conformation and are stereospecific (although this was not achieved without effort).

Orientation A is only one of the infinite number of conformers possible and apparently is not even the predominant form, at least in polar solvents.[1,2] It is suggested, however, that A may be the most reactive of the conformers, because the antiparallel arrangement of the C=O and C—Cl bonds allows the easy polarization of the carbonyl group in the transition state. Thus the transition state A_1 is regarded as being favored over B because of the lesser dipole repulsion.

Regardless of the detailed explanation, the products observed are those expected if attack occurs on A from the less hindered side, i.e., between the two smaller groups, in this case H and Cl (see Cram's rule).[3] Once this has occurred, the later products arise by a sequence of trans displacements.

---

[1] L. J. Bellamy, L. C. Thomas, and R. L. Williams, *J. Chem. Soc.*, **1956**, 3704; L. J. Bellamy and R. L. Williams, *J. Chem. Soc.*, **1957**, 4294.

[2] N. L. Allinger and J. Allinger, *Tetrahedron*, **2**, 64 (1958).

[3] D. J. Cram and F. A. A. Elhafez, *J. Am. Chem. Soc.*, **74**, 5828 (1952).

As would be expected from the sequence outlined, the other alkene stereoisomer can be prepared by

$$\underset{C_2H_5C-CHCH_3}{\overset{\overset{O}{\|}\quad\overset{Cl}{|}}{}} \xrightarrow{CH_3MgI} \rightarrow \rightarrow \rightarrow \quad \underset{C_2H_5}{\overset{H_3C}{}}C=C\underset{CH_3}{\overset{H}{}}$$

Although the reaction sequence is shown for only one of the enantiomers of the racemic mixture, it *must* hold for the other, except that the configurations of the products are reversed. This is invariably the case in the reaction of optically active compounds with symmetric reagents. Thus since the final step causes the loss of the asymmetric centers, all distinction between the paths vanishes, and the same product appears.

PROBLEM 66.   Suggest mechanisms for the following reactions:

(66.1)

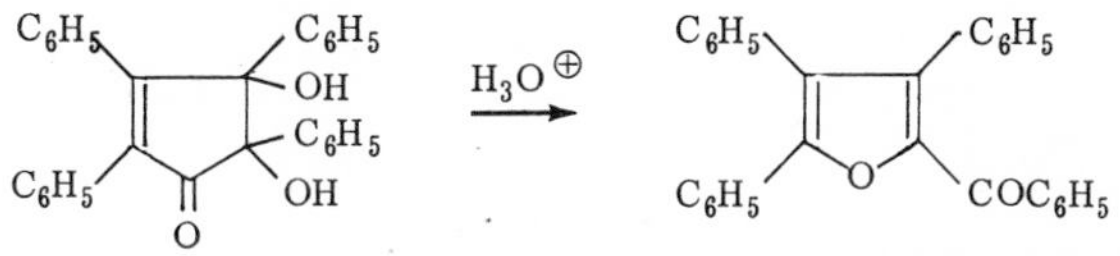

(66.2)

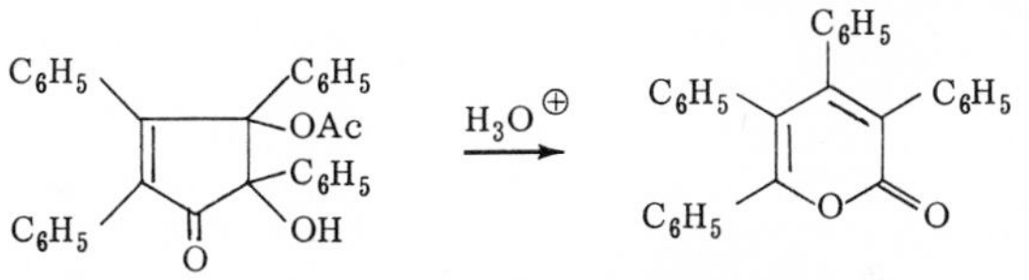

ANSWER 66.   [P. Yates and G. H. Stout, *J. Am. Chem. Soc.*, **76**, 5110 (1954).]
(66.1)   The suggested mechanism involves a retro-aldol reaction.

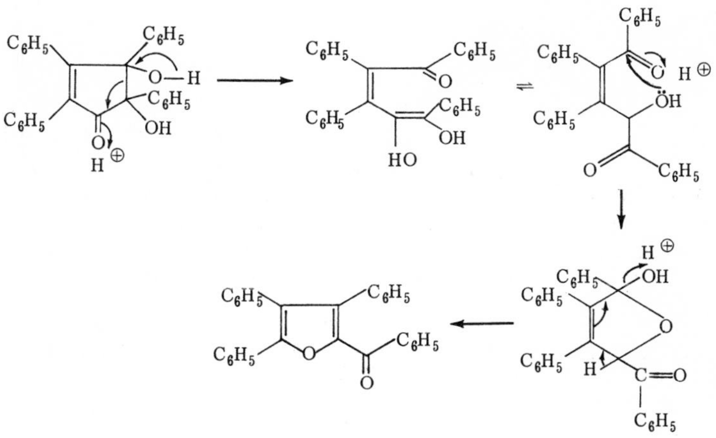

(66.2)   Unlike the hydroxyl group in (1), the acetoxyl group cannot undergo the retro-aldol ring opening, and an alternative reaction path must be found.

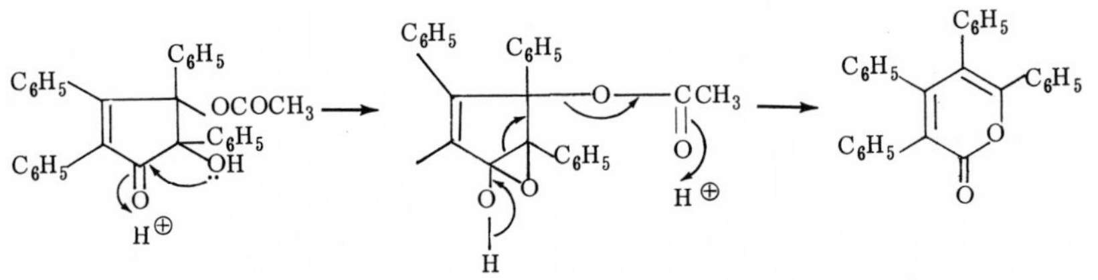

PROBLEM 67.   Suggest a mechanism for the following reaction:

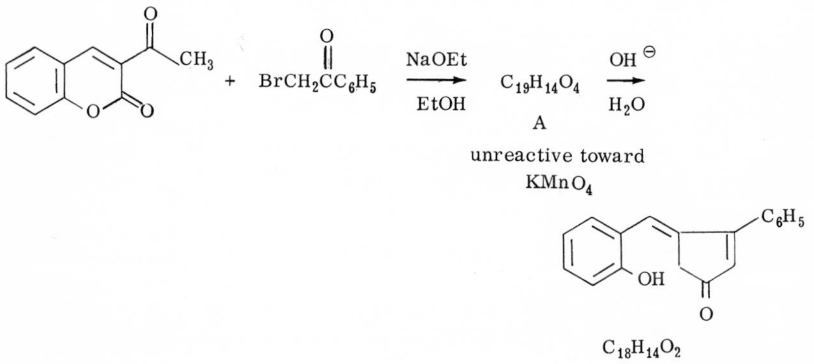

ANSWER 67.   [O. Widman, *Ber.*, **51**, 533 (1918); **52**, 1652 (1919); S. Wawzonek and C. E. Morreal, *J. Am. Chem. Soc.*, **82**, 439 (1960).]

The structure of the intermediate A has been confirmed by an independent synthesis[1]

---

[1] For a discussion of the reaction of diazoalkenes with conjugated double bonds, see B. Eistert in *Newer Methods of Preparative Organic Chemistry*, Wiley-Interscience, New York, 1948, pp. 513–570.

The sequence of steps in the subsequent hydrolysis of A is uncertain as usual, Wawzonek favoring hydrolysis of the lactone before, but suggesting that decarboxylation must follow, the cleavage of the cyclopropane ring.

PROBLEM 68.   Suggest mechanisms for the following reactions:

(68.1)

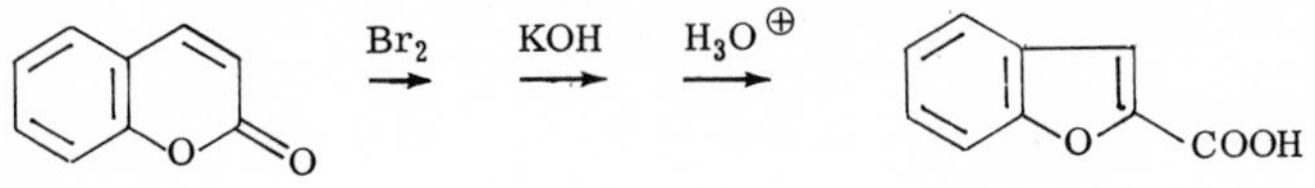

(68.2)

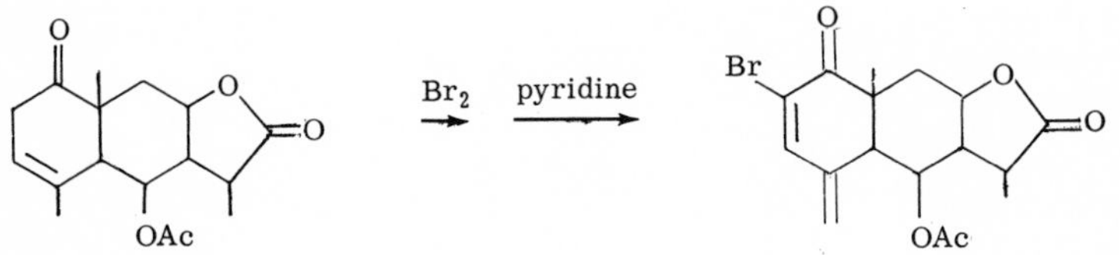

(68.3)

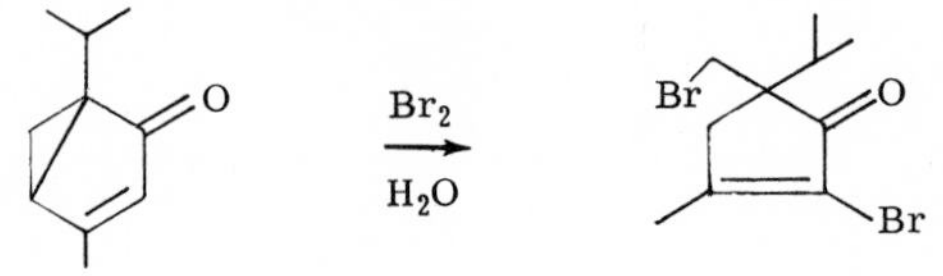

(68.4)

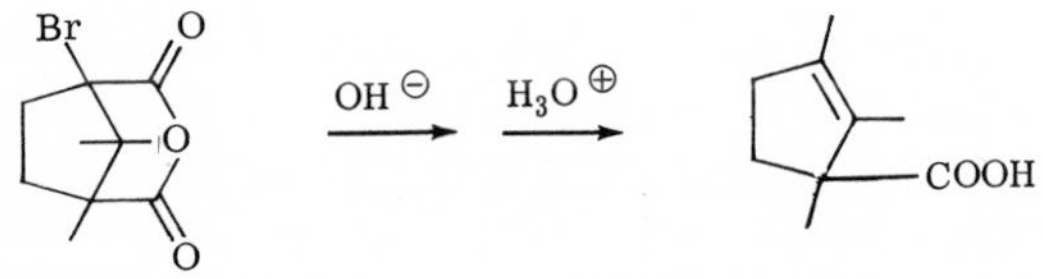

ANSWER 68.

(68.1)   [See R. C. Elderfield and V. B. Meyer in *Heterocyclic Compounds,* Vol. II (R. C. Elderfield, ed.), Wiley, New York, 1951, p. 5.]

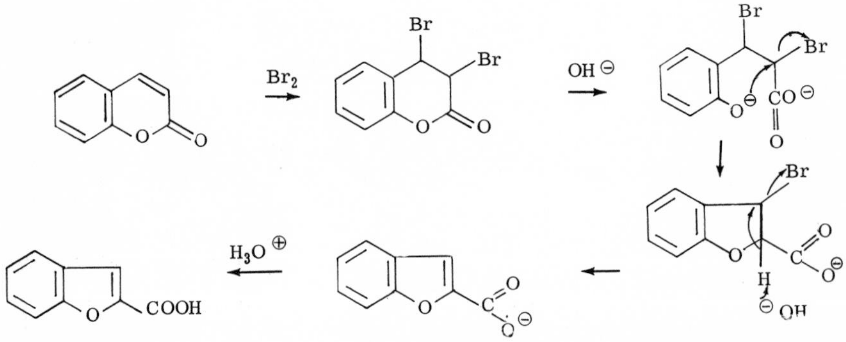

(68.2)   [D. H. R. Barton and P. de Mayo, *J. Chem. Soc.*, **1957**, 150; see also D. H. R. Barton, O. C. Böckman, and P. de Mayo, *J. Chem. Soc.*, **1960**, 2263.]

It has been proposed[1] that the reaction proceeds by selective bromination of the methylene group adjacent to the ketone, despite the presence of the double bond. Thus

Presumably the mechanism would be

but it is difficult to justify the unreactivity of the alkene system. A reasonable alternative would be

---

[1] P. de Mayo, *Mono- and Sesquiterpenoids*, Wiley-Interscience, New York, 1959, p. 232.

(68.3)　　[R. H. Eastman and A. Oken, *J. Am. Chem. Soc.*, **75**, 1029 (1953).]

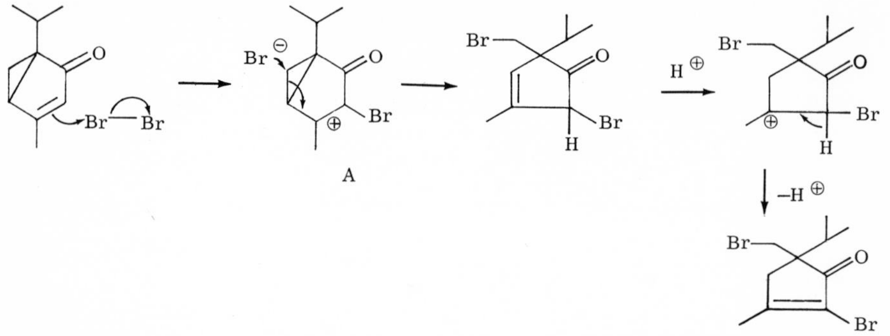

This is only one of a large number of possible routes. Another goes from A,

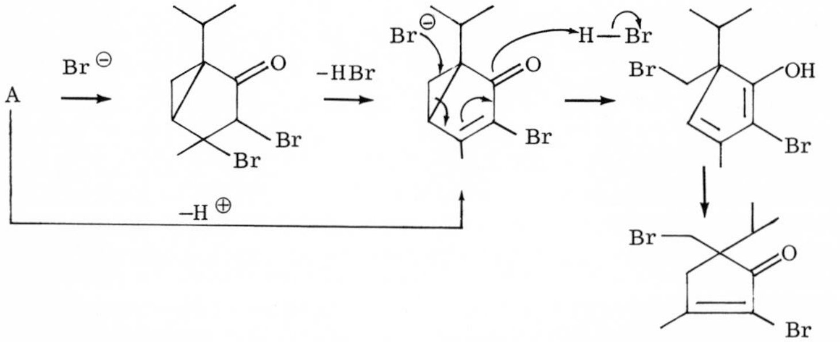

and yet a third involves opening of the cyclopropane ring before bromination
α to the ketone.[1]

(68.4)

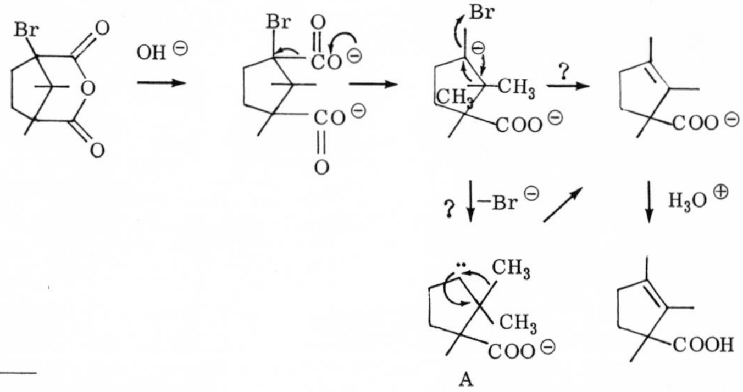

_____

[1] P. de Mayo, op. cit., p. 112.

The reaction may involve a concerted methyl migration and bromide loss as shown (possibly coupled with the decarboxylation), or it may proceed through the prior formation of the carbene intermediate A.

PROBLEM 69.   The derivative (1) of commic acid E does not give a simple elimination product on treatment with collidine, but affords instead the α,β-unsaturated aldehyde (2). Explain this fact and write a rational course for the formation of (2).

1	2

ANSWER 69.   [A. F. Thomas, K. Hensler, and J. M. Miller, *Tetrahedron*, **16**, 264 (1961).]

It is suggested that because of the high degree of substitution in ring A, the intermediate boat form (B) cannot be achieved so as to give the trans-antiparallel arrangement required for easy elimination of the tosyl group with the 2α-hydrogen. Instead, ring opening occurs, followed by an aldol condensation to give product **2**.

The hindrance between the 3β-tosyl and the 10β-methyl may be enough, however, to prevent the intermediacy of the boat form even without the extra substitution. Thus as the sole product.[1]

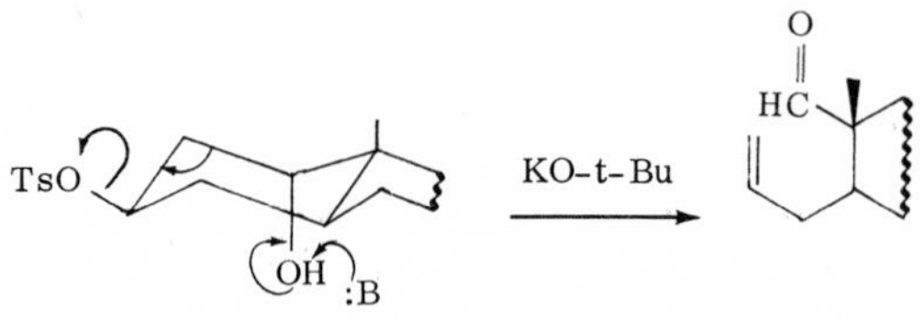

PROBLEM 70.   Suggest a mechanism for the following reaction:

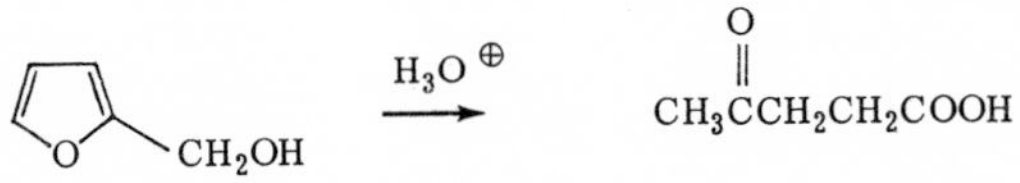

ANSWER 70.   [L. Birkofer and F. Beckmann, *Ann.*, **620**, 21 (1959).]

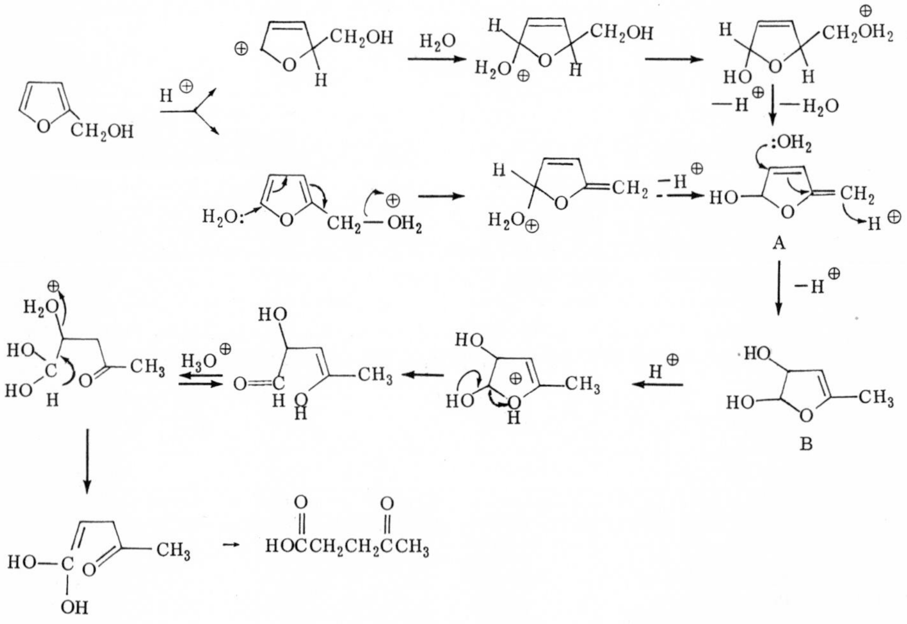

---

[1] R. B. Clayton, H. B. Henbest, and M. Smith, *J. Chem. Soc.*, **1957**, 1982.

This is only one of several proposed mechanisms.[1] There appears to be general agreement that A is an intermediate, and there is good evidence for the formation of B, but the other steps are unproved. If the reaction is carried out in methanolic acid, however, various suggestive intermediates can be observed.[2]

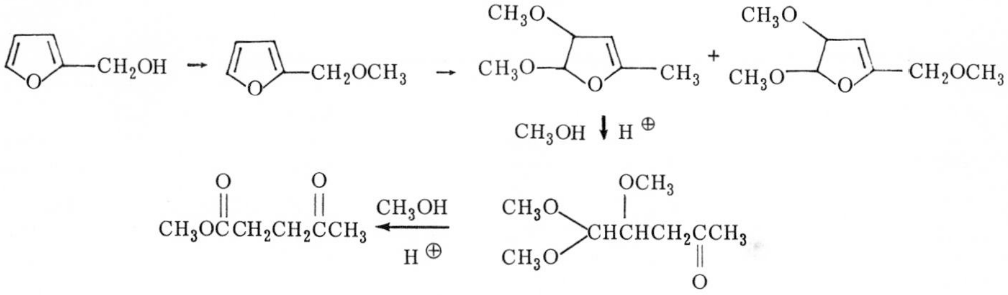

PROBLEM 71.   Suggest reasonable structures for the isomers, A and B, produced in the following reaction:

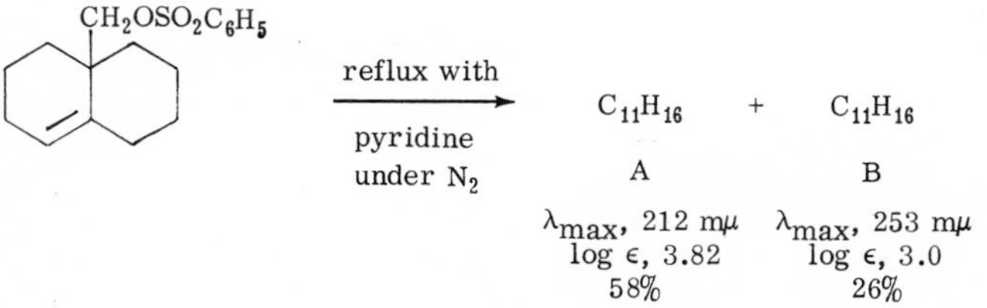

reflux with
⟶
pyridine
under N_2

$C_{11}H_{16}$ + $C_{11}H_{16}$

A   B

λ_{max}, 212 mμ λ_{max}, 253 mμ
log ϵ, 3.82   log ϵ, 3.0
58%   26%

ANSWER 71.   [J. W. Rowe, A. Melera, D. Arigoni, O. Jeger, and L. Ruzicka, *Helv. Chim. Acta,* **40**, 1 (1957).]
   The carbonium ion produced by the elimination of the benzenesulfonate group from the starting material may be regarded as either a homoallylic[1] or a neopentylic cation. The first point of view suggests the reaction sequence

whereas the second suggests a Wagner-Meerwein rearrangement[2]:

---

70 [1] See *Chemistry of Carbon Compounds,* Vol. IVA (E. H. Rodd, ed.), Elsevier, Amsterdam, 1957, p. 143.
    [2] L. Birkofer and R. Dutz, *Ann.,* **608**, 17 (1957).
71 [1] See pp. 93ff. in B. Capon, *Quart. Rev.,* **18**, 45 (1964).
    [2] Gould, pp. 584ff.

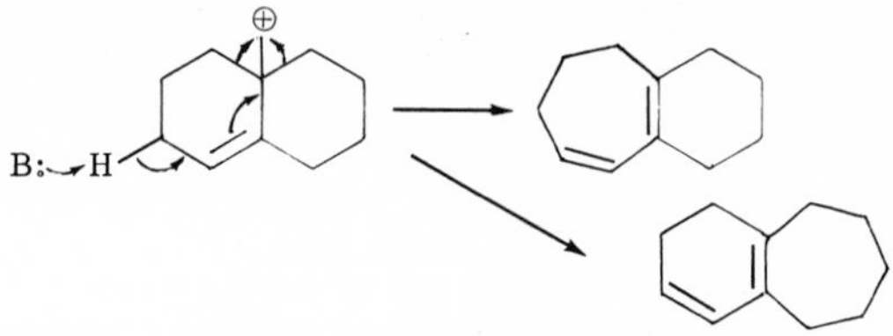

Of these, the first product is likely to be A, since the shortwave UV absorption is consistent with the lesser degree of conjugation in vinyl cyclopropanes as compared with 1,3-dienes. The evidence does not distinguish rigorously between the possible double bond arrangements for B, but B_1 might be preferred on the grounds that B_2, being a six-membered homoannular diene, might be expected to have its UV absorption around 270 mμ.[3] The seven-membered ring of B_1, being more flexible, might resemble more nearly an alicyclic structure and absorb at shorter wavelengths.

PROBLEM 72.   Predict the products of the following reactions:

(72.1)

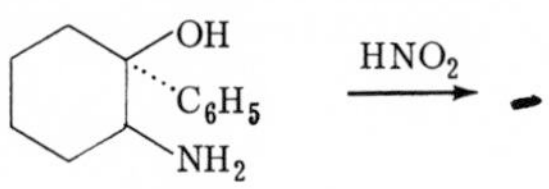

(72.2)

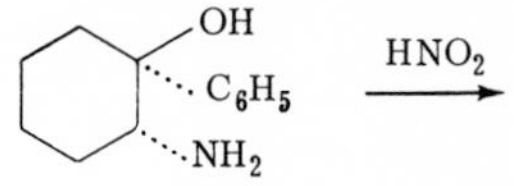

ANSWER 72.   [D. Y. Curtin and S. Schmukler, *J. Am. Chem. Soc.*, **77**, 1105 (1955).]

These reactions involve diazotization of the primary amine and then elimination of nitrogen from the resulting diazo group, with simultaneous participation of a bond or group which is trans-antiparallel to the diazo group. The loss of nitrogen appears to be so rapid that the direction of the resulting rearrangement is determined by the preferred conformation of the starting amine. Thus

(72.1)

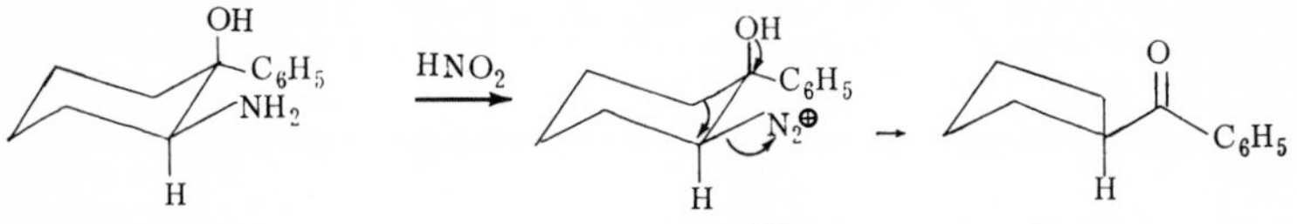

(72.2)

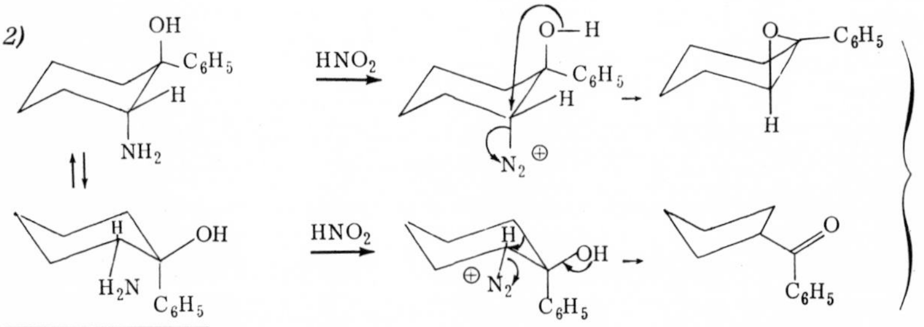

mixture of possible products

---

[3] L. F. Fieser and M. Fieser, *Steroids*, Reinhold, New York, 1959, pp. 15ff.

The absence of any products of phenyl migration in case (72.1) can be attributed either to the very low equilibrium concentration of the required conformation of the starting amine, or to extreme hindrance to migration of an axial phenyl group.

PROBLEM 73. Predict structures for the following products:

(73.1)

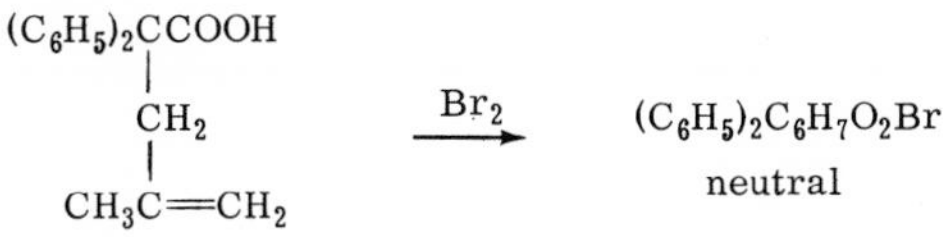

$(C_6H_5)_2CCOOH$
CH_2
$CH_3C{=}CH_2$
Br_2
$(C_6H_5)_2C_6H_7O_2Br$
neutral

(73.2)

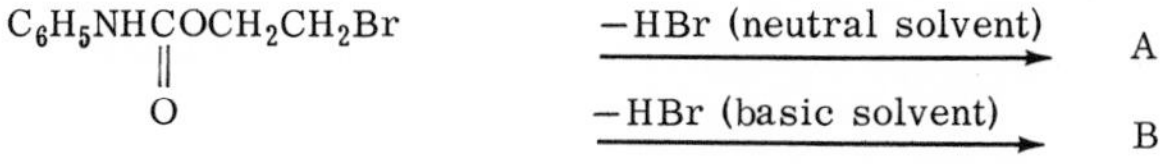

$C_6H_5NHCOCH_2CH_2Br$
O
−HBr (neutral solvent)
A
−HBr (basic solvent)
B

(73.3)

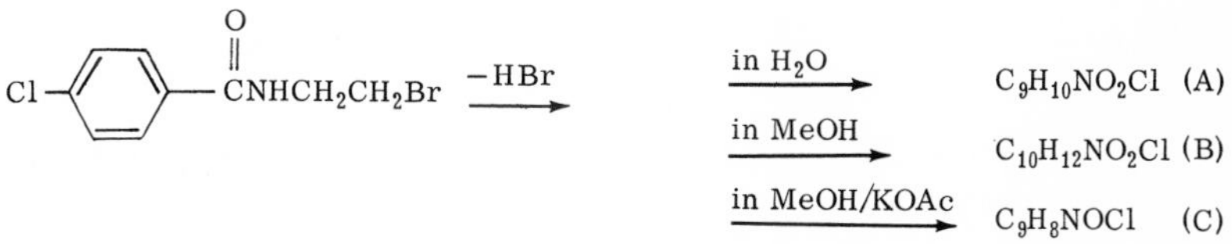

O
Cl
$CNHCH_2CH_2Br$
−HBr
in H_2O
$C_9H_{10}NO_2Cl$ (A)
in MeOH
$C_{10}H_{12}NO_2Cl$ (B)
in MeOH/KOAc
C_9H_8NOCl (C)

ANSWER 73.

(73.1) [P. N. Craig and J. H. Witt, *J. Am. Chem. Soc.*, **72**, 4925 (1950).]

C_6H_5
C_6H_5—C—C
O—H
O
CH_2—C=CH_2
CH_3
Br—Br
C_6H_5
C_6H_5—C—C
O
O
CH_2—C—CH_2Br
CH_3
+ HBr

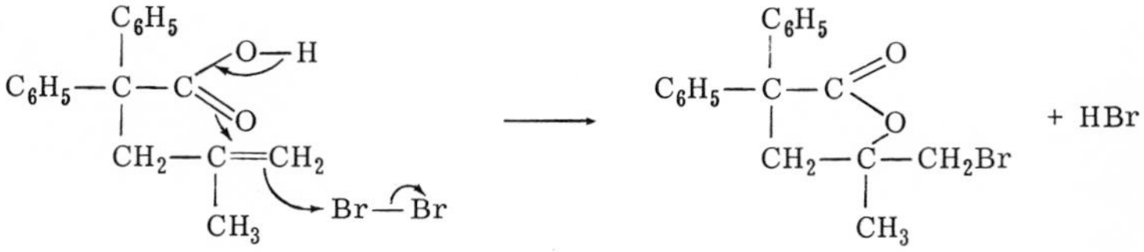

The addition of Br_2 to the double bond is accompanied by participation of the neighboring carboxyl group.[1] The γ-lactone structure may be suggested for the product, in preference to the alternative δ structure, because of the preference for attack by Br^+ ($Br^{\delta+}$—$Br^{\delta-}$) on the primary rather than the tertiary carbon.

(73.2) [F. L. Scott, R. E. Glick, and S. Winstein, *Experientia*, **13**, 183 (1957).]

[1] See E. E. van Tamelen and M. Shamma, *J. Am. Chem. Soc.*, **76**, 2315 (1954).

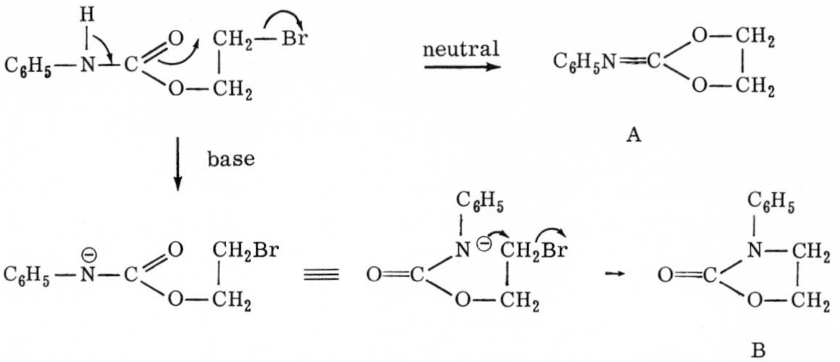

A

B

Under neutral conditions the oxygen is more nucleophilic than the nitrogen, whereas in the case of the anion the opposite is true. Since the anion can place its charge on either N or O, these results are difficult to explain, but they are observed consistently.

(73.3)   [H. W. Heine, *J. Am. Chem. Soc.*, **79**, 907 (1957).]

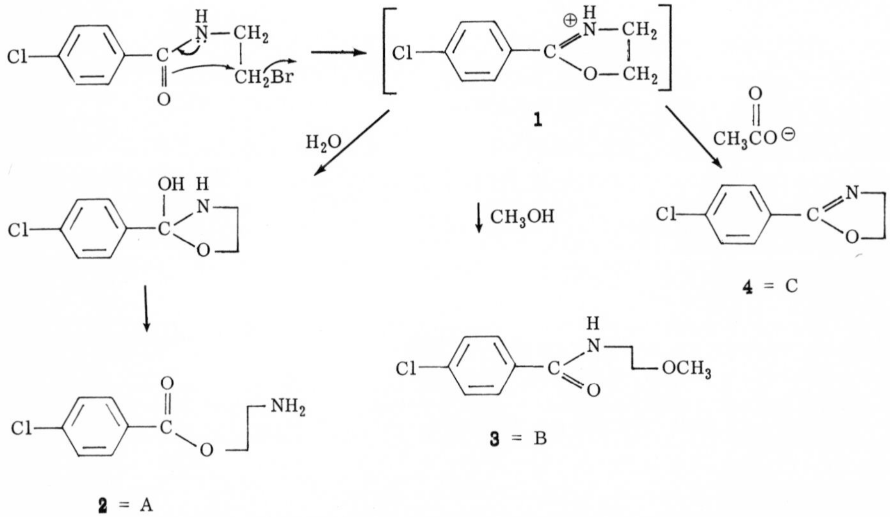

1

H_2O

$CH_3CO^\ominus$

CH_3OH

4 = C

2 = A

3 = B

The first step in all solvents is the internal displacement and ring closure leading to the oxazoline and HBr (=oxazolinium salt). In the presence of water the double bond is hydrated, and the resulting ortho acid derivative opens to give **2**. Presumably, the alternative opening to give **5** also occurs, but is reversible, whereas **2** accumulates in the form of the unreactive hydrobromide salt.

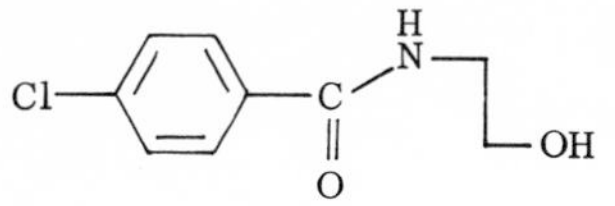

5 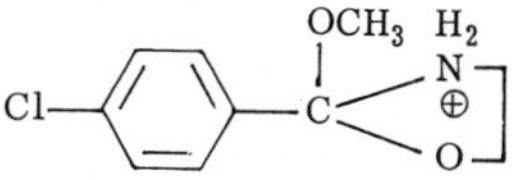   **6**

Similar addition of methanol to the oxazolium salt **1** leads to **6**, which represents a blind alley in equilibrium with **1**. **3** arises by another reaction,

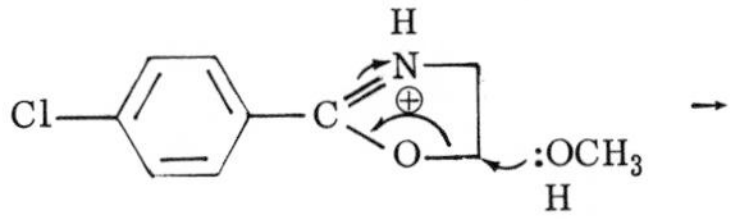

In the presence of the basic acetate ion, **1** merely loses a proton and remains
as the oxazoline, **4**.

PROBLEM 74.   Deduce structures for the following products; suggest explanations for the facts that the reaction A → B is much faster than the reaction A → B′
and that the bromination of B′ is difficult.

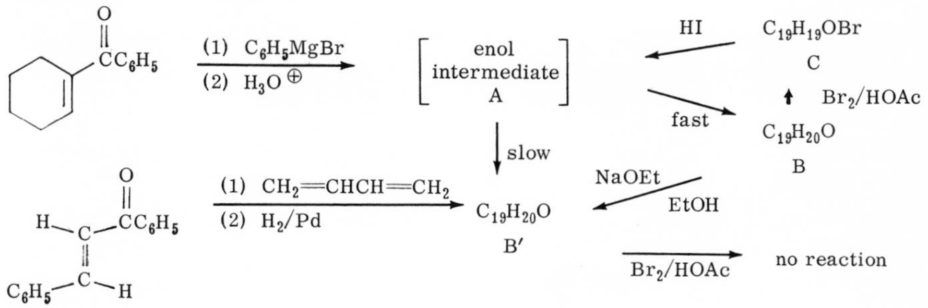

B′ is an isomer of B, and A is the (unisolated) enol from both B and B′.

ANSWER 74.   [H. E. Zimmerman, *J. Org. Chem.,* **20**, 549 (1955).]
The Diels-Alder reaction[1] is a cis addition, and hence the product B′ is the
trans compound shown below. Thus B must be the less stable cis isomer.

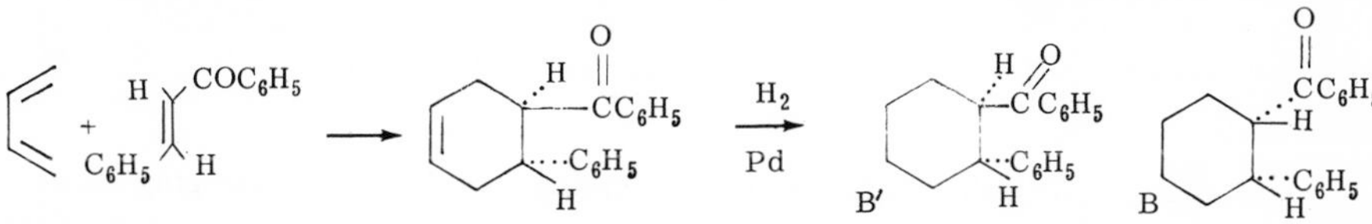

---

[1] Gould, p. 533; K. Alder in *Newer Methods of Preparative Organic Chemistry,* Interscience, New York, 1948, pp. 381–511.

From a consideration of the structures of B and B', it is clear that the Grignard reaction proceeds by a 1,4-addition to give[2]

A

The enol intermediate, A, arising from the 1,4-addition could lead to either stereoisomer, B or B'. That B is in fact formed means that of the two possible ketonization processes which occur during the acidification of A, that leading to the less stable ketonic product, B, is the faster. Two explanations have been proposed for this observation.

Zimmerman originally suggested that the reaction course is determined by a preferential proton attack at the less hindered side of the enol double bond. Thus, of the two possible approaches to the enol carbon undergoing attack by the proton donor (transition states **1** and **2**), that (**1**) leading to B is favored because of the relatively unhindered equatorial approach available to HA.

Recently, however, Johnson and Malhotra[3] have pointed out that conformations such as **1** and **2** are subject to considerable steric strain as a result of interaction between the equatorial 2-substituent and the groups attached to the double bond. They have provided evidence that in such systems the predominant conformer is **3**, with the substituent axial. Thus in order to account for the observed results, protonation must occur rapidly by axial attack (as is commonly

---

[2]See M. S. Kharasch and O. Reinmuth, *Grignard Reactions of Nonmetallic Substances,* Prentice-Hall, Englewood Cliffs, N. J., 1954, pp. 196ff. for an extensive review of such additions.

[3]F. Johnson and S. K. Malhotra, *J. Am. Chem. Soc.,* **87**, 5492 (1965); S. K. Malhotra and F. Johnson, *J. Am. Chem. Soc.,* **87**, 5493 (1965).

observed) on **3**, yielding B. Under equilibrating conditions a further, slow reaction can occur by either equatorial protonation on **3** or axial attack on **2** to give the stable product B'.

The two sets of authors agree that the differing reactivities of B and B' toward Br_2 arise from the much greater ease of enolization of B,[4] but their justifications differ and parallel the arguments given above for the reverse reaction.

---

[4]Note that the energy of activation for enolization of B' must be much larger than that of B, because the ground state of the former is more stable, and the transition state B' → A less stable, than that of B → A (cf. the rates of the reverse reactions).

CHAPTER 5

MISCELLANEOUS REACTIONS

PROBLEM 75. Deduce structures for the following reaction products:

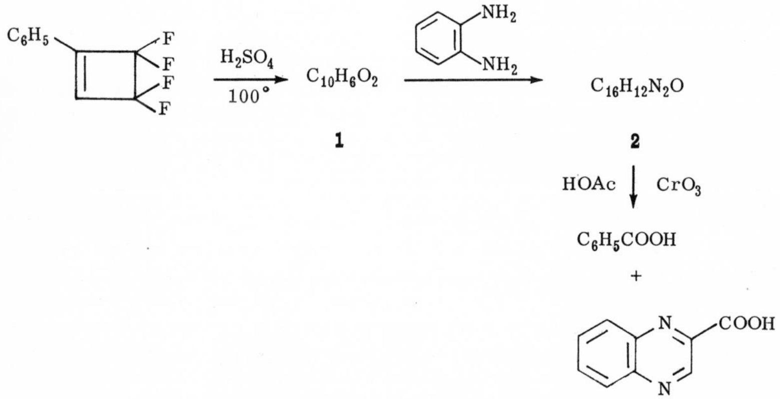

$$\text{C}_6\text{H}_5\text{—} \begin{array}{c} \text{F} \\ \text{F} \\ \text{F} \\ \text{F} \end{array} \xrightarrow[100^\circ]{\text{H}_2\text{SO}_4} \text{C}_{10}\text{H}_6\text{O}_2 \xrightarrow{} \text{C}_{16}\text{H}_{12}\text{N}_2\text{O}$$

1　　　　　　　　　　　**2**

$$\text{HOAc} \Big\downarrow \text{CrO}_3$$

$$\text{C}_6\text{H}_5\text{COOH}$$

$$+$$

ANSWER 75.　[E. J. Smutny, M. C. Caserio, and J. D. Roberts, *J. Am. Chem. Soc.*, **82**, 1793 (1960).]

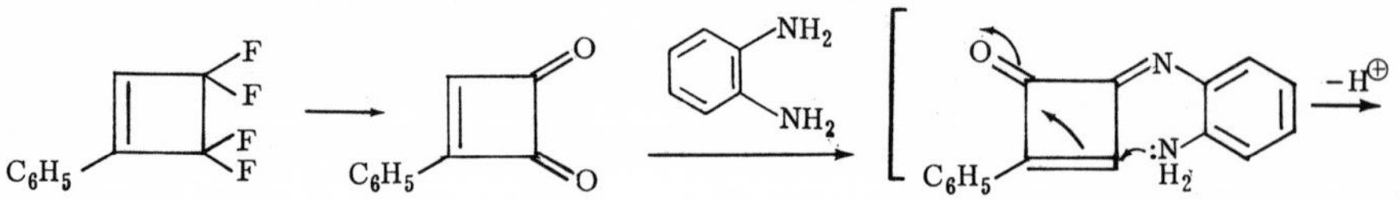

132

The first reaction is a characteristic hydrolysis in the fluorinated cyclobutane series.

PROBLEM 76.   The compound below forms a semicarbazone which, when heated with acid, is converted back into the starting material. Propose mechanisms for these reactions.

ANSWER 76.   [G. Buchi and N. C. Yang, *Chem. Ind. (London),* **1955,** 357; *Helv. Chim. Acta,* **38,** 1338 (1955).]

The compound can be regarded as being capable of a tautomeric equilibrium:

A   B

Because of the differences in geometry, the two structures do not contribute to a resonance hybrid, although the activation energy required to pass from one to the other should be small. As might be expected, the closed form A is more stable and is the normal species, but the open form is presumably present in traces which can be removed by an alternative reaction (e.g., semicarbazone formation). Hydrolysis of the semicarbazone gives back the ketone, which immediately forms the pyran.

A concerted mechanism involving attack by semicarbazide in the ring opening has been suggested but does not seem necessary.

An analogous mechanism can be used to explain the remarkably easy degradation of 2,2-dimethylchromenes under relatively mild basic conditions. Thus

PROBLEM 77.   Suggest mechanisms for the following reactions:

(77.1)

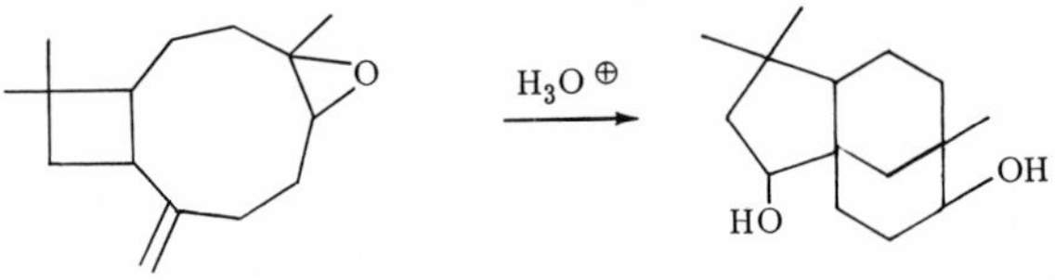

(77.2)

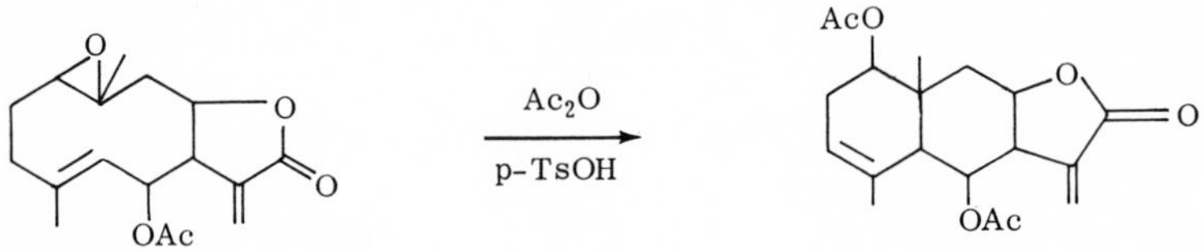

(77.3)

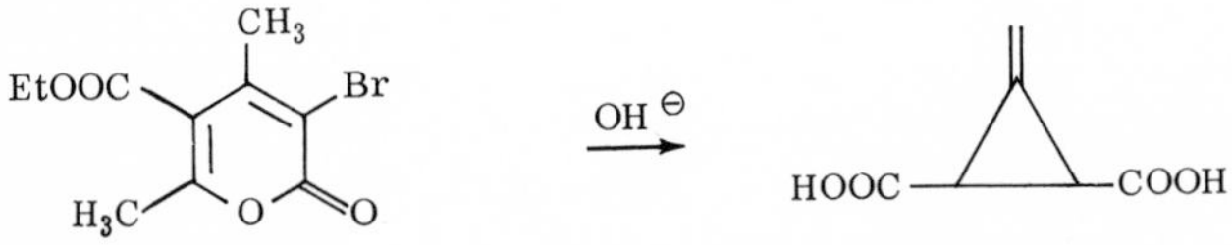

ANSWER 77.

(77.1)   [A. Aebi, D. H. R. Barton, and A. S. Lindsey, *J. Chem. Soc.*, **1953**, 3124.]

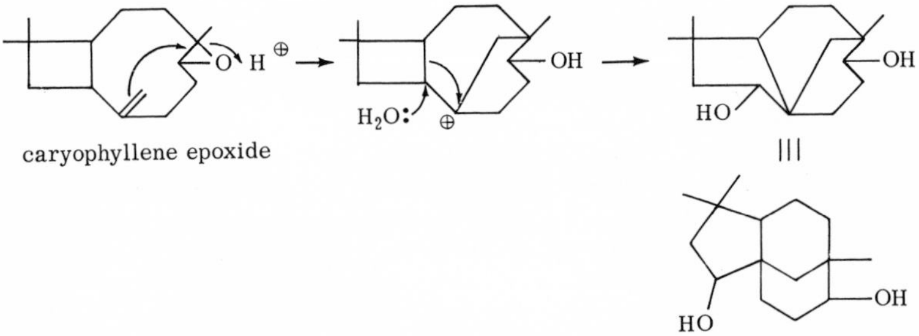

caryophyllene epoxide

Cleavage of the epoxide bond is followed by transannular formation of a C—C bond. The strain of the four-membered ring facilitates the final 1,2-shift to give the product.

(77.2)   [D. H. R. Barton, O. C. Bockman, and P. de Mayo, *J. Chem. Soc.*, **1960**, 2263; see also D. H. R. Barton and P. de Mayo, *J. Chem. Soc.*, **1957**, 150.]

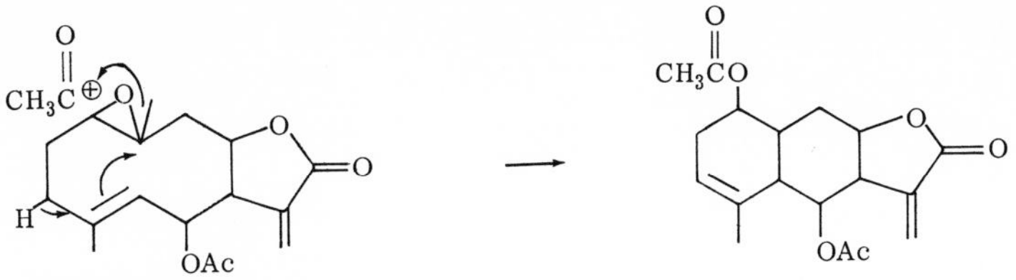

pyrethosin

(77.3)   [E. F. Ullman, *J. Am. Chem. Soc.*, **81**, 5386 (1959).]

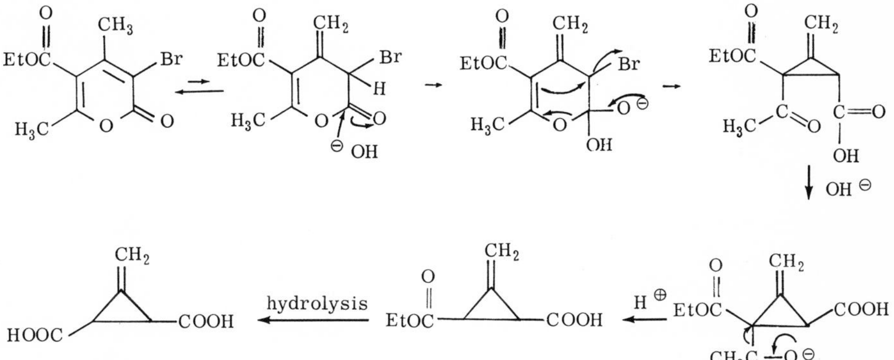

Feist's
acid

The following reaction has also been observed in this series.[1]

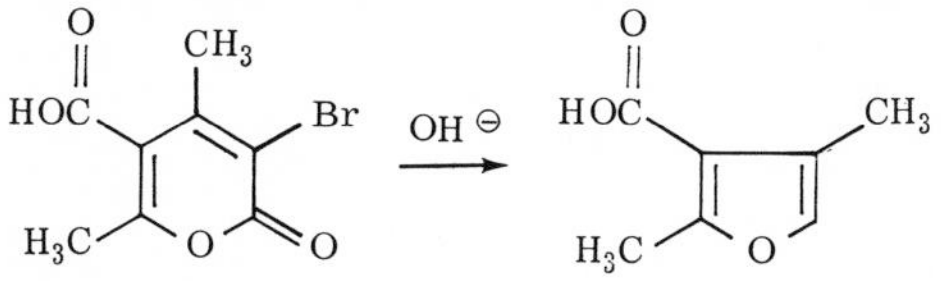

PROBLEM 78.   Suggest mechanisms for the following reactions:

(78.1)

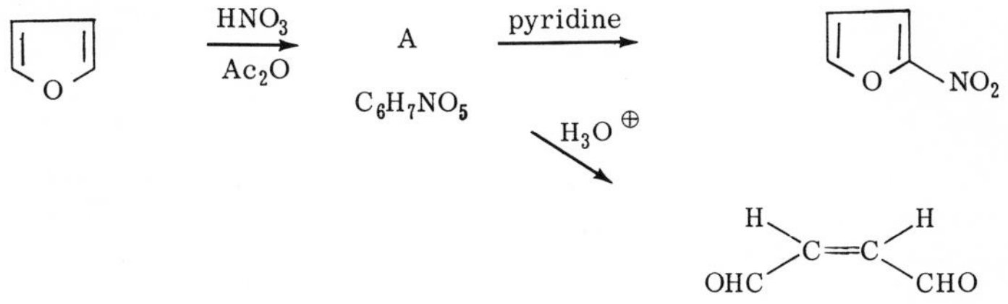

$$\text{HNO}_3 / \text{Ac}_2\text{O} \longrightarrow A \quad C_6H_7NO_5 \xrightarrow{\text{pyridine}}$$

$$\xrightarrow{\text{H}_3\text{O}^{\oplus}}$$

[1] F. Feist, *Ber.*, **26**, 747 (1893).

(*cont.*)

(78.2)

ANSWER 78.

(78.1)   [See N. Clauson-Kaas and J. Fakstorp, *Acta Chem. Scand.*, **1**, 210 (1947).]

(78.2)   [A. T. Blomquist, Y. C. Meinwald, C. G. Bottomley, and P. W. Martin, *Tetrahedron Letters*, **1960** (24), 13.]

The elimination to form the intermediate A is quite similar to the more common conversion of 1,2-dibromides to alkenes by I^{-1}.

In some similar cases, the o-quinodimethane intermediate cyclizes to give a benzocyclobutene product, rather than undergoing dimerization. Thus

But even here the intermediate can be trapped in the presence of a good dieno-phile.[2]

PROBLEM 79.

(79.1)   Suggest a mechanism for

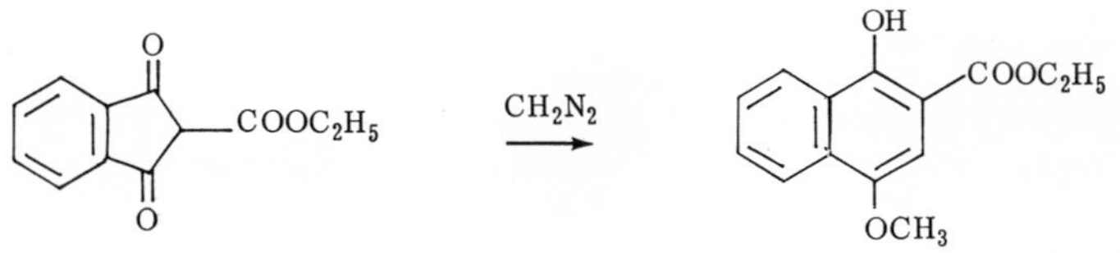

(79.2)   Deduce the structure of the product and suggest a mechanism for

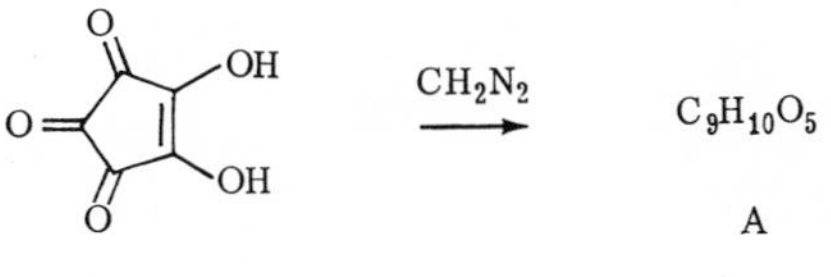

ANSWER 79.   (For a general discussion of ring enlargments with CH_2N_2, see B. Eistert in *Newer Methods of Preparative Organic Chemistry*, Wiley-Interscience, New York, 1948, pp. 513–570.)

(79.1)   [A. Hantzsch and E. Czapp, *Ber.*, **63**, 566 (1930); F. Arndt, *Ber.*, **63**, 1180 (1930).]

---

[1] Gould, pp. 494ff.
[2] M. P. Cava, A. A. Deana, and K. Muth, *J. Am. Chem. Soc.*, **81**, 6458 (1959).

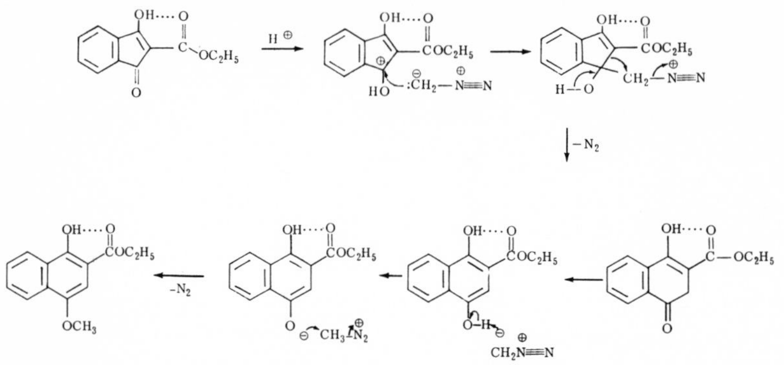

The failure to methylate chelated hydroxyl groups is common with diazomethane.

(79.2)   [K. Yamada and Y. Hirata, *Bull. Chem. Soc. Japan*, **31**, 550 (1958).]

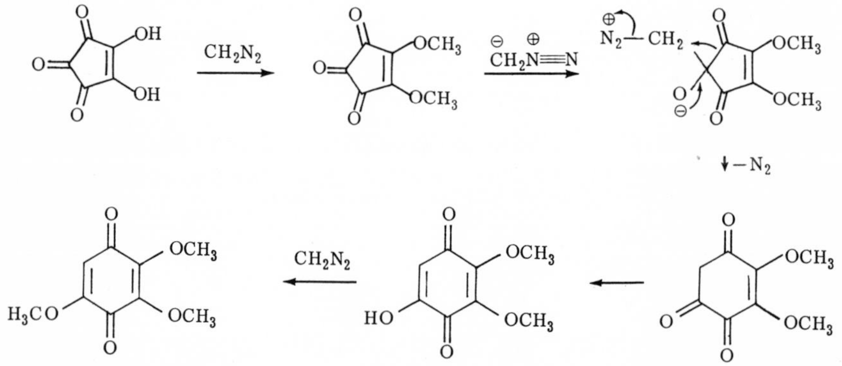

PROBLEM 80.   That the following reaction involves a benzyne intermediate has been shown by a tracer experiment using C^{14} (indicated by asterisks). Suggest reaction sequences in which the product is degraded to appropriate compounds, from which the distribution pattern of C^{14} in the product can be deduced.

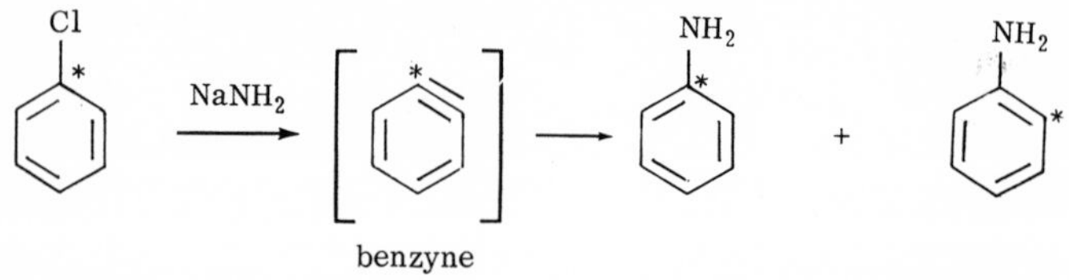

ANSWER 80.   [J. D. Roberts, D. A. Semenow, H. E. Simmons, Jr., and L. A. Carlsmith, *J. Am. Chem. Soc.,* **78**, 601 (1956).]

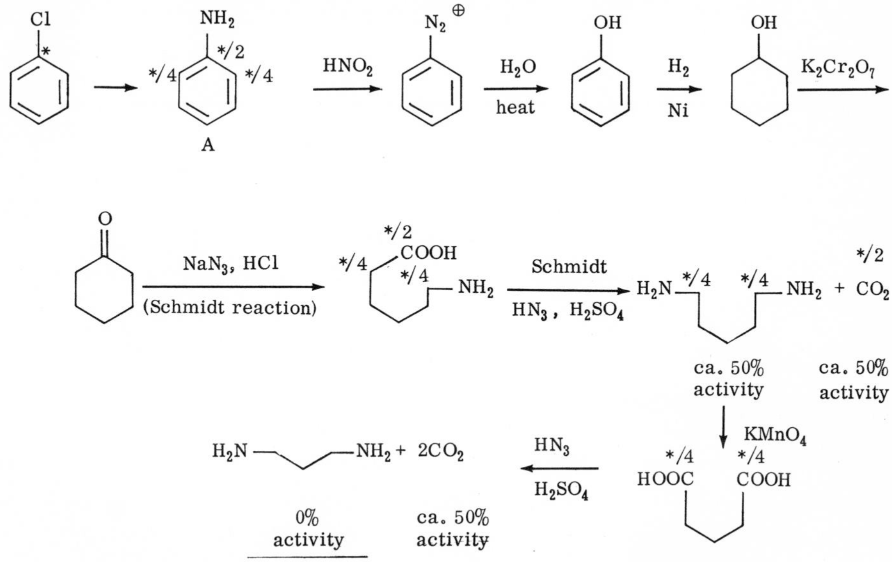

The distribution of C^{14} in the product, aniline, is expected to be as shown in A. Radioactivity measurements of the degradation products in the reaction sequence have clearly shown the validity of this assumption.

PROBLEM 81.   Suggest mechanisms for the following reactions:

(81.1)

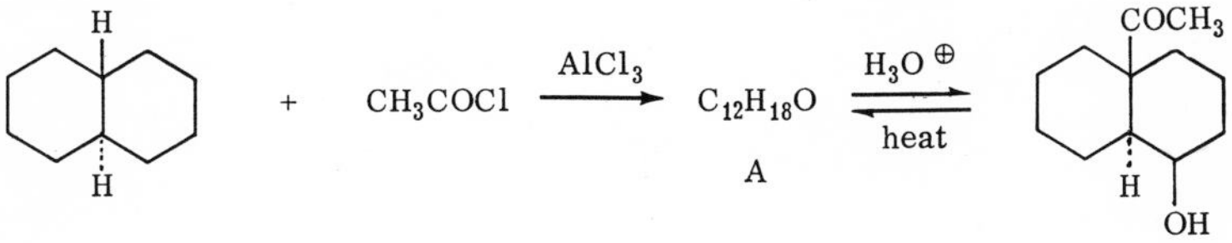

(81.2)

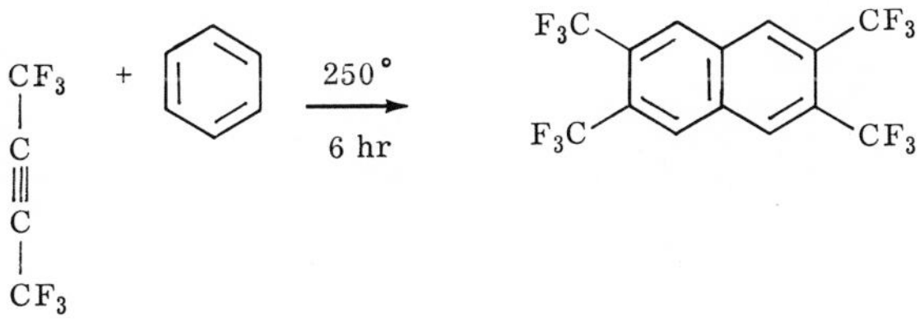

ANSWER 81.

(81. 1)   [G. Baddeley, B. G. Heston, and J. W. Rosburn, *J. Chem. Soc.*, **1960**, 4713; (1960); *J. Chem. Soc.*, **1961**, 3828.]

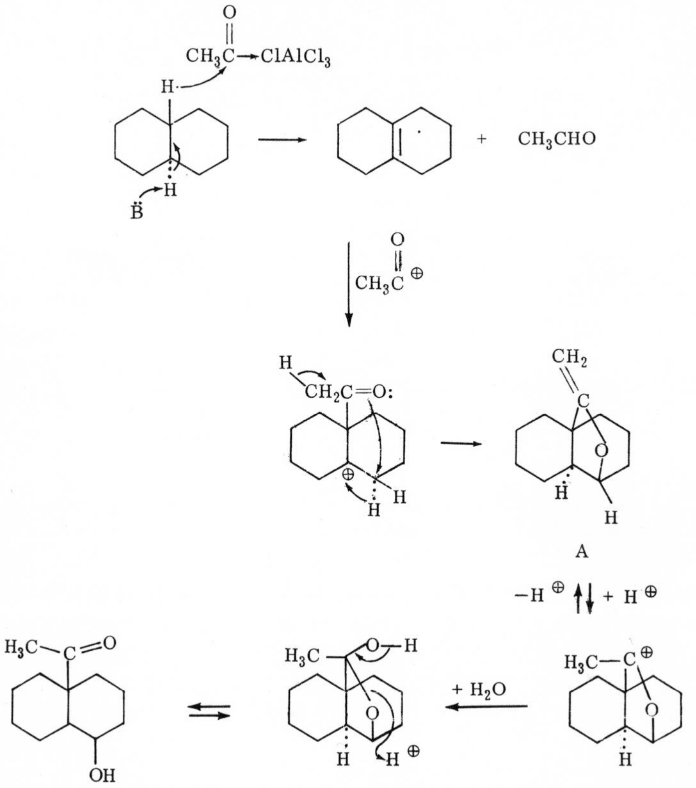

A

$-H^{\oplus}$ ⇅ $+ H^{\oplus}$

The first step is a dehydrogenation of decalin to Δ^9-octalin, which then undergoes Friedel-Crafts acylation. It has been suggested[1] that the first step from the octalin may lead to

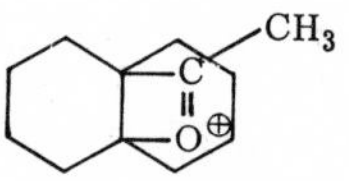

which then rearranges to give A.

_____

[1] M. S. Ahmad, G. Baddeley, B. G. Heston, and J. W. Rosburn, *Proc. Chem. Soc.*, **1959**, 395.

(81.2)   [C. G. Krespan, B. C. McKusick, and T. L. Cairns, *J. Am. Chem. Soc.*, **83**, 3428 (1961).]

Hexafluoro-2-butyne is an extremely active dienophile[1] and is capable of attacking aromatic rings to form bridged compounds such as A. The presence of A during the reaction is shown by the isolation of D as one of the other products.

1,5-Additions to the bridged system such as A have been observed[2] to give products resembling B, and a rearrangement allows the system to assume a less strained form. The mechanism of the rearrangement is not known, but, considering the vigorous conditions, it is not surprising, at least in retrospect. Finally, dehydrogenation yields the stable aromatic system.

---

[1] For an extensive discussion of the normal Diels-Alder (diene) synthesis, see K. Alder in *Newer Methods of Preparative Organic Chemistry*, Wiley-Interscience, New York, 1948, pp. 381-512.

[2] A. T. Blomquist and Y. C. Meinwald, *J. Am. Chem. Soc.*, **81**, 667 (1959).

PROBLEM 82.   Suggest mechanisms for the following reactions:

(82.1)

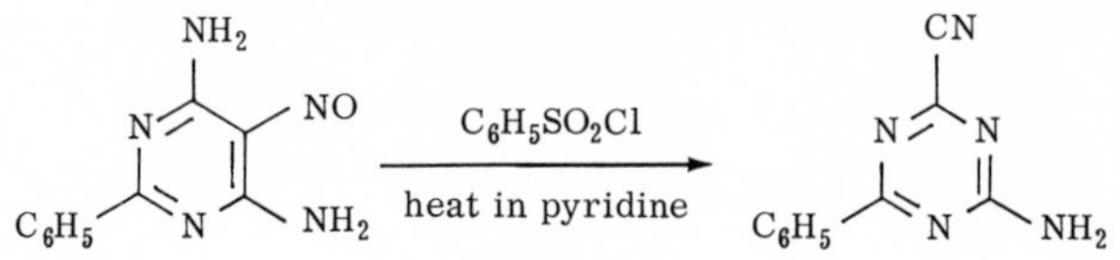

$$\text{(pyrimidine)} \xrightarrow[\text{heat in pyridine}]{C_6H_5SO_2Cl} \text{(triazine)}$$

(82.2)

$$\text{(pteridine-SH)} \xrightarrow[\text{reflux}]{ClCH_2COOH,\ aq.\ NaHCO_3} \text{(pyrazine)}$$

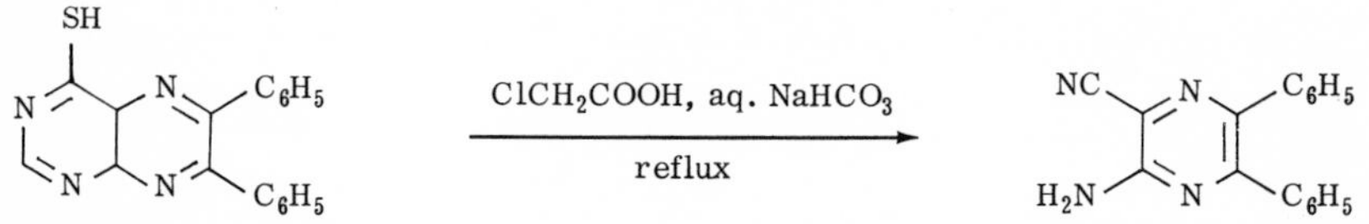

ANSWER 82.

(82.1)   [E. C. Taylor, C. W. Jefford, and C. C. Cheng, *J. Am. Chem. Soc.*, **83**, 1261 (1961).]

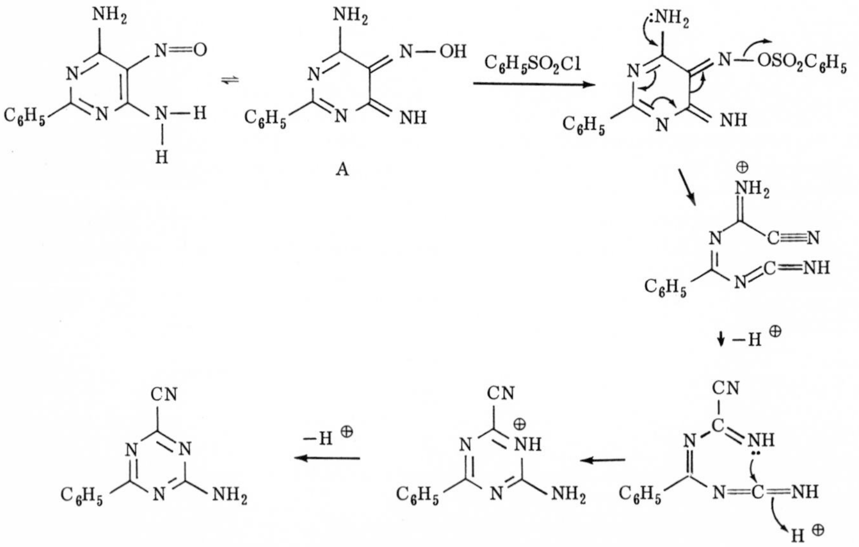

The first step need not proceed through the oxime form A, since the same product can be obtained by attack of $C_6H_5SO_2Cl$ on the nitroso oxygen, accompanied or followed by loss of a proton from one of the amino groups.

(82.2)   [E. C. Taylor, R. J. Knopf, J. A. Cogliano, J. W. Barton, and W. Pleiderer, *J. Am. Chem. Soc.*, **82**, 6058 (1960).]

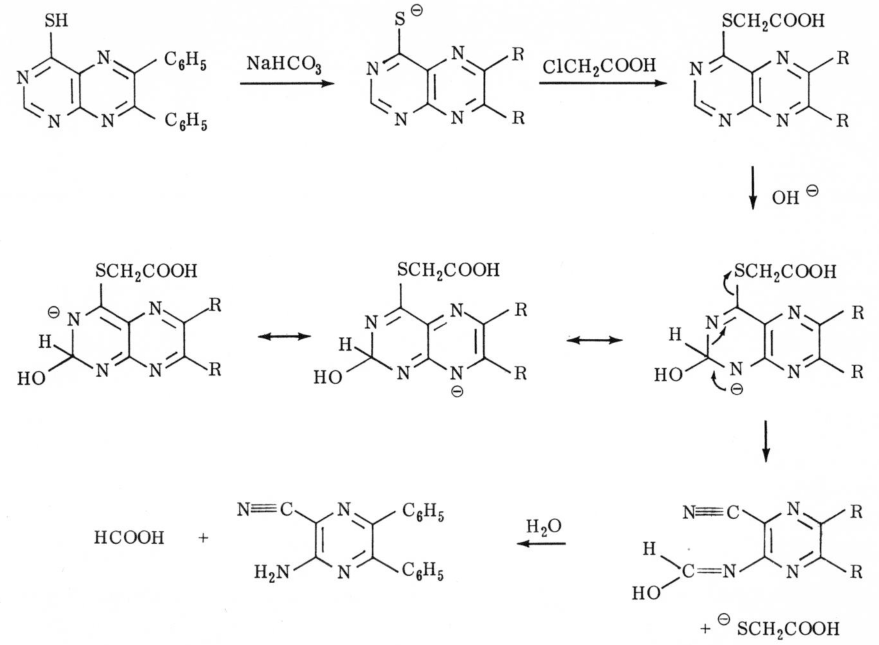

The ease of reaction even under the mildly basic conditions used apparently depends on the ability of the ring system to stabilize the intermediate anion by placing the charge on electronegative atoms, and on the presence of a group which can be lost irreversibly. Pyrimidine rings fused to other systems which can help stabilize the first formed anion have also been found to undergo this reaction.

PROBLEM 83.   Suggest mechanisms for the following reactions:

(83.1)

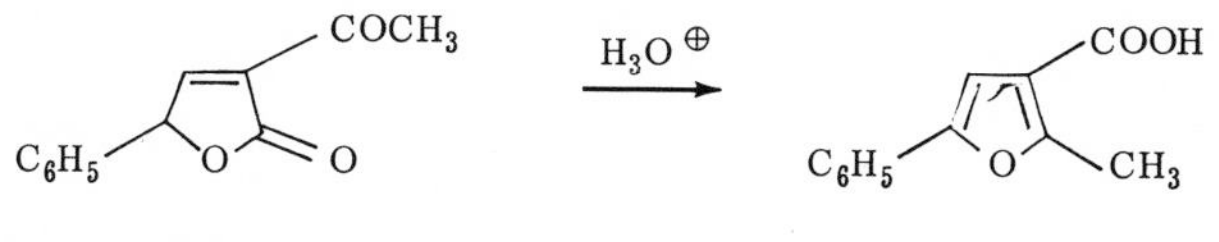

(83.2)

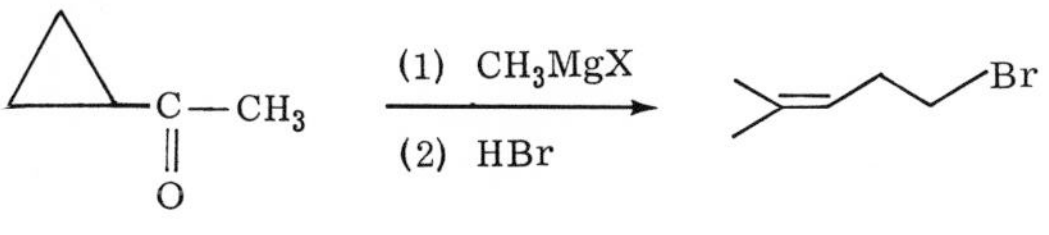

(83.3)

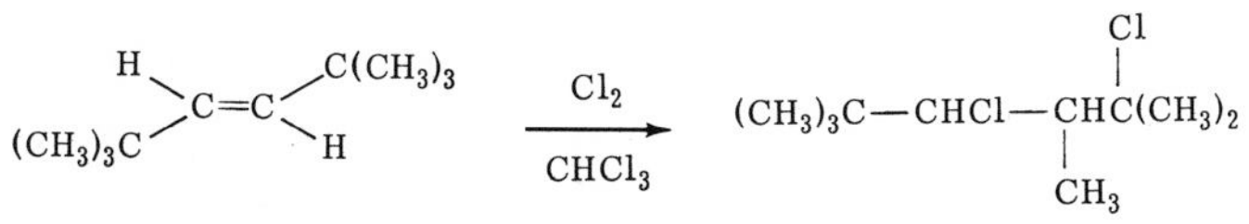

(cont.)

(83.4)

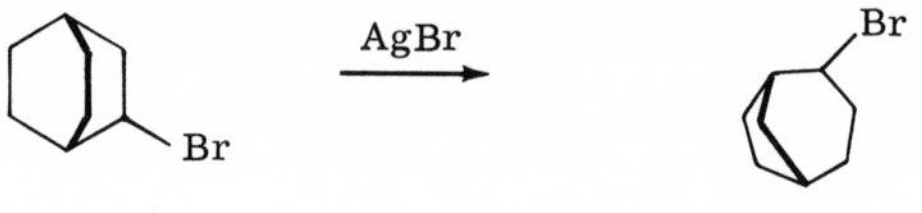

ANSWER 83.

(83.1)   [F. Korte and K. H. Buchel, *Angew. Chem.*, **71**, 709 (1959).]

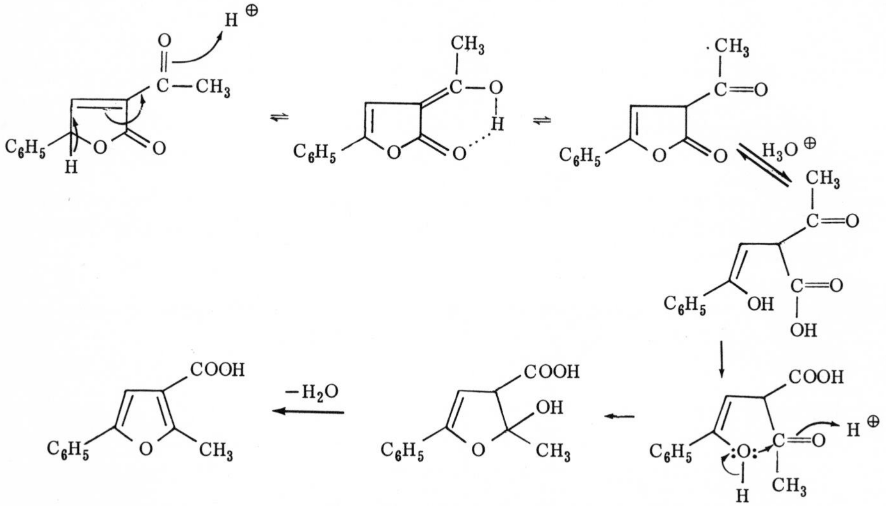

Alternative mechanisms have been proposed[1] but seem less likely.

(83.2)   [M. Julia, S. Julia, and R. Guegan, *Compt. Rend.*, **248**, 820 (1959).]

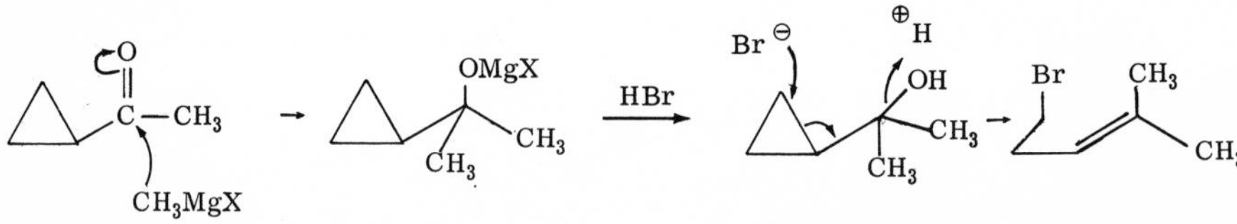

   This reaction is an example of the ready rearrangement of cyclopropylcar-
binyl derivatives to allyl carbinyl products.[2] The halide product can be converted
to the Grignard reagent and used to repeat the process. In this way a chain of iso-
prenoid units can be built up, although there is always one more terminal carbon
than in the true terpenes.[3]

---

[1] R. N. Lacey, *J. Chem. Soc.*, **1954**, 822.

[2] See J. D. Roberts and R. H. Mazur, *J. Am. Chem. Soc.*, **73**, 2509 (1951).

[3] M. Julia and C. Descoins, *Bull. Soc. Chim. France*, **1962**, 1939.

(83.3)   [W. H. Puterbaugh and M. S. Newman, *J. Am. Chem. Soc.,* **81,** 1611 (1959).]

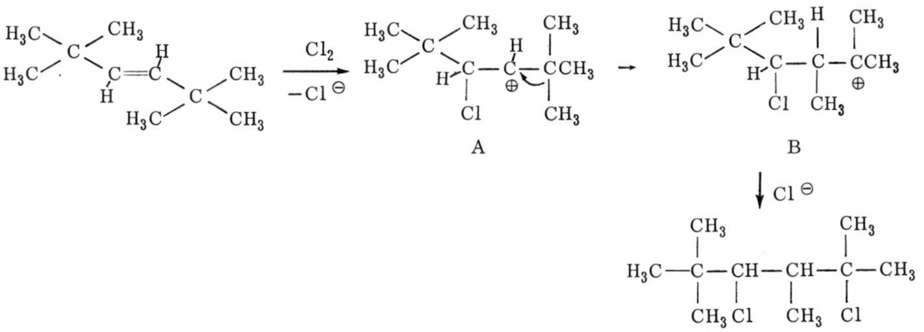

A   B

It is suggested that the extreme steric crowding of the ion A prevents its solvation and destabilizes it with respect to the rearranged ion B, in which the positive carbon is more accessible.

(83.4)   [See J. A. Berson in *Molecular Rearrangements,* Vol. I (P. de Mayo, ed.), Wiley-Interscience, New York, 1963, pp. 213ff.]

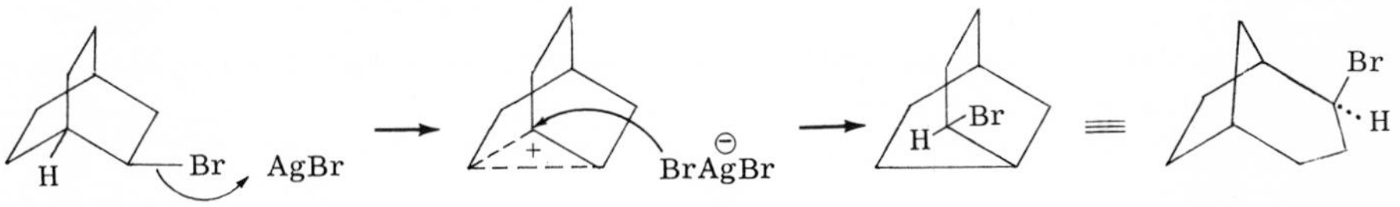

PROBLEM 84.   Suggest mechanisms for the following Grignard reactions which do not yield normal products:

(84.1)

$$C_6H_5COOC(C_6H_5)_3 \xrightarrow{CH_3MgI} \xrightarrow{H_2O} C_6H_5COOH + C_6H_5-\underset{\underset{C_6H_5}{|}}{\overset{\overset{CH_3}{|}}{C}}-C_6H_5$$

(84.2)

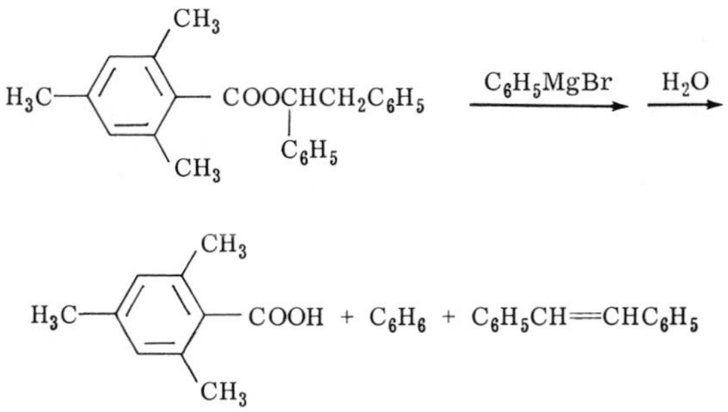

(cont.)

(84.3)

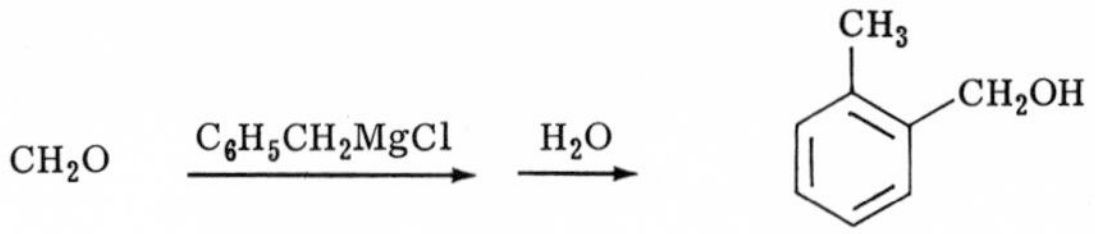

$$CH_2O \quad \xrightarrow{C_6H_5CH_2MgCl} \quad \xrightarrow{H_2O}$$

(84.4)

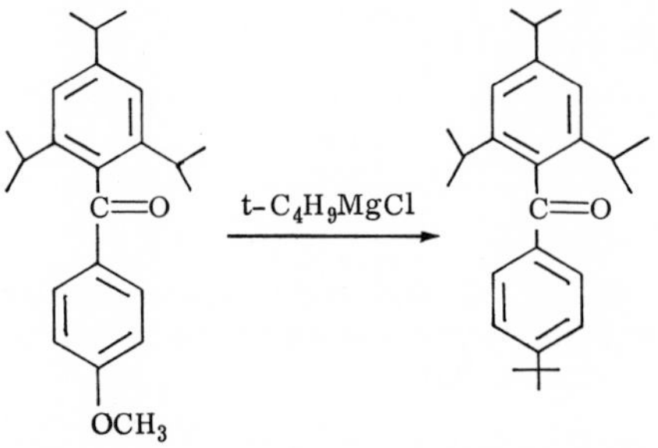

ANSWER 84.   [For very extensive discussions of the various Grignard reactions see M. S. Kharasch and O. Reinmuth, *Grignard Reactions of Nonmetallic Substances*, Prentice-Hall, Englewood
Cliff, N.J., 1954.]

The nature of the Grignard reagent and the mechanism of its reaction with
carbonyl groups are very complex and involve various highly solvated molecular
species. The addition reaction has been suggested to go by way of a cyclic six-
membered transition state containing two molecules of the reagent. A similar
process, with one molecule of the reagent, can be visualized to account for
the frequent 1,4-additions to $\alpha\beta$-unsaturated systems.

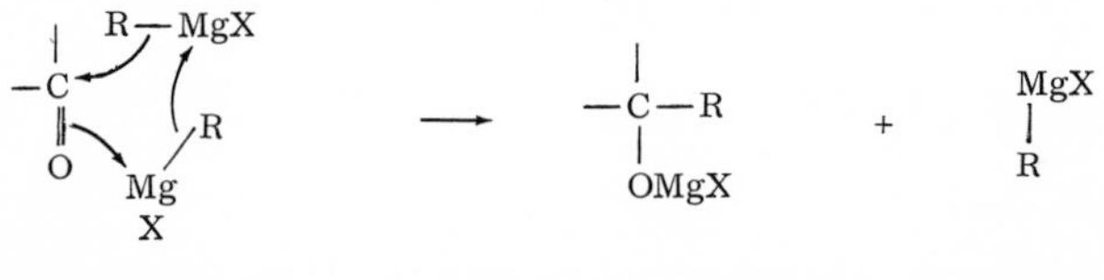

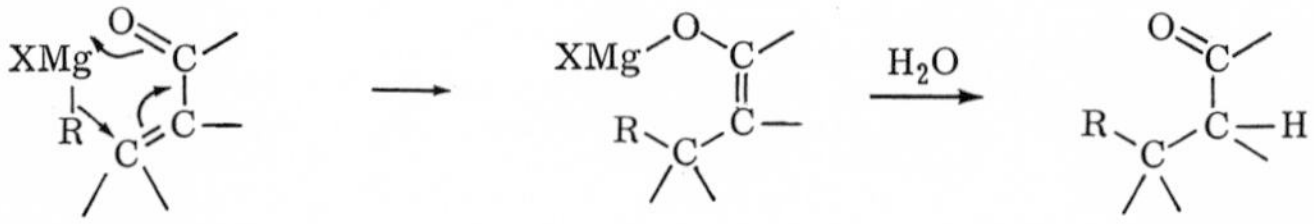

In practice, Grignard products can usually be predicted by regarding the reagent
effectively as $R^- MgX^+$.

Those reactions which do not give the simply expected product are lumped together as "abnormal Grignard reactions." These occur for various reasons, among them steric hindrance at the normal reaction site and particular electronic effects in the reactants.

(84.1)   [C. R. Hauser, P. O. Saperstein, and J. C. Shivers, *J. Am. Chem. Soc.*, **70**, 606 (1948); M. S. Kharasch and O. Reinmuth, op. cit., pp. 567ff.]

Various mechanisms can be suggested for this reaction, and there is no evidence to distinguish among them. Thus there have been proposed

A

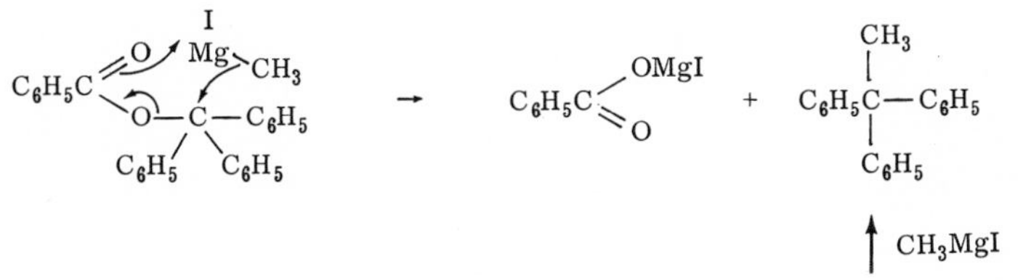

B

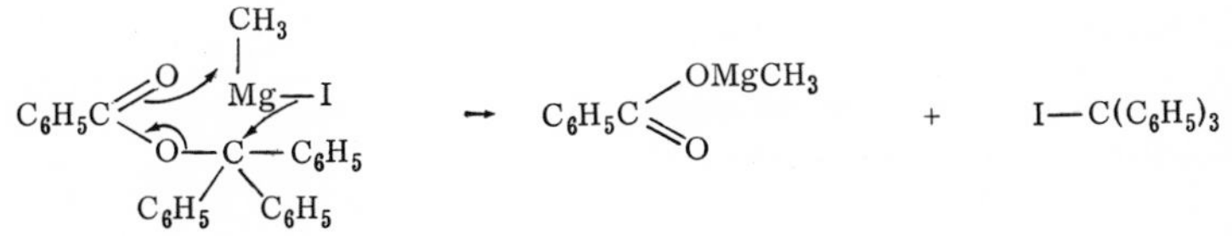

The second path has analogies in the cases of hindered acids,

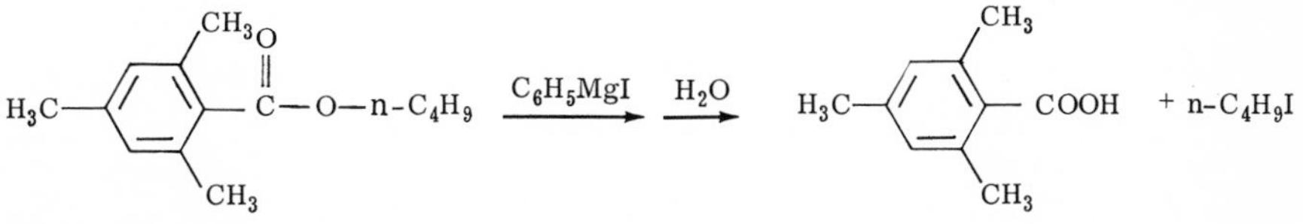

and the alkylation of triphenylmethyl halides by Grignard reagents is known. Nevertheless, both routes suffer from severe steric problems in conducting the displacement at a quaternary center.

An alternative mechanism, which resembles that proposed for the triphenylmethyl halides, would be

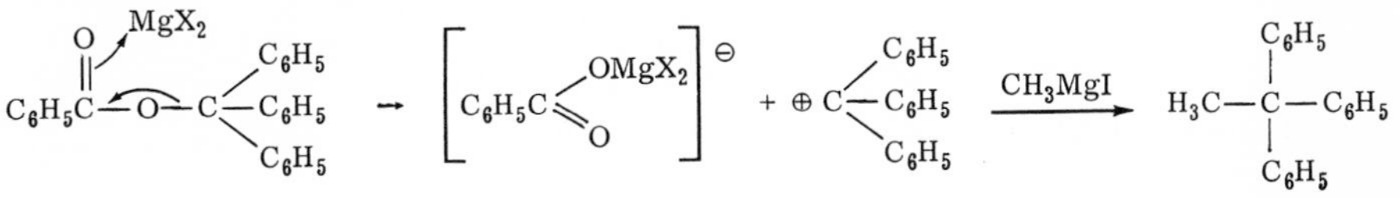

(*cont.*)

since the magnesium salts present in the reagent are capable as acting as Lewis acids.

(84.2)   [M. S. Kharasch and O. Reinmuth, op. cit.]

As above, there are two proposed mechanisms and no evidence. The second has the advantage of analogy, however.

(84.3)   [S. Siegel, W. M. Boyer, and R. R. Jay, *J. Am. Chem. Soc.*, **73**, 3237 (1951); M. S. Kharasch and O. Reinmuth, op. cit., pp. 1133ff.]

This is one of the classic abnormal Grignard reactions. It should be noted that with aldehydes other than formaldehyde, addition occurs both on the ring and on the side chain.

This presumably involves transformation of the intermediate A into a new Grignard-like reagent,

or

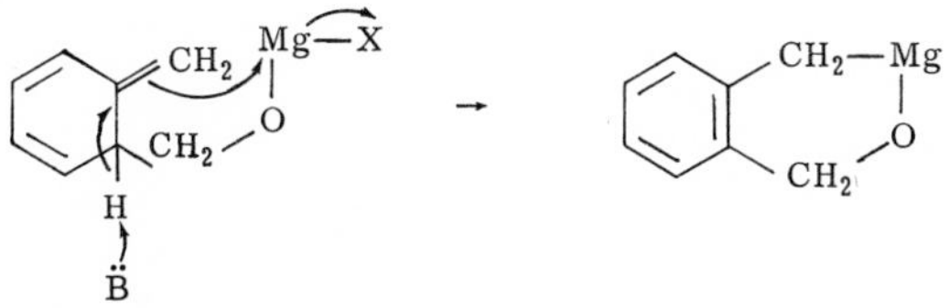

although it is not clear why this should fail to occur with formaldehyde.

(84.4)   [R. C. Fuson and W. S. Friedlander, *J. Am. Chem. Soc.*, **75**, 5410 (1953).]

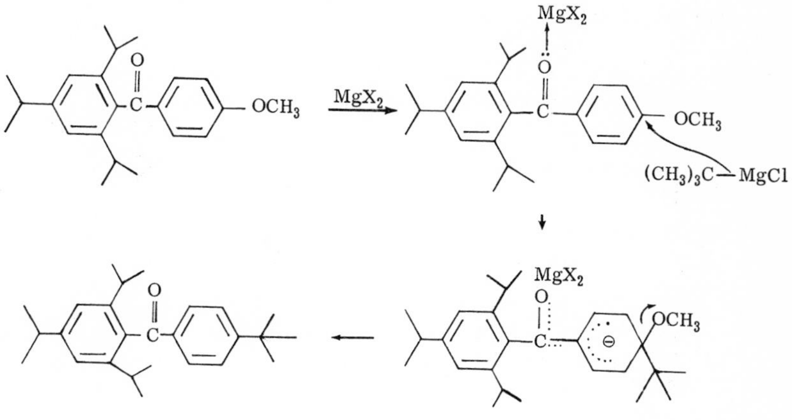

PROBLEM 85.   Suggest explanations why reactions A and B, in each of the following pairs, give different results.

(85.1)

A $C_6H_5COCHN_2 + C_6H_5NH_2 + C_6H_5NH_3Br^{\ominus}$ $\xrightarrow{\text{heat}}$

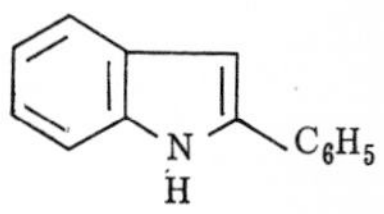

(*cont.*)

B

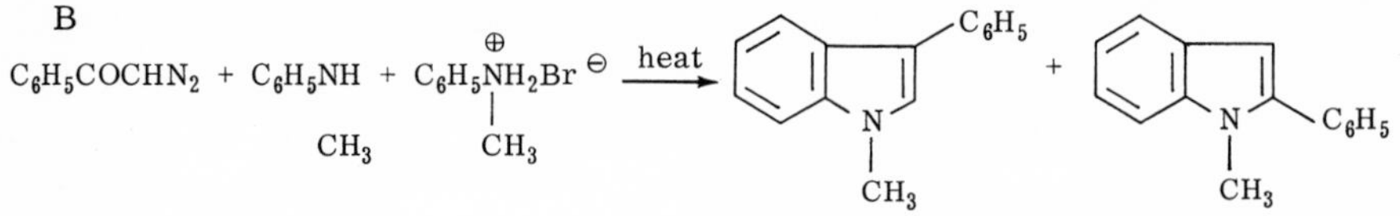

$$C_6H_5COCHN_2 + C_6H_5\overset{\underset{\displaystyle CH_3}{|}}{N}H + C_6H_5\overset{\underset{\displaystyle CH_3}{|}}{\overset{\oplus}{N}}H_2Br^{\ominus} \xrightarrow{\text{heat}}$$

(85.2)

A

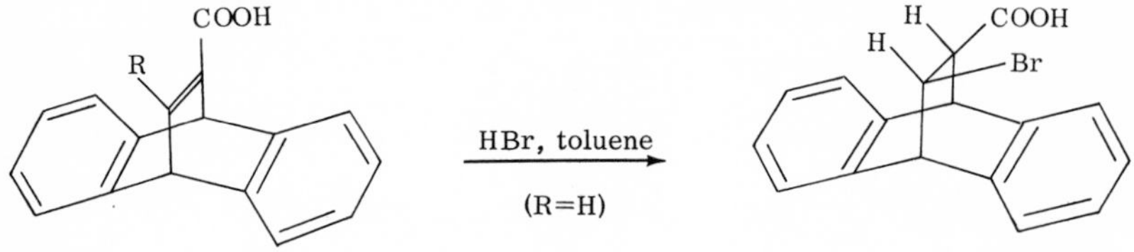

HBr, toluene

(R=H)

B   "

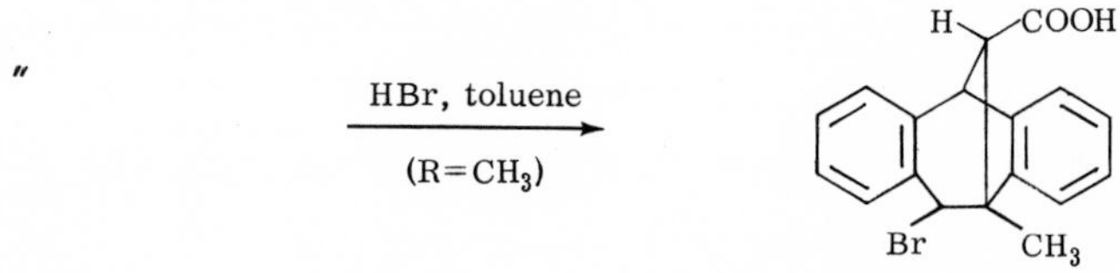

HBr, toluene

(R=CH₃)

(85.3)

A

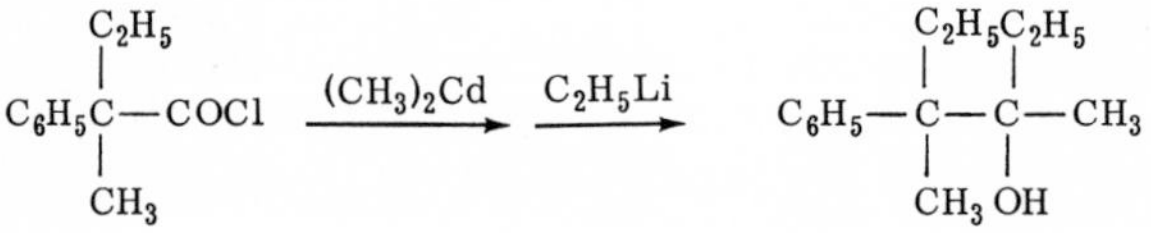

$$C_6H_5\overset{\underset{\displaystyle CH_3}{|}}{\overset{\displaystyle C_2H_5}{|}}C-COCl \xrightarrow{\text{(CH}_3)_2\text{Cd}} \xrightarrow{\text{C}_2\text{H}_5\text{Li}} C_6H_5-\overset{\underset{\displaystyle CH_3}{|}}{\overset{\displaystyle C_2H_5}{|}}C-\overset{\underset{\displaystyle OH}{|}}{\overset{\displaystyle C_2H_5}{|}}C-CH_3$$

B   " $\xrightarrow{\text{(C}_2\text{H}_5)_2\text{Cd}} \xrightarrow{\text{CH}_3\text{Li}}$ "

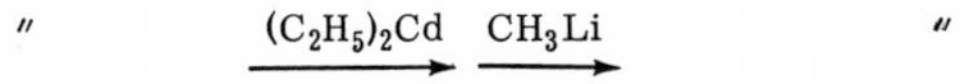

The products obtained by the reactions A and B are diastereoisomers.

ANSWER 85.

(85.1)   [C. E. Blades and A. L. Wilds, *J. Org. Chem.*, **21**, 1013 (1956).]

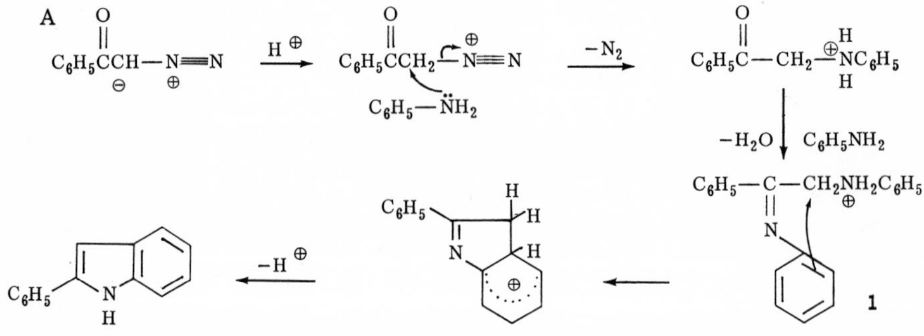

B

The difference between the two reactions may be ascribed to the fact that with aniline conversion to the imino intermediate **1** is complete and cyclization occurs on it. With alkyl anilines, however, imines corresponding to **1** cannot be formed. As a result the equilibrium addition of amine to the carbonyl group is less favored, and the alternative cyclization through **2** is allowed. An alternative suggestion is that since the initial addition product **3** cannot form the imine it cyclizes both by the route shown and by

The increasing yield of 3-phenylindoles as the N-alkyl group is made larger can be justified by either mechanism.

This reaction is quite closely related to the Bischler indole synthesis, in which the starting material is the α-haloacetophenone rather than the diazo-ketone.

(85.2)   [W. R. Vaughan and A. C. Schoenthaler, *J. Am. Chem. Soc.,* **79,** 5777 (1957).]

The first reaction A is a normal addition. In nonpolar solvents the transition state is known to involve several molecules of hydrogen halide, and it is probable that the addition of the bromine is more or less concerted with the protonation. In this way the formation of a secondary carbonium ion is avoided. In case B, the developing charge is on a tertiary carbon and may now have a sufficient lifetime for rearrangement to occur. It is possible that the methyl group also provides a certain amount of steric hindrance to the approach of the bromine, thus increasing the time available for rearrangement.

(85.3)   [For reviews see Y. Gault and H. Felkin, *Bull. Soc. Chim. France*, **1960**, 1342; E. L. Eliel, *Stereochemistry of Carbon Compounds*, McGraw-Hill, New York, 1962, pp. 68–74.]

When a new asymmetric unit is generated adjacent to one already in existence, the configuration of the product will be more or less determined by that of
the starting material. Cram's rule[1] states that, for addition to a carbonyl group,
the product may be predicted by orienting the group between the two smallest
substituents (M, S) on the asymmetric carbon and assuming that the incoming
reagent (R) approaches from the side of the smallest group (S):

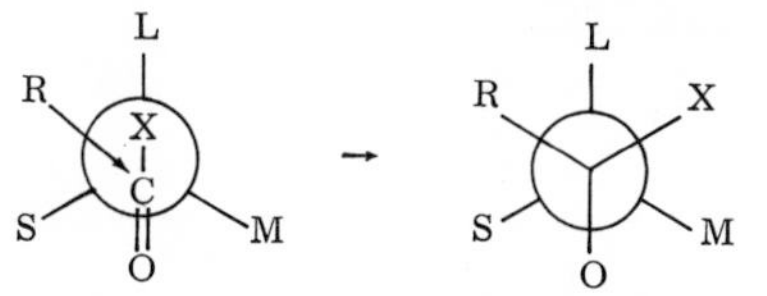

In the example given, it is assumed that phenyl > ethyl > methyl.

PROBLEM 86.

86.1)   Suggest a mechanism for the following reaction: The numbers in parentheses are total observed atom % of O^{18} ($\pm 0.01\%$).

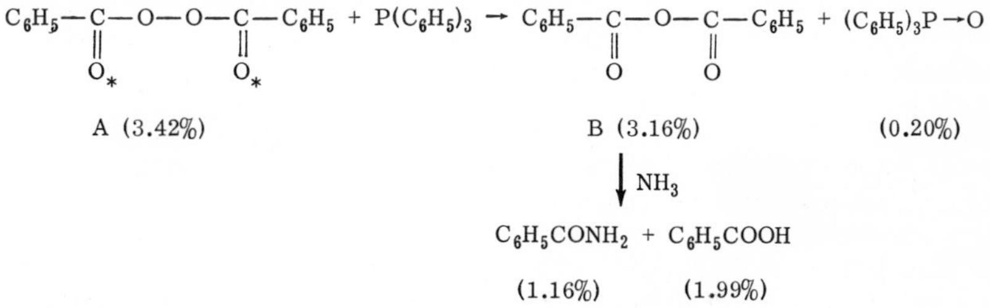

$$C_6H_5-\underset{\underset{*}{\overset{\|}{O}}}{C}-O-O-\underset{\underset{*}{\overset{\|}{O}}}{C}-C_6H_5 + P(C_6H_5)_3 \rightarrow C_6H_5-\underset{\overset{\|}{O}}{C}-O-\underset{\overset{\|}{O}}{C}-C_6H_5 + (C_6H_5)_3P \rightarrow O$$

$$\qquad\text{A (3.42\%)} \qquad\qquad\qquad\qquad\qquad \text{B (3.16\%)} \qquad\qquad\text{(0.20\%)}$$

$$\downarrow NH_3$$

$$C_6H_5CONH_2 + C_6H_5COOH$$

$$\quad(1.16\%) \qquad\quad (1.99\%)$$

(N.B.: The natural concentration of O^{18} is 0.2 atom %.)

86.2)   With reference to the above results, deduce which oxygen atom is abstracted
by PR_3 in the following reaction:

$$O_2N-\left\langle\!\!\!\bigcirc\!\!\!\right\rangle-\underset{\underset{*}{\overset{\|}{O}}}{C}-O-O-\underset{\overset{\|}{O}}{C}-\left\langle\!\!\!\bigcirc\!\!\!\right\rangle-OMe \xrightarrow{PR_3}\ \text{acid anhydride}\ \xrightarrow{NH_3}$$

$$\qquad\qquad\qquad\qquad\qquad\qquad\qquad\qquad\quad(1.07\%)$$

$$O_2N-\left\langle\!\!\!\bigcirc\!\!\!\right\rangle-CONH_2$$

$$(1.12\%)$$

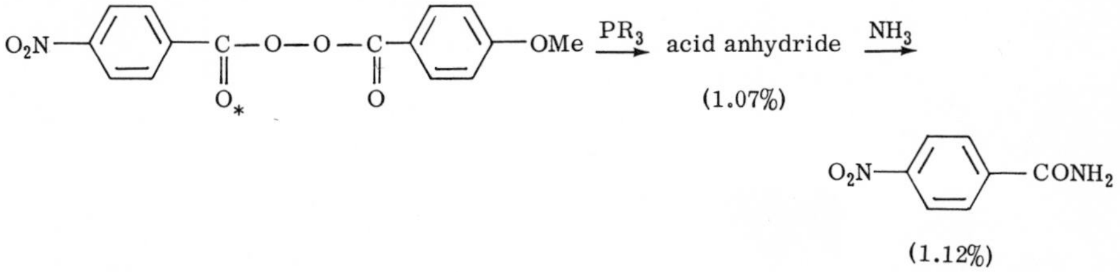

(N.B.: The O^{18} percentages given here refer to the *excess* over natural abundance.)

---

[1] D. J. Cram and F. A. Abd Elhafez, *J. Am. Chem. Soc.*, **74**, 5828 (1952).

ANSWER 86.

(86. 1)   [M. A. Greenbaum, D. B. Denney, and A. K. Hoffman, *J. Am. Chem. Soc.*, **78**, 2563 (1956).]

The O^{18} content (in atom %) of the original peroxide is given by A. The content of the peroxide oxygens is the natural abundance.

$$\begin{array}{c} 0.20 \quad 0.20 \\ C_6H_5-\overset{\displaystyle \|}{\underset{\displaystyle O}{C}}-O-O-\overset{\displaystyle \|}{\underset{\displaystyle O}{C}}-C_6H_5 \qquad A\\ \quad 1.51 \qquad\quad 1.51 \end{array}$$

The O^{18} content of the phosphine oxide formed is natural and indicates that a peroxidic oxygen was abstracted. The O^{18} content (3.16 atom %) of the anhydride product may be visualized as being distributed in a number of possible ways (B_{1-4}); see Table 5-1. The O^{18} contents are predicted for the products of ammonolysis on the assumption that attack by ammonia will occur with equal probability at either carbonyl and that the values found will be the average of those obtained for the two alternative cleavages.

Table 5-1

	Label	Distribution	Acid	Amide
B_1	$\overset{O^*}{\overset{\|}{-}}C-O-\overset{O^*}{\overset{\|}{}}C-$	$\overset{O^{1.48}}{\overset{\|}{-}}C-\underset{0.20}{O}-\overset{O^{1.48}}{\overset{\|}{}}C-$	1.68	1.48
B_2	$\overset{O^*}{\overset{\|}{-}}C-\overset{*}{O}-\overset{O}{\overset{\|}{}}C-$	$\overset{O^{1.48}}{\overset{\|}{-}}C-\underset{1.48}{O}-\overset{O^{0.20}}{\overset{\|}{}}C-$	2.32	0.84
B_3	$\overset{O^*}{\overset{\|}{-}}C-\overset{*/2}{O}-\overset{O^{*/2}}{\overset{\|}{}}C-$	$\overset{O^{1.48}}{\overset{\|}{-}}C-\underset{0.84}{O}-\overset{O^{0.84}}{\overset{\|}{}}C-$	2.00	1.16
B_4	$\overset{O^{*/3}}{\overset{\|}{-}}C-\underset{*/3}{O}-\overset{O^{*/3}}{\overset{\|}{}}C-$	$\overset{O^{1.05}}{\overset{\|}{-}}C-\underset{1.05}{O}-\overset{O^{1.05}}{\overset{\|}{}}C-$	2.10	1.05

The excellent agreement between the observed values and those predicted for B_3 suggests that this represents the actual distribution. The following mechanism is suggested to account for these results.

$$C_6H_5-\overset{\overset{*}{O}}{\overset{\|}{C}}-O\!\!\rightarrow\!\!\underset{\overset{\displaystyle \cdot\cdot}{P R_3}}{O}-\overset{\overset{*}{O}}{\overset{\|}{C}}-C_6H_5 \;\rightarrow\; \left[R_3\overset{\oplus}{P}-O-\overset{\overset{*}{O}}{\overset{\|}{C}}C_6H_5 \;+\; C_6H_5\overset{\overset{*}{O}}{\overset{\|}{C}}-O^{\ominus} \;\longleftrightarrow\; C_6H_5\overset{\overset{*}{O}^{\ominus}}{\overset{|}{C}}\!\!=\!\!O \right]$$

$$\downarrow$$

$$C_6H_5\overset{\overset{*}{O}}{\overset{\|}{C}}-O-\overset{\overset{*/2}{O}}{\overset{\|}{C}}C_6H_5 \;+\; R_3P\rightarrow O$$

The intermediate probably exists as an ion pair in the nonpolar solvents used. The two oxygens of the benzoate anion are equivalent, thus accounting for the equipartition of the O^{18} label. The displacement reaction leading from the intermediate to the products is probably to be represented by

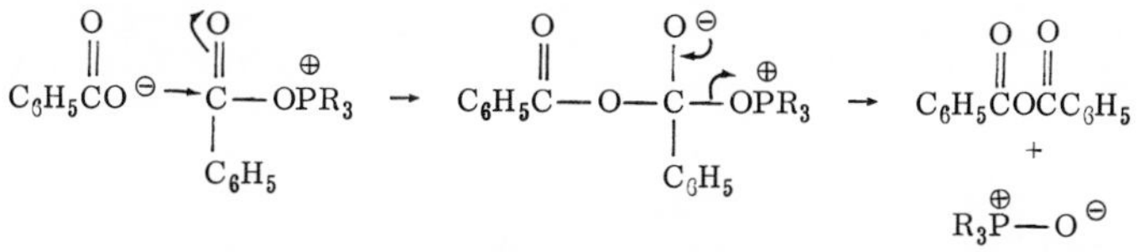

$$C_6H_5CO^{\ominus} \rightarrow \overset{O}{\underset{C_6H_5}{\overset{\|}{C}}} - OPR_3 \quad \rightarrow \quad C_6H_5\overset{O}{\overset{\|}{C}} - O - \overset{O^{\ominus}}{\underset{C_6H_5}{C}} \overset{\oplus}{OPR_3} \quad \rightarrow \quad C_6H_5\overset{O}{\overset{\|}{C}}O\overset{O}{\overset{\|}{C}}C_6H_5$$

$$+$$

$$R_3\overset{\oplus}{P} - O^{\ominus}$$

(86.2)   [D. B. Denney and M. A. Greenbaum, *J. Am. Chem. Soc.*, **79**, 979 (1957).]
This peroxide is unsymmetrical and has two nonequivalent oxygen atoms, α and β, which can be attacked by the phosphine. Such attacks will lead to the ion pairs and products shown below.

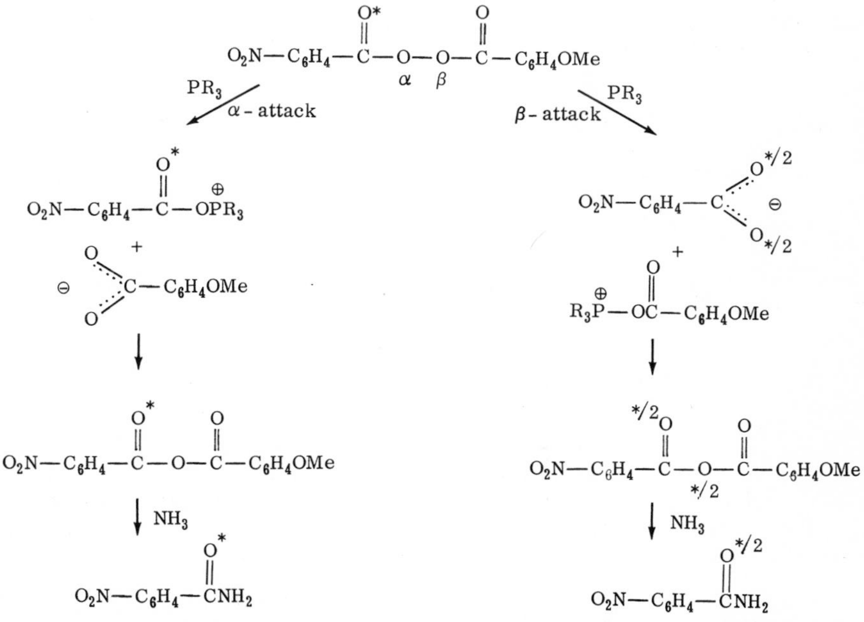

$$O_2N - C_6H_4 - \overset{O^*}{\overset{\|}{C}} - O - O - \overset{O}{\overset{\|}{C}} - C_6H_4OMe$$
$$\qquad\qquad\qquad\qquad \alpha \quad \beta$$

PR$_3$ α - attack   PR$_3$ β - attack

$$O_2N - C_6H_4 - \overset{O^*}{\overset{\|}{C}} - \overset{\oplus}{O}PR_3$$

$$\overset{\ominus}{\underset{O}{\overset{O}{}}}C - C_6H_4OMe$$

$$O_2N - C_6H_4 - C\overset{O^{*/2}}{\underset{O_{*/2}}{}}{}^{\ominus}$$

$$+$$

$$R_3\overset{\oplus}{P} - O\overset{O}{\overset{\|}{C}} - C_6H_4OMe$$

$$\downarrow$$

$$O_2N - C_6H_4 - \overset{O^*}{\overset{\|}{C}} - O - \overset{O}{\overset{\|}{C}} - C_6H_4OMe$$

$$\downarrow NH_3$$

$$O_2N - C_6H_4 - \overset{O^*}{\overset{\|}{C}}NH_2$$

$$\downarrow$$

$$O_2N - C_6H_4 - \overset{*/2 \, O}{\overset{\|}{C}} - O - \overset{O}{\overset{\|}{C}} - C_6H_4OMe$$
$$\qquad\qquad\qquad {}^{*/2}$$

$$\downarrow NH_3$$

$$O_2N - C_6H_4 - \overset{O^{*/2}}{\overset{\|}{C}}NH_2$$

Thus if the initial reaction occurs on the α-oxygen, no distribution of the label should be found. Reaction on the β-oxygen, however, produces a symmetrical benzoate ion containing the O^{18}, so this will be divided between the carbonyl and anhydride positions. The observation that all the excess O^{18} of the anhydride appears in the derived amide indicates that the label is retained in the carbonyl group and thus that α-attack has occurred.

Since the ion pair produced by the favored α-attack is less stable thermo-dynamically (anion of weaker acid, $\oplus$ charge associated with the fragment bearing a NO_2 group) than that expected from β-attack, the direction of reaction must be determined by the polarization of the starting peroxide. The α-oxygen is more positive than the β-oxygen because of the electron-withdrawing effects of the nitro group, and apparently is more reactive toward the phosphine because of this.

PROBLEM 87.   On being heated with potassium acetate in ethanol at 60°, compounds 1, 2, and 3 undergo cyclization to give a Δ^2-oxazoline, 4. The cis isomers 5, 6, and 7, on the other hand, undergo solvolysis to give a mixture of elimination and displacement products.

R = H (1)
R = t-C$_4$H$_9$ (2,3)

Ms = CH$_3$SO$_2$—

The observed first-order (or pseudo-first-order) rate constants for these reactions are [in 10^6 k(sec^{-1})]:

1	252	5	0.69
2	6280	6	0.69
3	76	7	2.95

(87.1)   Suggest an explanation for the relative reactivities of 1, 2, 3, and the cis compounds.

(*cont.*)

(87.2)   Discuss quantitatively the importance of possible intermediates in the reaction of **1**, as compared with those for **2** and **3**.

ANSWER 87.   [J. Sicher, M. Tichy, F. Sipos, and M. Pankova, *Collection
Czech. Chem. Commun.,* **26**, 2418 (1961); *Proc. Chem. Soc.,*
1960, 384.]

(87. 1)   The concerted displacement reaction leading to the oxazoline requires the
antiperiplanar arrangement A; the problem is to accommodate this arrangement
within the restrictions imposed by the bulky t-butyl group, which requires an
equatorial position.[1,2]

A   B

The orientation A is provided naturally by the trans-diaxial arrangement of
2, and the steric strain inherent in two axial groups destabilizes the ground
state, so the reaction proceeds at the maximum rate. On the other hand, the
corresponding conformation (B) for **3** is much too strained to serve as an intermediate. Nevertheless, the reaction gives the product which results from
concerted displacement and at a rate which, in comparison with the cis compounds, indicates considerable neighboring-group assistance in the transition
state. The alternative which is proposed involves the twisted boat form (C),[3]
which also provides the required geometry, but without placing the t-butyl group
in an axial position.

C   OMs

The parent system **1** can react either through the trans-diaxial conformer
(D) or through the twisted boat (E). It is suggested that both of these are involved
[see part (2)]. In any case, the diequatorial ground state of **1** is more stable than
the diaxial one of **2**, and so the reaction is slower.

[1] S. Winstein and N. J. Holness, *J. Am. Chem. Soc.,* **77**, 5562 (1955).
[2] E. L. Eliel, *J. Chem. Educ.,* **37**, 126 (1960).
[3] See E. L. Eliel, *Stereochemistry of Carbon Compounds,* McGraw-Hill, New York,
1962, pp. 206-207.

The cis compounds cannot attain the arrangement A, and in the absence of the neighboring group assistance react more slowly by normal solvolytic paths.

(87.2)   The reaction of the conformationally mobile cyclohexane derivative **1** may involve either of the intermediate conformations D or E, which are in equilibrium with the diequatorial form F:

The observed rate v is given by[1,2]

$$v = k[1] = k_D[D] + k_E[E]$$

$$K_D = \frac{[D]}{[F]} \qquad K_E = \frac{[E]}{[F]}$$

Since [F] is known to be significantly more stable than D or E, $[F] \approx [1]$; so $[D] \approx K_D[1]$ and $[E] \approx K_E[1]$. Thus

$$k[1] = k_D K_D[1] + k_E K_E[1] \qquad \text{or} \qquad k = k_D K_D + k_E K_E$$

As a very rough approximation, it may be suggested that the rate through the twisted boat form is the same for **1** and **3**, since both involve the diequatorial to diaxial conversion, and the orientation of the t-butyl group remains roughly unchanged in the transition state for **3**. Thus, substituting the observed rate **3** for $k_E K_E$, we have

$$252 \times 10^{-6} = k_D K_D + 76 \times 10^{-6}$$

$$k_D K_D = 172 \times 10^{-6}$$

$$\frac{k_D K_D}{k_E K_E} = \frac{172 \times 10^{-6}}{76 \times 10^{-6}} = 2.4$$

Thus the reaction proceeds somewhat more by way of the chair intermediate than by the boat, although both appear to be involved.

CHAPTER **6**

CONDENSATIONS AND RELATED REACTIONS

This chapter contains an assemblage of problems related mainly by the fact that they involve the reaction of a resonance stabilized carbanion or its equivalent with an electrophilic center. No single reference can cover all these topics, but classical carbonyl condensations are treated at length in Royals. The following are further references.

1. H. O. House, *Modern Synthetic Reactions*, Benjamin, New York, 1965, pp. 163-281. A practical survey of condensation reactions, alkylations, and acylations.
2. J. Szmuszkovicz in *Advances in Organic Chemistry*, Vol. 4, Wiley-Interscience, New York, 1963, pp. 1-113. A survey of enamine chemistry.
3. B. C. L. Weedon in *Elucidation of Structures by Physical and Chemical Methods*, Part 2 (K. W. Bentley, ed.), Wiley-Interscience, 1963, pp. 655-705. A discussion of the processes which can occur under the vigorous conditions of alkali fusion.

PROBLEM 88. Predict the position at which halogenation will occur when each of the following compounds reacts with 1 mole of bromine in the presence of base:

$$\underset{\text{A}}{CH_3CCH_2CH_3} \qquad \underset{\text{B}}{\qquad CH_3} \qquad \underset{\text{C}}{ClCH_2CCH_3}$$

ANSWER 88.   (See Gould, pp. 372-384.)

$$\underset{\text{A}}{BrCH_2\overset{\displaystyle O}{\overset{\displaystyle \|}{C}}CH_2CH_3}$$

B

$$\underset{\text{C}}{Cl\underset{\displaystyle Br}{\overset{\displaystyle O}{\overset{\displaystyle \|}{C}}HC}CH_3}$$

The base-catalyzed halogenation of ketones generally proceeds via the slow formation of an enolate anion by removal of an α-H and the rapid reaction of this anion with the halogen. Thus

$$CH_3\overset{\displaystyle O}{\overset{\displaystyle \|}{C}}CH_3 + OH^{\ominus} \xrightarrow{\text{slow}} CH_3\overset{\displaystyle O}{\overset{\displaystyle \|}{C}}\overset{\ominus}{\cdots}CH_2 \xrightarrow[\text{fast}]{Br_2} CH_3\overset{\displaystyle O}{\overset{\displaystyle \|}{C}}CH_2Br$$

In unsymmetrical molecules the structure of the product will be determined by the stability of the intermediate anion or the similar transition state leading to it. As a result, substitution favors I° > II° > III° halogenation, in line with the corresponding sequence of anion stabilities (note that $-CH_3$ is electron releasing as compared with $-H$). Substitution by electron-withdrawing groups such as halogen, however, helps stabilize the anion and leads to polyhalogenation on one carbon. The iodoform reaction, for example, depends on both these effects. The first iodination occurs on the methyl group because of the preference for primary substitution, and the subsequent ones because of the anion stabilization by the iodine already present.

PROBLEM 89.   Explain why cyanide ion is essential as a catalyst in the benzoin condensation.

ANSWER 89.   [Gould, pp. 394ff.; W. S. Ide and J. S. Buck in *Organic Reactions,* Vol. 4, Wiley, New York, 1948, p. 269.]

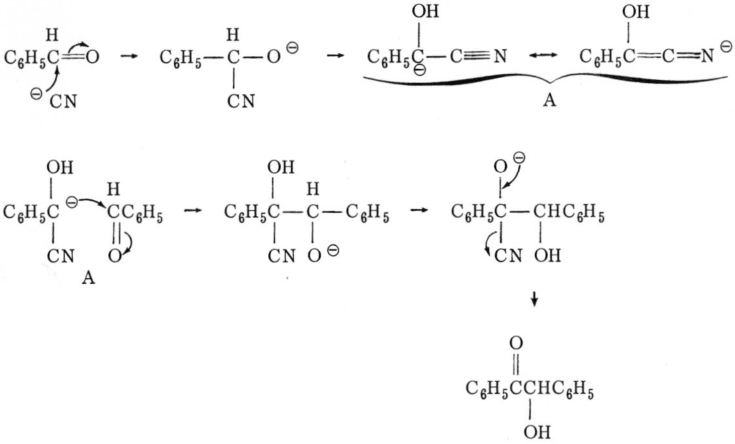

Because of the ability of the —CN group to stabilize adjacent negative charges by resonance, the cyanohydrin resulting from the addition of HCN to an aldehyde can lose a proton to form the anion A. This anion can then add to a second molecule of aldehyde in a step which is essentially the same as an aldol reaction.[1]

The benzoin condensation is usually restricted to aldehydes lacking α-hydrogen atoms, since, if these are present, the CN⁻ is a sufficiently strong base to cause aldol condensations to occur.

PROBLEM 90.   Show methods for the following selective methylations:

(90.1)

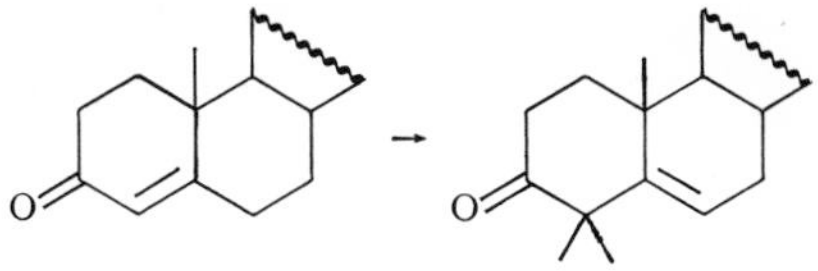

(90.2)

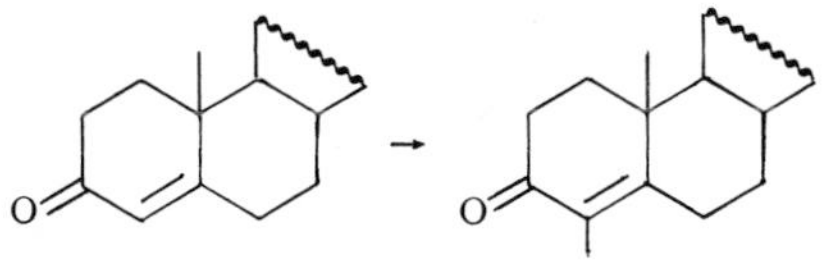

---

[1]Royals, pp. 751ff.

ANSWER 90.

(90. 1)   [R. B. Woodward, A. A. Patchett, D. H. R. Barton, D. A. J. Ives, and R. B. Kelley, *J. Am. Chem. Soc.,* **76**, 2852 (1954).]

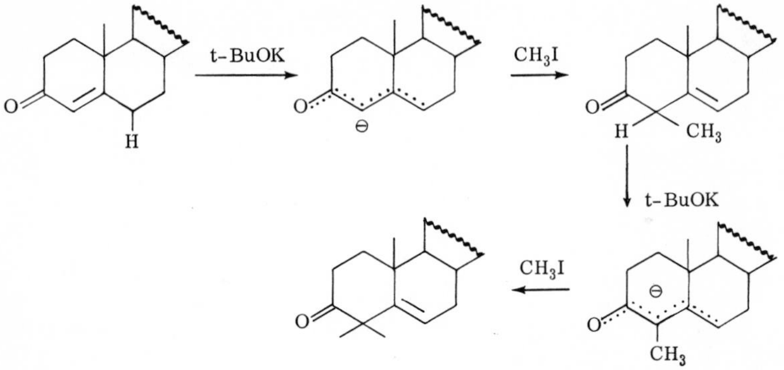

(90. 2)   [See J. Szmuszkovicz in *Advances in Organic Chemistry,* Vol. 4, Wiley, New York, 1963, pp. 1, 86, and references there cited.]

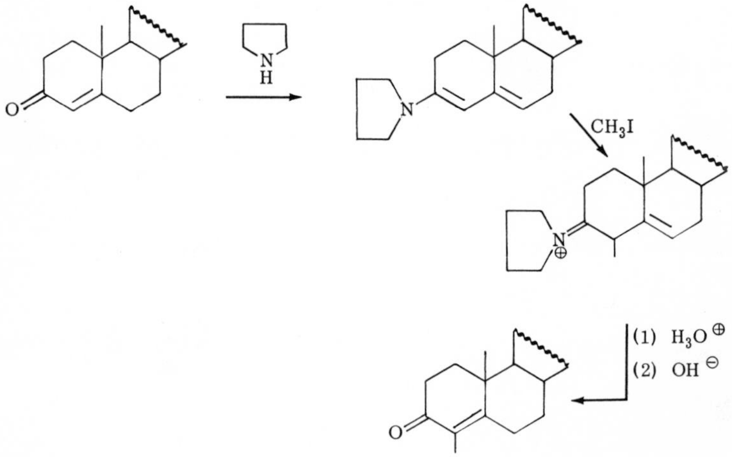

PROBLEM 91.   Suggest mechanisms for the following reactions:

(91.1)

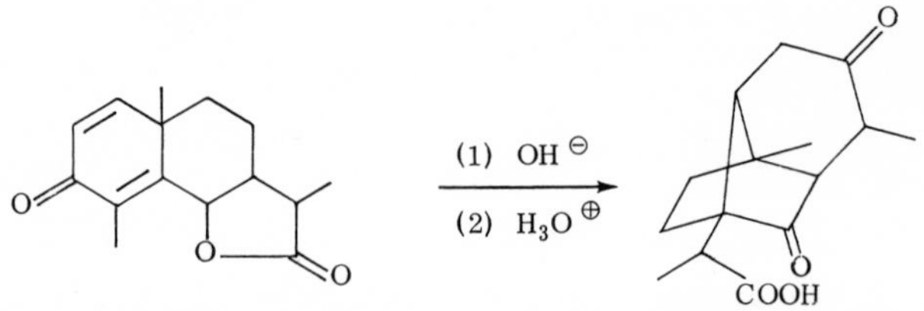

(cont.)

(91.2)

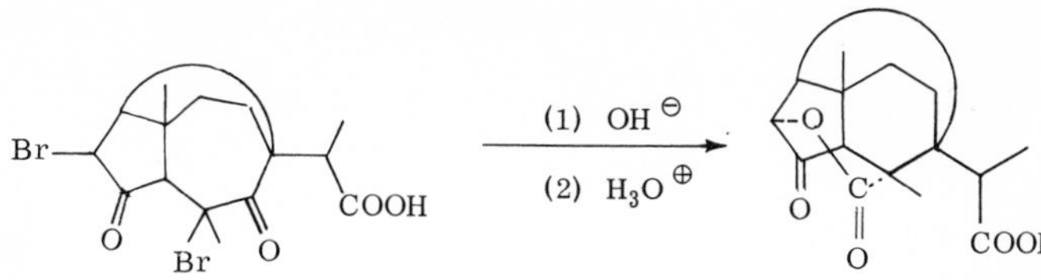

(91.3)

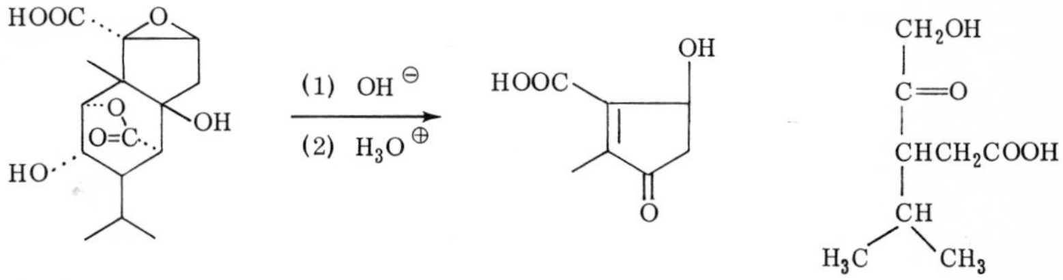

ANSWER 91.

(91.1)   [R. B. Woodward, F. J. Brutschy, and H. Baer, *J. Am. Chem. Soc.*, **70**, 4216 (1948).]

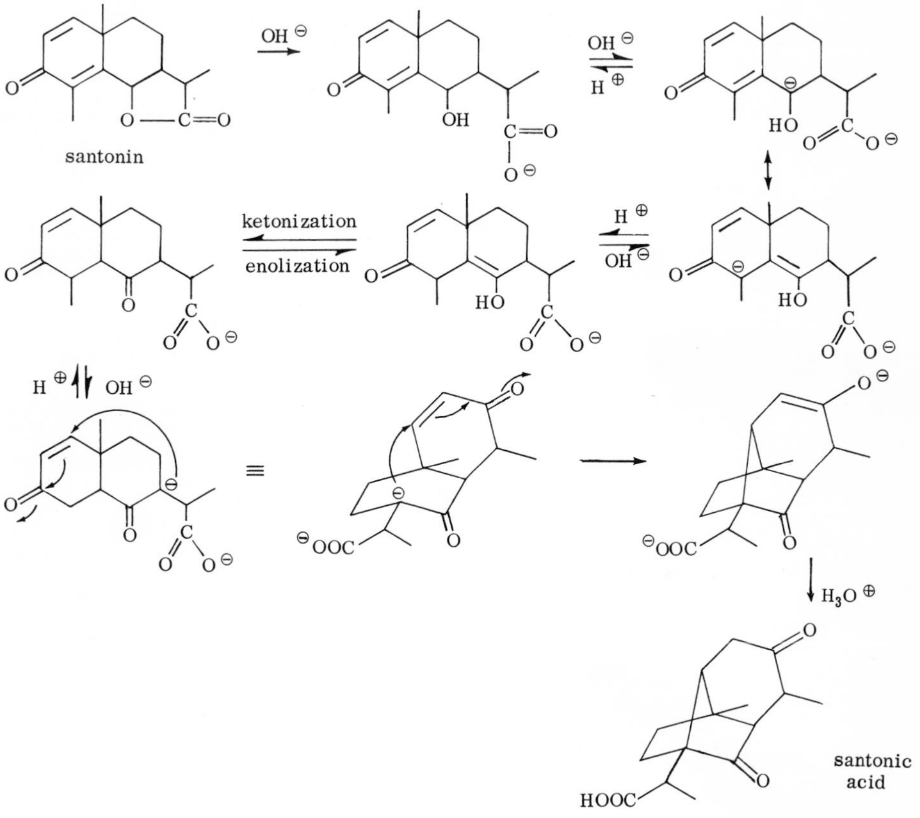

santonin

ketonization
enolization

H$^{\oplus}$ \quad OH$^{\ominus}$

$\equiv$

H$_3$O$^{\oplus}$

santonic acid

HOOC

(91.2)   [R. B. Woodward and E. G. Kovach, *J. Am. Chem. Soc.,* **72**, 1009 (1950).]

This is an example of the Favorskii reaction,[1] but since the starting material lacks α-hydrogens, it cannot proceed through the usual cyclopropanone intermediate.[2]

(91.3)   [H. Conroy, *J. Am. Chem. Soc.,* **79**, 1726 (1957).]

dihydro-α-picrotoxinic acid

---

[1] A. Kende, in *Organic Reactions,* Vol. 11, Wiley, New York, 1960, p. 261.
[2] R. B. Loftfield, *J. Am. Chem. Soc.,* **73**, 4707 (1951).

PROBLEM 92.   Suggest mechanisms for the following reactions:

(92.1)

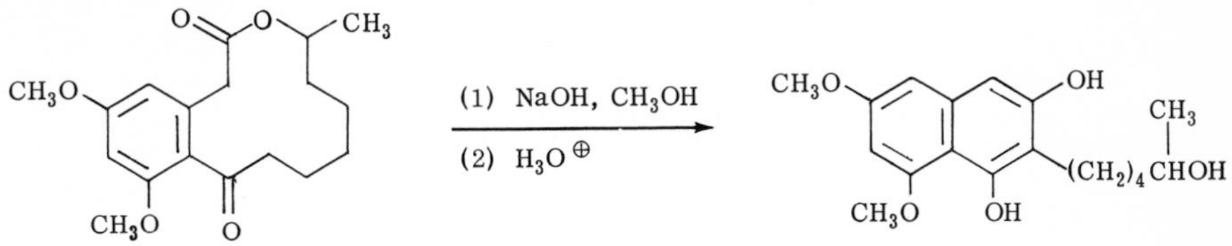

CH$_3$O

CH$_3$O   O

(1) NaOH, CH$_3$OH

(2) H$_3$O$^\oplus$

CH$_3$O   OH

CH$_3$

(CH$_2$)$_4$CHOH

CH$_3$O   OH

(92.2)

KMnO$_4$ H$_3$O$^\oplus$

COOH

OH

+

COOH

COOH

KMnO$_4$ H$_3$O$^\oplus$

MgSO$_4$

COOH

OH

only

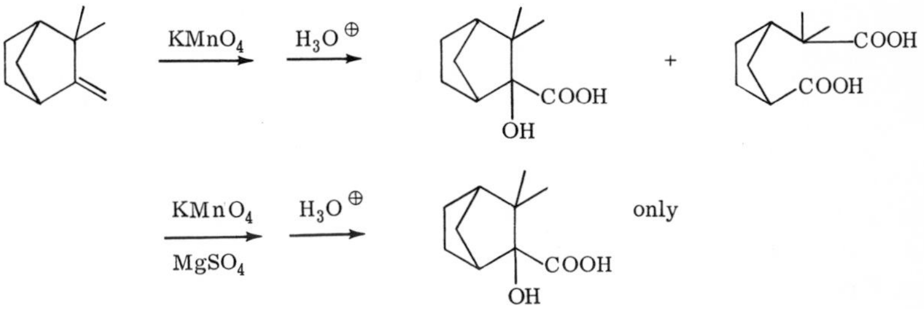

ANSWER 92.

(92.1)   [A. J. Birch, O. C. Musgrave, R. W. Rickards, and H. Smith, *J. Chem. Soc.*, **1959**, 3146.]

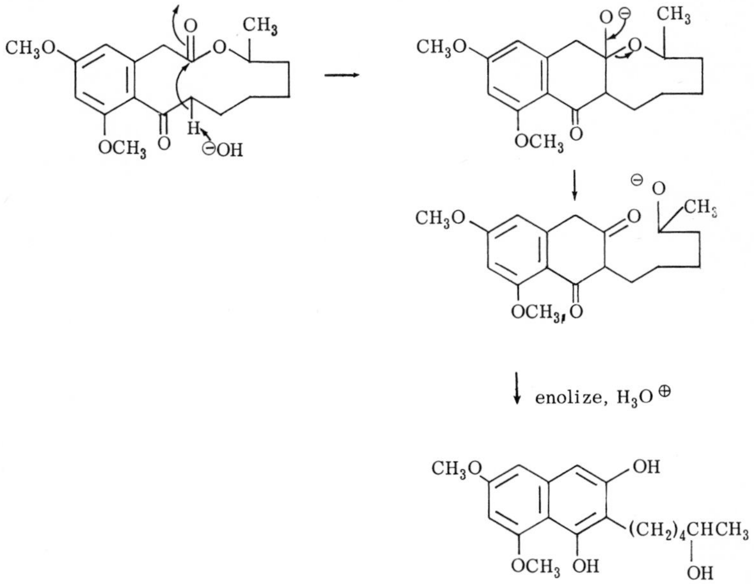

CH$_3$O   CH$_3$ O

OCH$_3$ O   H

$^\ominus$OH

→

CH$_3$O   O$^\ominus$ CH$_3$

OCH$_3$ O

CH$_3$O   O   CH$_3$

OCH$_3$,O $^\ominus$O

enolize, H$_3$O$^\oplus$

CH$_3$O   OH

(CH$_2$)$_4$CHCH$_3$

OCH$_3$ OH   OH

The reaction is a transannular Claisen condensation leading to the naphthalene product. Such a ring closure is quite similar to those suggested (at least formally) in the biosynthesis of polyphenols from acetate.[1]

(92.2)   [See J. L. Simonsen, *The Terpenes,* Vol. II, Cambridge University Press, Cambridge, 1949, pp. 280-289; P. de Mayo, *Mono- and Sesquiterpenoids,* Wiley-Interscience, New York, 1959, p. 130.]

Permanganate oxidations involve the reaction

$$3e^- + 2H_2O + MnO_4^- \rightarrow MnO_2 + 4OH^-$$

and the reaction mixtures become strongly basic unless buffered. In the present example, the formation of acid **3** (and the corresponding glycol **1**, also isolated) is unexceptional. In the presence of base, however, the intervening aldehyde **2** undergoes a base-catalyzed rearrangement, presumably with the relief of ring strain, to give **4**. Further oxidation of this ketol system leads to **5**.

The added magnesium sulfate removes the base formed as the insoluble $Mg(OH)_2$ and leaves the solution essentially neutral. Under these conditions no rearrangement occurs.

PROBLEM 93.   Suggest mechanisms for the following reactions:

(93.1)

---

[1] See J. H. Richards and J. B. Hendrickson, *The Biosynthesis of Steroids, Terpenes, and Acetogenins,* Benjamin, New York, 1964, Chap. III.

(cont.)

(93.2) $C_6H_5—CH=CHCOOEt + CH_3CH(COOEt)_2$ $\xrightarrow{\text{NaOEt}}$ $\xrightarrow{\text{neutralize}}$

$$C_6H_5—CH—CH(CO_2Et)_2$$
$$\underset{\underset{\displaystyle CO_2Et}{|}}{\overset{\displaystyle |}{CH_3CH}}$$

ANSWER 93.

(93.1)   [C. E. Berkoff and L. Crombie, *Proc. Chem. Soc.*, **1959**, 400.]

Other routes may be devised to go from A to the final product, but they are similar in outline.

(93.2)   [O. Simamura, N. Inamoto, and T. Suehiro, *Bull. Chem. Soc. Japan,* **27,** 221 (1954).]

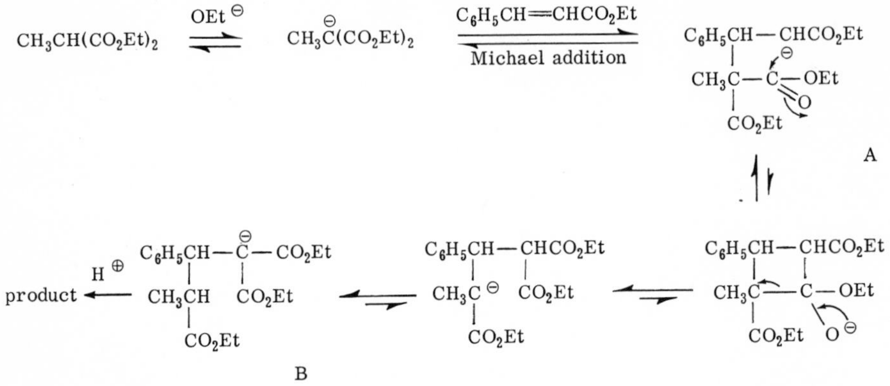

$$CH_3CH(CO_2Et)_2 \rightleftarrows \overset{\ominus}{CH_3C}(CO_2Et)_2 \xrightarrow[\text{Michael addition}]{C_6H_5CH=CHCO_2Et}$$

A

B

product

The product of the normal Michael addition[1] (A) has a reactive, strongly basic carbanion stabilized by only one adjacent carbonyl group. By the rearrangement shown this is converted to B, containing a more weakly basic, doubly stabilized ion. The stability of B in the strongly basic reaction medium causes it to accumulate.

The mechanism of this "abnormal Michael reaction," has been confirmed by tracer studies.

PROBLEM 94.   Suggest mechanisms for the following reactions:

(94.1)

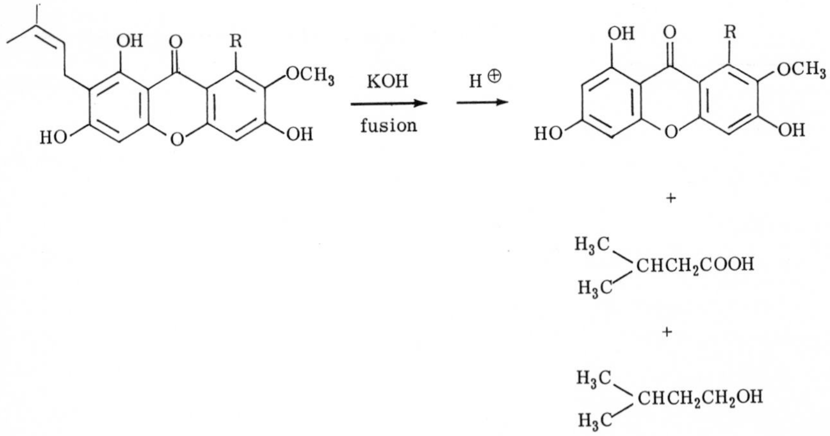

+

+

---

[1]Royals, pp. 790ff.

(cont.)

(94.2)

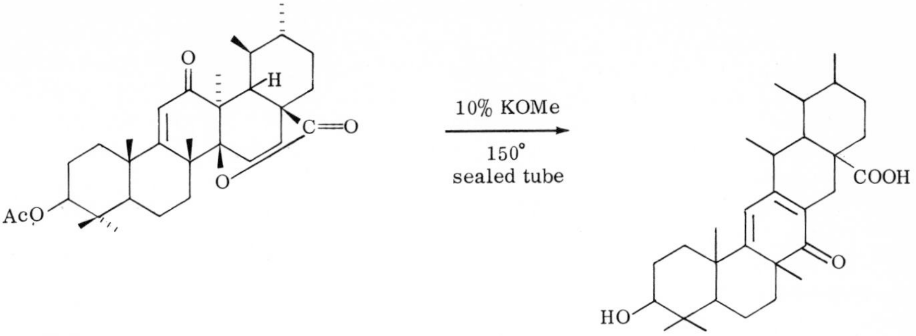

10% KOMe
150°
sealed tube
COOH
HO
AcO

ANSWER 94.

(94.1) [P. Yates and G. H. Stout, *J. Am. Chem. Soc.*, **80**, 1691 (1958).]

(1) OH ⊖
(2) H2O
products

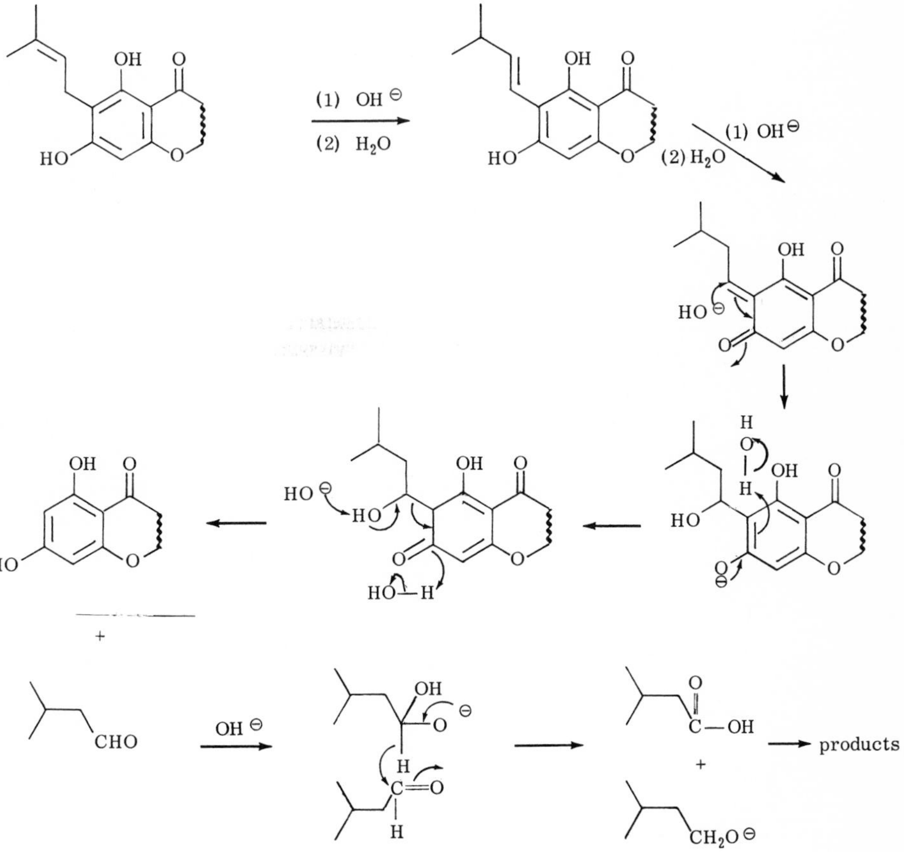

The elimination involves migration of the side-chain double bond into conjugation with the carbonyl group(s) produced by ketonization of the phenolic
hydroxyls. The conjugated system is hydrated by a Michael addition,[1] and the
resulting hydroxy ketone is cleaved by a reverse aldol reaction[2] to split off
isovaleraldehyde. Under the extremely vigorous basic conditions used, the
aldehyde disproportionates by hydride transfer to give the corresponding acid
and alcohol. Although this disproportionation is well known for aldehydes
which cannot undergo condensation (Cannizzaro reaction),[3] normally the aldol
condensation takes precedence when possible. The aldol reaction is reversible,
however, and the disproportionation is not; so under vigorous conditions its
products tend to accumulate.

(94.2)   [D. Arigoni, H. Bossard, J. Dreiding, and O. Jeger, *Helv. Chim. Acta,* **37**,
          2173 (1954).]

---

[1]Gould, pp. 392ff.
[2]Royals, pp. 751ff.
[3]Royals, 717ff.

The reaction involves hydrolysis of the lactone, a reverse aldol cleavage, and then a recondensation in the other direction.

PROBLEM 95. Suggest mechanisms for the following reactions:

(95.1)

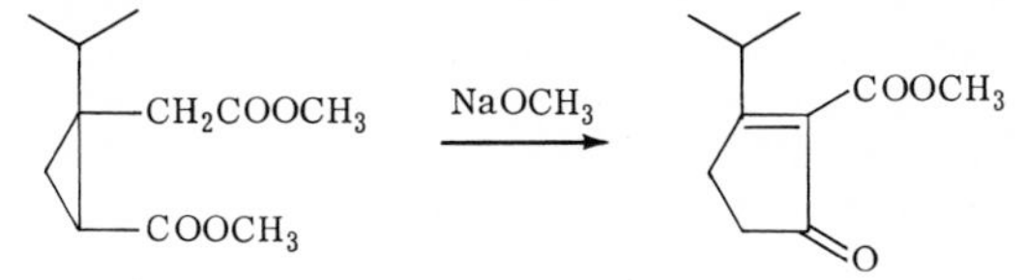

$-CH_2COOCH_3$ $\xrightarrow{\text{NaOCH}_3}$ $COOCH_3$

$-COOCH_3$

(95.2)

CH_3 $\xrightarrow{\text{NaNH}_2}$

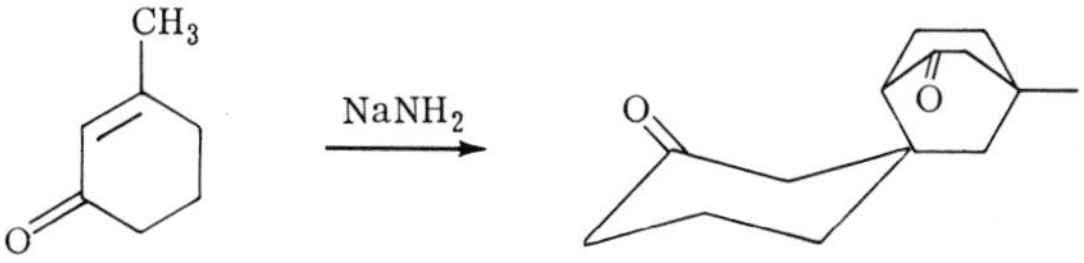

ANSWER 95.

(95.1) [E. E. van Tamelen and G. T. Hildahl, *J. Am. Chem. Soc.*, **78**, 4405 (1956).]

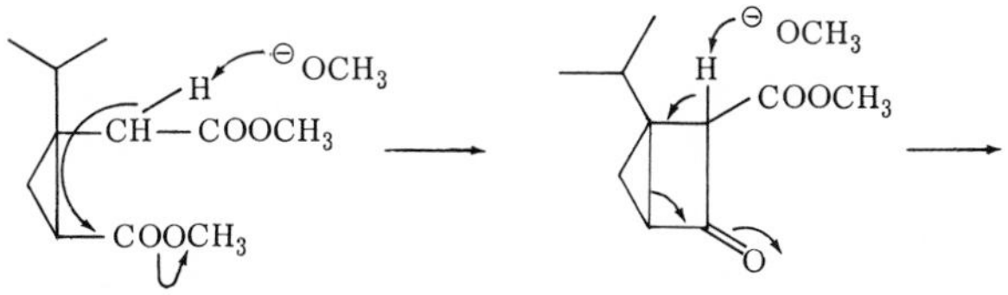

$-CH-COOCH_3$ H—$^\ominus OCH_3$

$-COOCH_3$

A

$COOCH_3$ $\xrightarrow{H^\oplus}$ $COOCH_3$

$O^\ominus$

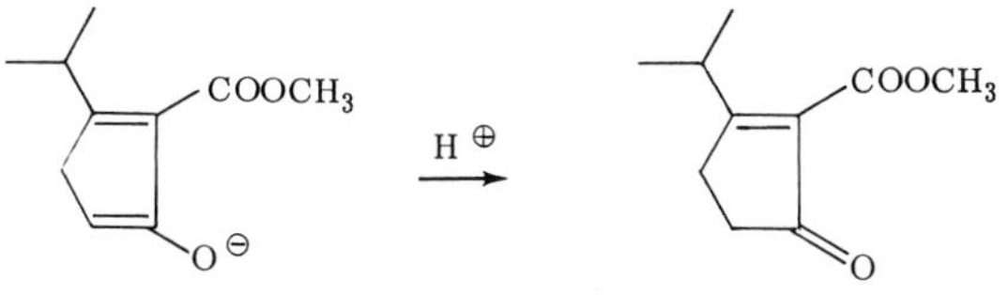

B

It is suggested that the reaction proceeds by a Dieckmann ring closure to A, followed by a reverse Michael reaction which relieves the strain of the fused ring system. It is also possible to arrive at B without going through A, i.e., by opening the cyclopropane ring first, but since bicyclic compounds of this sort have been shown[1] to be formed by Dieckmann condensations, and to be unstable in base, the above mechanism would seem satisfactory. Systems A and B appear to be readily interconvertible, and may actually exist in tautomeric equilibrium in solution.

---

[1] E. H. Farmer, C. K. Ingold, and J. F. Thorpe, *J. Chem. Soc.*, **121**, 128 (1922).

(95.2)   [G. Büchi, J. H. Hansen, D. Knutson, and E. Koller, *J. Am. Chem. Soc.*, **80**, 5517 (1959).]

Although the proof for the gross structures of the product appears sound, there is no evidence which determines whether the carbonyls are syn (B) or anti (A). It has been suggested that the anti form is to be preferred, since the transition state leading to it has better overlap geometry and has the negatively charged oxygen atoms at the greatest possible separation. On the other hand, there is no reason not to suppose that the reaction is equilibrium- rather than rate-controlled as far as A and B are concerned, particularly since the product appears to be stable under basic conditions which lead to ionization at all α positions (shown by deuterium exchange). In this case, too, however, the anti form would probably be favored as providing the minimum dipole-dipole repulsion of the carbonyl groups.

PROBLEM 96.   Suggest a mechanism for:

$$R = -CH_2CH_2NMe_2$$

ANSWER 96.   [K. W. Bentley, J. Dominguez, and J. P. Ringe, *J. Org. Chem.*,
22, 418 (1957).]

The carbon skeleton of the product is present in the starting material, and all that is required is a ring opening of the cyclohexenone by hydration and a reverse aldol reaction. The loss of the aldehyde group probably depends on the ability of the methoxylated benzene rings to stabilize the partial negative charge which develops α to them during the decomposition of A.

PROBLEM 97.   Suggest a mechanism for the following condensation:

ANSWER 97.   [R. B. Davis and L. C. Pizzini, *J. Org. Chem.*, **25**, 1884 (1960).]

This reaction is insensitive to the nature of substituents on the ring of the phenylacetonitrile, but is easily subverted by changes in the nitrobenzene moiety. Thus

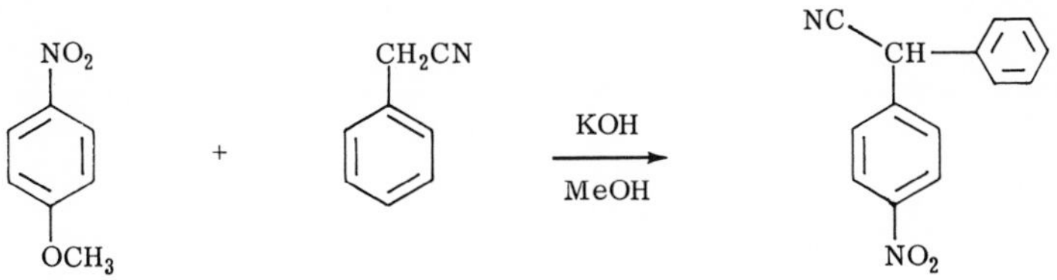

It is also affected by solvent, since

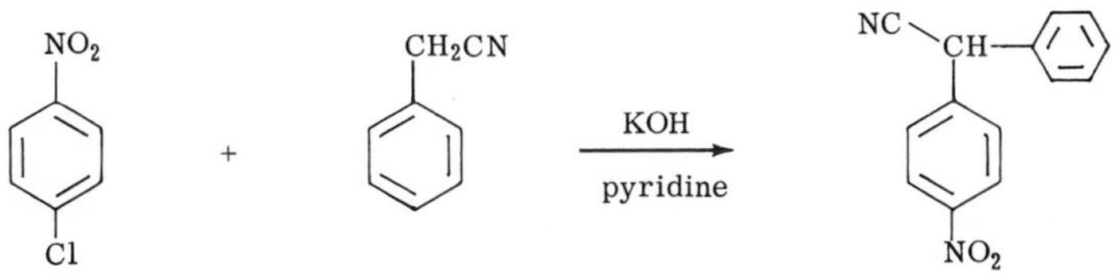

PROBLEM 98.   Suggest mechanisms for the following transformations:

(98.1)

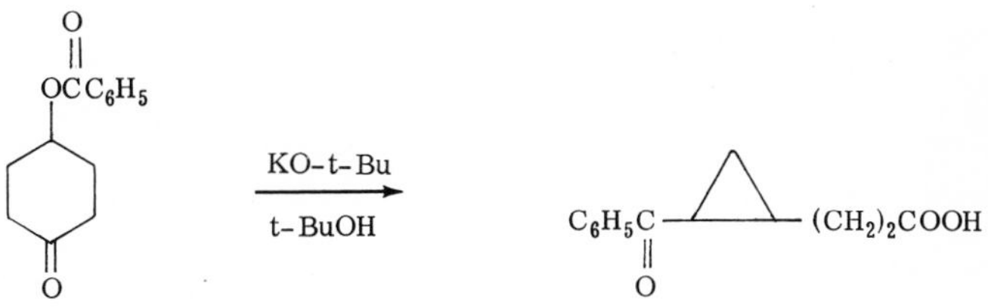

(98.2)

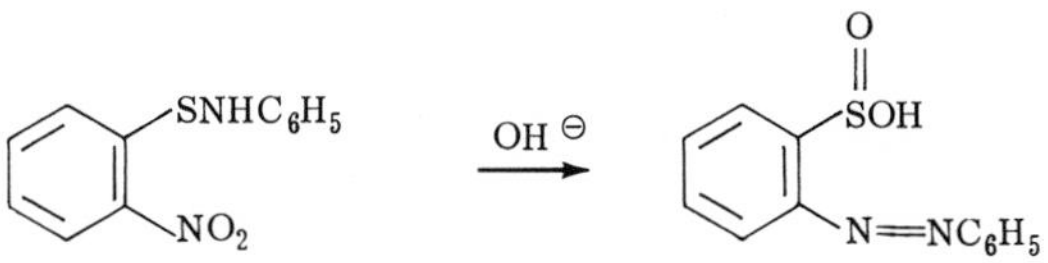

ANSWER 98.

(98.1)   [P. Yates and C. D. Anderson, *J. Am. Chem. Soc.*, **80**, 1264 (1958); **85**, 2937 (1963); R. L. Clarke and W. T. Hunter, *J. Am. Chem. Soc.*, **80**, 5304 (1958).]

In confirmation of this suggested route, the lactone A has been isolated in small yield by Clarke and Hunter from the reaction mixture, while Yates and Anderson have shown that it is converted in base to B.

In a similar reaction,

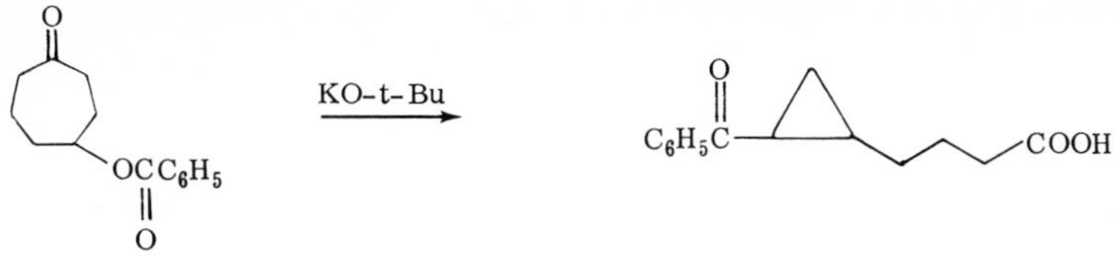

(98.2)   [M. P. Cava and C. E. Blake, *J. Am. Chem. Soc.*, **78**, 5444 (1956).]

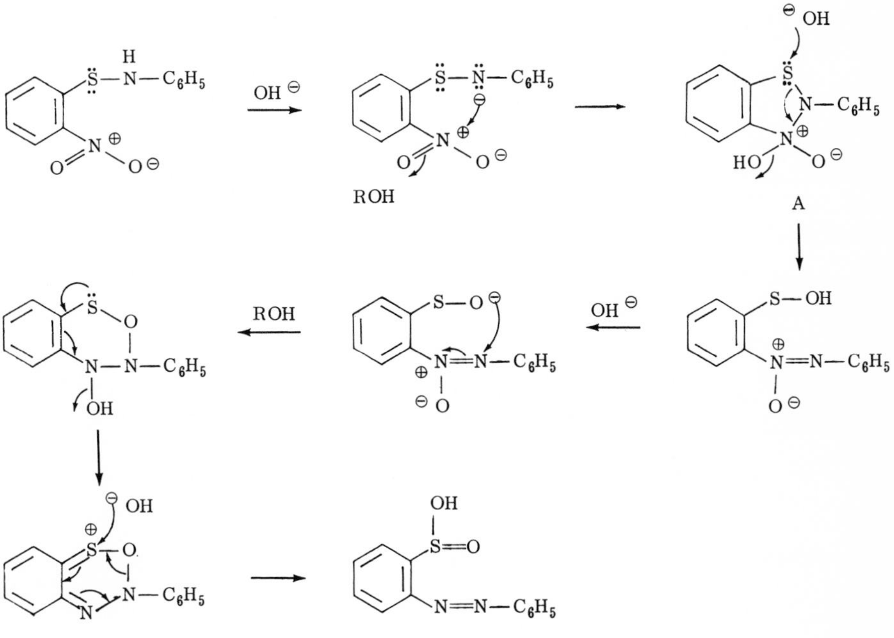

This mechanism has been proposed to account for the internal oxidation-reduction reaction which occurs. Since the para isomer (B) of the starting material does not react, an intramolecular route is assumed.

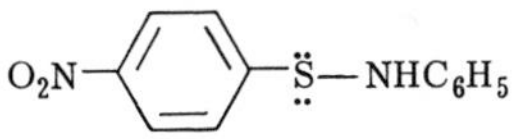

B

No real evidence for the course of the reaction exists, however, so a number of other routes are also possible. Thus the intermediate A, which seems highly probable, might transfer an oxygen internally and then rearrange to the product.

Other routes, e.g., ones similar to the Favorskii reaction,[1] are conceivable but unlikely because of strain.

PROBLEM 99.   Predict the structures of the following products:

(99.1)

(99.2)

---

[1]See R. B. Loftfield, *J. Am. Chem. Soc.*, **73**, 4707 (1951).

(cont.)

(99.3)   [enamine structure] + $\begin{array}{l} CH_2COCl \\ | \\ CH_2COCl \end{array}$ $\begin{array}{l}(1)\ Et_3N \\ \xrightarrow{\hspace{1.5cm}} \\ (2)\ H_2O\end{array}$ $C_{10}H_{12}O_3$

ANSWER 99.   [For extensive discussions of enamine chemistry, see J. Szmuszkovicz, *Advances in Organic Chemistry,* Vol. 4, Wiley-Interscience, New York, 1963, p. 1; G. Stork, A. Brizzolara, H. Landesman, J. Szmuszkovicz, and R. Terrell, *J. Am. Chem. Soc.,* **85**, 207 (1962).]

(99.1)   [S. Hünig, E. Benzing, and E. Lucke, *Ber.,* **90**, 2833 (1957); J. Szmuszkovicz, op. cit., p. 47.]

[reaction scheme 99.1 with chemical structures]

$$\ldots \xrightarrow[H_2O]{H^\oplus} \ldots$$

The triethylamine is used to prevent the HCl formed from tying up half of the starting enamine.

(99.2)   (S. Hünig *et al.,* loc. cit.)

[reaction scheme 99.2 with chemical structures]

The intermediate formed by acylation of the enamine can react with a second molecule of acid chloride to give the product shown.

(99.3)   [S. Hünig and E. Lucke, *Ber.*, **92**, 652 (1959).]

This reaction is an intramolecular version of that described in answer 99.2.

PROBLEM 100.   Suggest a rational course for each of the following transformations:

(100.1)

(100.2)

(100.3)

ANSWER 100.   [For a general discussion of enamine syntheses, see J. Szmuszkovicz in *Advances in Organic Chemistry*, Vol. 4, Wiley-Interscience, New York, 1963, p. 1.]

(100.1)   [G. A. Berchtold, G. R. Harvey, and C. E. Wilson, *J. Org. Chem.*, **26**, 4776 (1961); J. Szmuszkovicz, op. cit., p. 38.]

B = a base

(100.2)   [S. Hünig, E. Benzing, and K. Hubner, *Ber.*, **94**, 486 (1961); J. Szmuszkovicz, op. cit., p. 53.]

(100.3)   [G. Stork and H. K. Landesman, *J. Am. Chem. Soc.*, **78**, 5129 (1956);
J. Szmuszkovicz, op. cit., p. 38.]

The water required for this mechanism may arise from the in situ preparation of the original enamine.

Although all these mechanisms are speculative, it has been shown in the last
one that the pyrrolidine transfer probably passes through the stage of a free amine.
Thus a reaction involving two initial enamines gave products corresponding to all
four possible combinations of amine and ketone fragments.[1]

---

[1]K. G. Untch, Doctoral thesis, Columbia University, New York, 1959; *Dissertation
Abstr.* **20**, 3962 (1960).

CHAPTER 7

REARRANGEMENT REACTIONS

Discussions of rearrangement reactions are to be found in Gould and Hine, as well as in other texts in advanced organic chemistry. By far the most comprehensive general coverage, however, is the following.

1. *Molecular Rearrangements*, Vols. I and II (P. de Mayo, ed.), Wiley-Interscience, New York, 1963.

PROBLEM 101. Give structures for the products:

(101.1)

$$(C_6H_5)_2C - CHC_6H_5 \xrightarrow[-H_2O]{\text{conc. } H_2SO_4}$$
with OH and OH below the two central carbons

(101.2)

$$(C_6H_5)_2C - C \equiv CH \xrightarrow{H_2SO_4} \text{isomer}$$
with OH below the first carbon

(101.3)

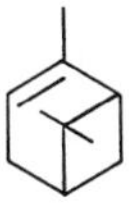

$\xrightarrow{\text{HCl}}$ HCl – adduct

(101.4)

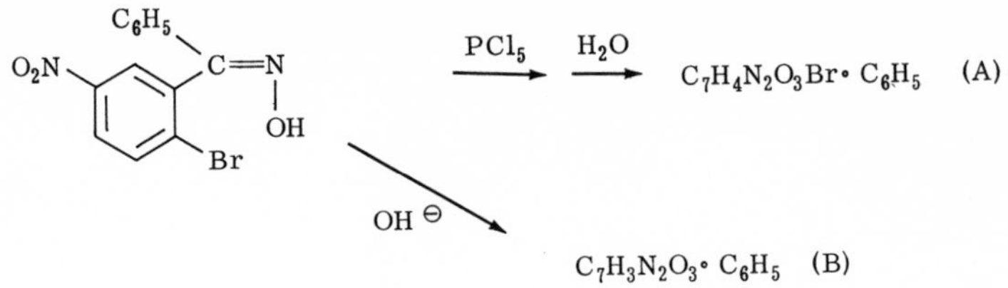

$$C_7H_4N_2O_3Br \cdot C_6H_5 \quad (A)$$

$$C_7H_3N_2O_3 \cdot C_6H_5 \quad (B)$$

ANSWER 101.

(101.1)   [C. J. Collins, *Quart. Rev.*, **14**, 357 (1960); Y. Pocker in *Molecular Rearrangements,* Vol. 1 (P. de Mayo, ed.), Wiley-Interscience, New York, 1963, pp. 15ff.]

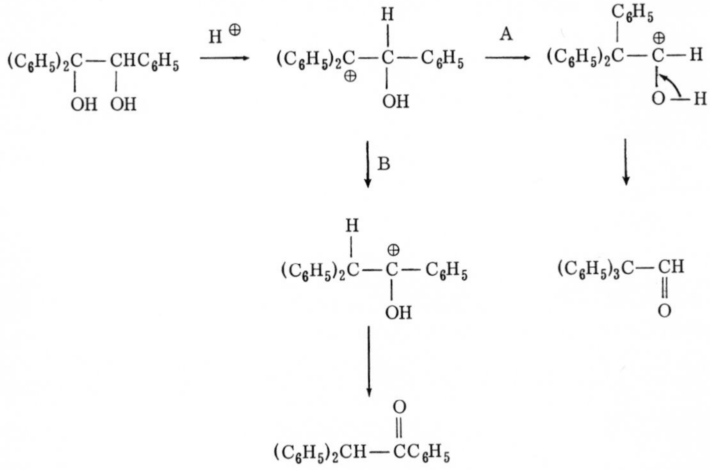

This is an example of the pinacol rearrangement of an unsymmetrical compound. The tertiary hydroxyl is lost more readily because it gives the more stable carbonium ion. This ion can then rearrange by either phenyl or hydrogen migration, and both are observed. It has been shown[1] that the migratory aptitudes of the two groups are strongly affected by the reaction medium, the ratio of A/B varying from 7.3 in conc. H_2SO_4 to 0.04 in HCl-dioxane.

(101.2)   [See P. B. D. de la Mare in *Molecular Rearrangements*, Vol. 1 (P. de Mayo, ed.), Wiley-Interscience, New York, 1963, p. 87.]

---

[1] C. J. Collins, *J. Am. Chem. Soc.*, **77**, 5517 (1955).

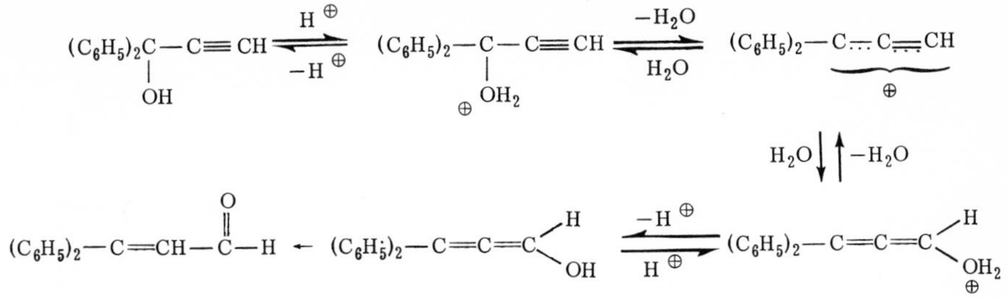

This is an example of the Meyer-Schuster rearrangement (conversion of an acetylenic alcohol to an unsaturated aldehyde or ketone).

(101.3)   [See J. A. Berson in *Molecular Rearrangements,* Vol. 1 (P. de Mayo, ed.), Wiley-Interscience, New York, 1963, pp. 185ff.]

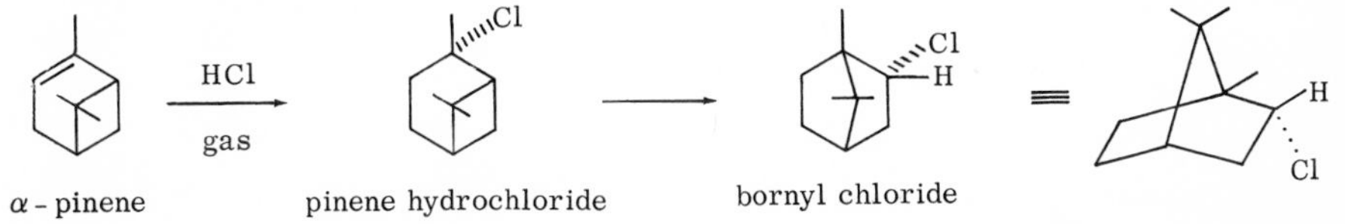

α-pinene   pinene hydrochloride   bornyl chloride

If the addition of HCl to α-pinene is carried out at very low temperatures and with the rigorous exclusion of moisture, it is possible to obtain pinene hydrochloride. This rearranges very easily, however, by migration of one of the one-carbon bridges to give bornyl chloride. The migration of the other bridge is at most a very minor route in this case, but has been observed in the hydration of α-pinene and in the rearrangement of the stereoisomeric alcohols related to pinene hydrochloride.[2]

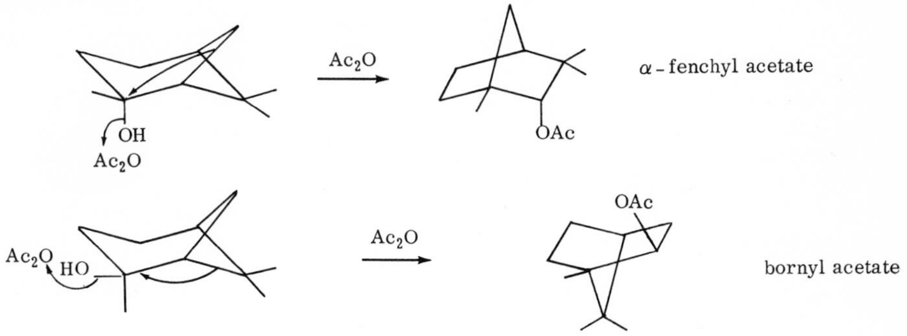

α-fenchyl acetate

bornyl acetate

---

[2]W. D. Burrows and R. H. Eastman, *J. Am. Chem. Soc.,* **81,** 245 (1959).

These rearrangements presumably involve the usual Walden-inversion-like rearrangement path, but it is not known whether they are concerted.

(101.4)   [J. Meisenheimer, P. Zimmermann, and U. von Kummer, *Ann.*, **446**, 205 (1926).]

The first reaction is simply a Beckmann rearrangment of an oxime.[3,4] The second is an internal nucleophilic displacement of an aromatic halide activated by a p-nitro group. Taken together they provide one of the classical pieces of evidence that the Beckmann rearrangement involves the migration of the group trans (anti) to the —OH.

---

[3]P. A. S. Smith in *Molecular Rearrangements*, Vol. I (P. de Mayo, ed.), Wiley-Interscience, New York, 1963, pp. 483ff.

[4]L. G. Donaruma and W. Z. Heldt in *Organic Reactions*, Vol. 11, Wiley, New York, 1960, p. 1.

PROBLEM 102.   Deduce the structures of the following reaction products.

(102.1)

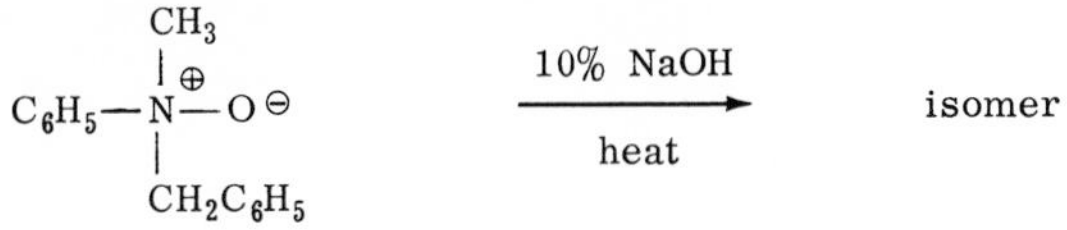

$$
C_6H_5-\underset{\underset{CH_2C_6H_5}{|}}{\overset{\overset{CH_3}{|}}{N}}{}^{\oplus}-O^{\ominus}
$$

$\xrightarrow[\text{heat}]{10\% \text{ NaOH}}$ isomer

(102.2)

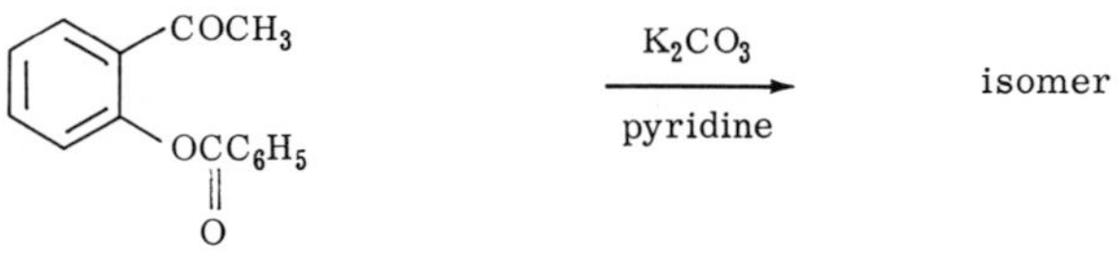

$$
\begin{array}{c}
\text{COCH}_3 \\
\text{OCC}_6\text{H}_5 \\
\| \\
\text{O}
\end{array}
$$

$\xrightarrow[\text{pyridine}]{\text{K}_2\text{CO}_3}$ isomer

(102.3)

$$
\begin{array}{c}
\text{C}_6\text{H}_5 \quad \text{NHCl}
\end{array}
$$

$\xrightarrow[\text{pyridine}]{\text{NaOCH}_3}$ $C_{19}H_{13}N$

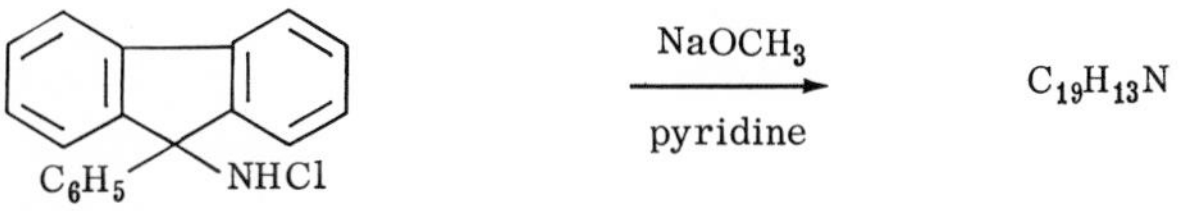

ANSWER 102.

(102.1)   [J. Meisenheimer, H. Greeske, and A. Willmersdorf, *Ber.*, **55**, 513 (1922).]

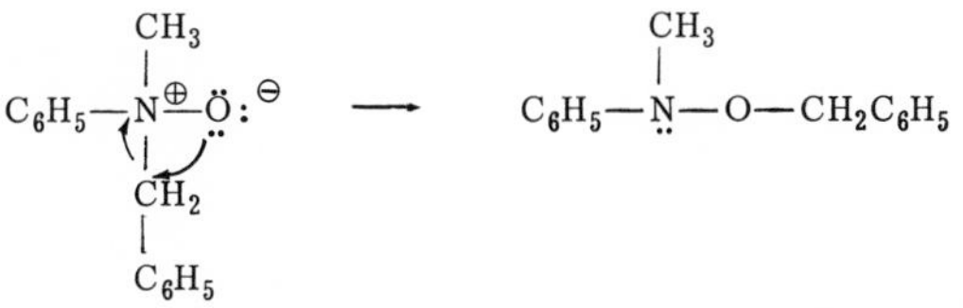

$$
C_6H_5-\underset{\underset{\underset{C_6H_5}{|}}{\overset{|}{CH_2}}}{\overset{\overset{CH_3}{|}}{N}}{}^{\oplus}\ddot{O}:^{\ominus} \longrightarrow C_6H_5-\underset{\cdot\cdot}{\overset{\overset{CH_3}{|}}{N}}-O-CH_2C_6H_5
$$

The mechanism of this reaction has not been elucidated, but the over-all process is isoelectronic with the Stevens rearrangement,[1] and the suggested mechanism is analogous. The reaction is apparently somewhat limited in scope, since Meisenheimer has shown that it requires a phenyl attached to nitrogen and an allyl[2] or benzyl substituent as the migrating group.

The base used in the reaction is not required by the proposed mechanism and probably serves only to liberate the amine oxide from the salt form in which it is isolated and stored.

---

[1] H. E. Zimmerman in *Molecular Rearrangements*, Vol. I (P. de Mayo, ed.), Wiley-Interscience, New York, 1963, pp. 378–382; Gould, p. 640.

[2] J. Meisenheimer, *Ber.*, **52**, 1667 (1919).

(102.2)   [W. Baker, *J. Chem. Soc.*, **1933**, 1381.]

This is sometimes referred to as the Baker-Venkataraman rearrangement, but it is essentially just an intramolecular Claisen reaction.

(102.3)   [L. A. Pinck and H. E. Hilbert, *J. Am. Chem. Soc.*, **59**, 8 (1937).]

This is an example of the Stieglitz rearrangement,[3] which is formally analo-gous to the Hofmann rearrangement. In this reaction, too, it is not known whether the nitrene A is actually formed as an intermediate or whether the rearrangement is concerted with the loss of Cl⁻.

---

[3] P. A. S. Smith in *Molecular Rearrangements*, Vol. I (P. de Mayo, ed.), Wiley-Interscience, New York, 1963, p. 481.

PROBLEM 103.   Predict the chief products in the benzylic acid rearrangements of the following compounds:

(103.1)

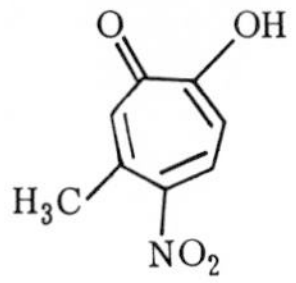

(103.2)

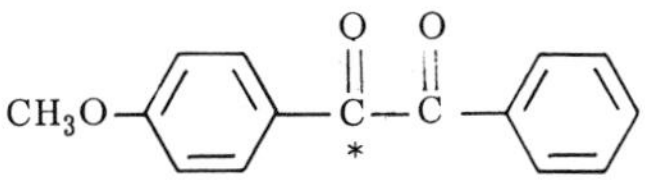

*= C^{14}

(103.3)

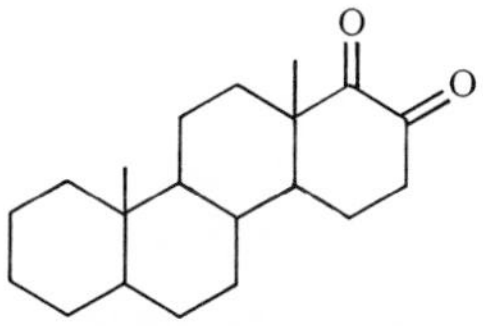

ANSWER 103.   [For a survey and discussion of the benzylic acid rearrangement see S. Selman and J. F. Eastham, *Quart. Rev.*, **14**, 221 (1960).]

(*103. 1*)   [R. D. Haworth and P. R. Jefferies, *J. Chem. Soc.*, **1951**, 2067.] Ring contraction in strong base is a typical reaction of tropolones.[1]

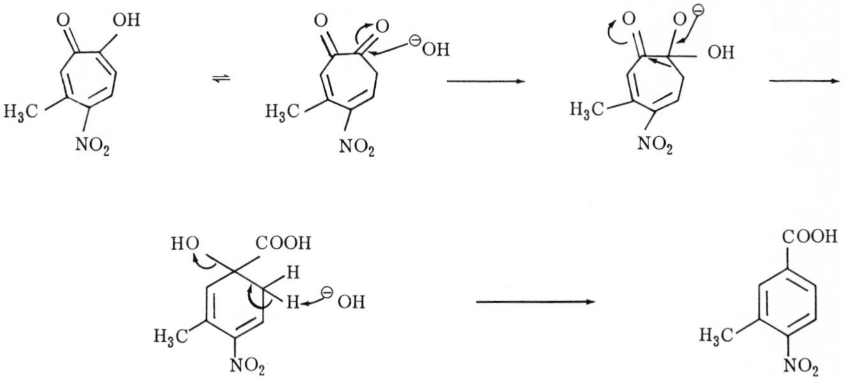

---

[1] P. L. Pauson, *Chem. Rev.*, **55**, 1 (1955).

(103.2)   [J. D. Roberts, D. R. Smith, and C. C. Lee, *J. Am. Chem. Soc.*, **73**, 619 (1951).]

$$CH_3O-\!\!\!\bigcirc\!\!\!-\overset{*}{\underset{\overset{\|}{O}}{C}}-\overset{\underset{\overset{\|}{O}}{}}{C}-\!\!\!\bigcirc \quad \xrightarrow{OH^{\ominus}} \quad CH_3O-\!\!\!\bigcirc\!\!\!-\underset{OH}{\overset{*}{\underset{|}{C}}}-\overset{O^{\ominus}}{\overset{\|}{C}}-\!\!\!\bigcirc$$

Left branch:

$$\downarrow OH^{\ominus}$$

$$CH_3O-\!\!\!\bigcirc\!\!\!-\underset{\underset{OH}{|}}{\overset{*}{\overset{\overset{O}{\|}}{C}}}-\overset{O^{\ominus}}{\overset{\|}{C}}-\!\!\!\bigcirc$$

$$\downarrow$$

$$CH_3O-\!\!\!\bigcirc\!\!\!-\underset{\underset{C_6H_5}{|}}{\overset{OH}{\overset{|}{C}}}\!\!\overset{*}{-}COOH$$

2

Right branch:

$$\downarrow$$

$$HOOC-\underset{\underset{\bigcirc}{|}}{\overset{OH}{\overset{|}{C}}}\!\!\overset{*}{-}C_6H_5$$

with lower ring bearing OCH_3

1

Hydroxide ion can attack either of the two carbonyl groups, and thus lead to either **1** or **2**. In fact, **2** is found to be the major product, and it is suggested that the labeled carbonyl, being stabilized by conjugation with the electron-releasing methoxyl group, is less reactive toward addition. The problem is complicated, however, by the fact that the observed product ratios reflect differences both in the equilibrium constants for the addition of the hydroxide and in the rates of re-arrangement of the two intermediates.[2] These last, in turn, depend on the relative migratory aptitudes of the two aromatic rings, and to a lesser extent on the at-tractiveness of the different carbonyls as sites to which to carry out the rear-rangement.

---

[2]For a more extensive discussion, see Selman and Eastham, loc. cit.

(103.3)   [V. Georgian and N. Kundu, *Chem. Ind. (London)*, **1958**, 1322; also N. L. Wendler, D. Taub, and R. P. Graber, *Tetrahedron*, **7**, 173 (1959).]

The reaction proceeds stereoselectively to give the 17β-hydroxyl group. This stereochemistry corresponds to preferential attack by OH⁻ on the 17a- rather than the 17-carbonyl. Two explanations have been proposed for this selectivity. In the first, attack at 17 would lead to the intermediate B, which is unfavorable because of the axial-axial interaction of the O⁻ and the methyl group. Consequently, the reaction goes by the other route.

The alternative notes that such α-diketones exist largely, if not entirely, as the enolate anions C in basic solution. Thus only the 17a-carbonyl is actually available for attack by hydroxide. Once OH⁻ has added to 17a, the driving force for enolization is lost, and protonation on carbon would give A. If necessary, the problem of OH⁻ attack on an already negatively charged species can be avoided by having the reaction occur with the small amount of enol in equilibrium with C.

There is no evidence available to distinguish between these two proposals, but the latter would seem to provide a more compelling argument for selective attack.

PROBLEM 104.   Deduce structures for the following products.

(104.1)

(cont.)

(104.2)

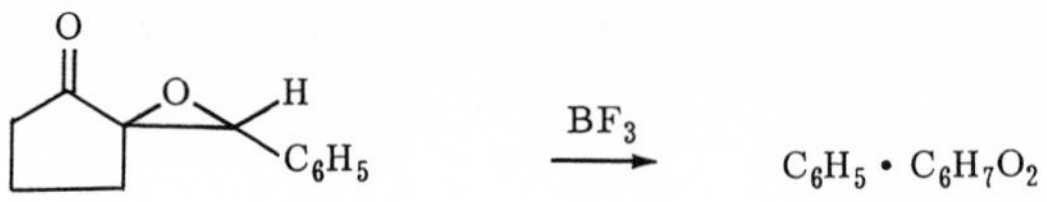

$$C_6H_5 \cdot C_6H_7O_2$$

ANSWER 104.
(104.1)   [H. O. House and D. J. Reif, *J. Am. Chem. Soc.*, **77**, 6525 (1955).]

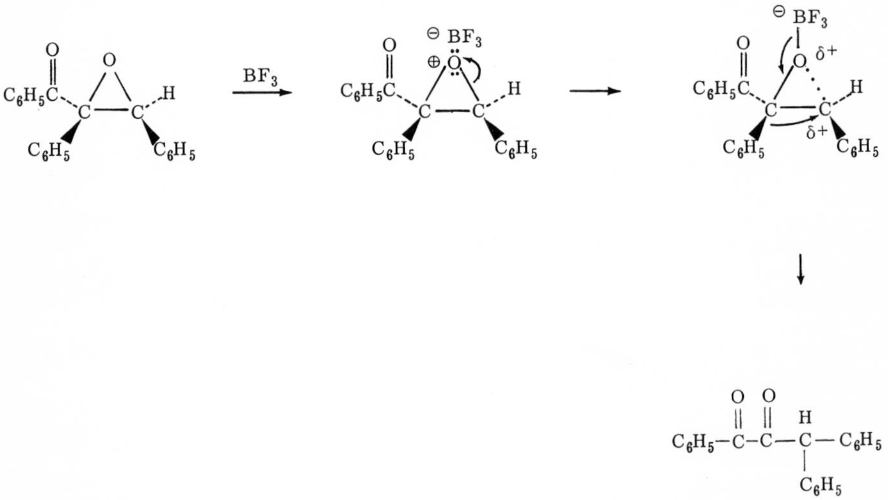

Epoxides may be opened, with rearrangement, by Lewis acids such as BF_3. The ring opening takes place so as to locate the intermediate carbonium ion (partial or full; see below) at the most stable position. In the case shown, this is on the carbon which is *not* substituted by the electron-withdrawing acyl group.[1]

The rearrangement has been shown to go intramolecularly,[2] and it has been suggested[3] that in this case, but not in many others, it is concerted.

---

[1] It has, however, been proposed that the effects of $-H$ and $-\overset{\overset{\textstyle O}{\textstyle \|}}{C}Ar$ on an adjacent carbonium ion are approximately the same. See H. O. House, D. J. Reif, and R. L. Wasson, *J. Am. Chem. Soc.*, **79**, 2490 (1957).
[2] H. O. House, *J. Am. Chem. Soc.*, **78**, 2298 (1956).
[3] H. O. House and D. J. Reif, *J. Am. Chem. Soc.*, **79**, 6491 (1957).

(104.2)   [H. O. House and R. L. Wasson, *J. Am. Chem. Soc.*, **78**, 4394 (1956).]

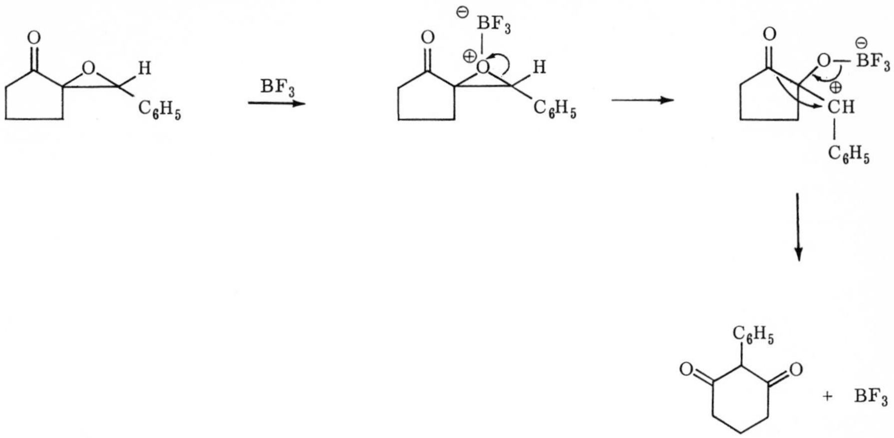

This reaction is proposed to go by the opening of the epoxide to give the more stable (benzylic) carbonium ion. This then rearranges with migration of the acyl group to give the product.[4]

The order of migratory aptitudes in this reaction has been shown to be aryl > acyl > alkyl > H.[5]

PROBLEM 105.   Suggest mechanisms for the following reactions:

(105.1)

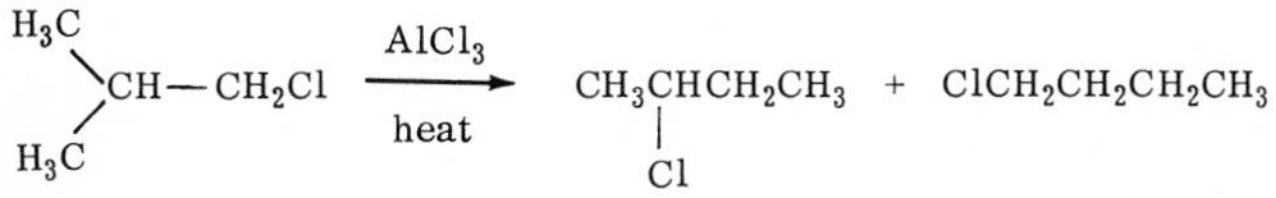

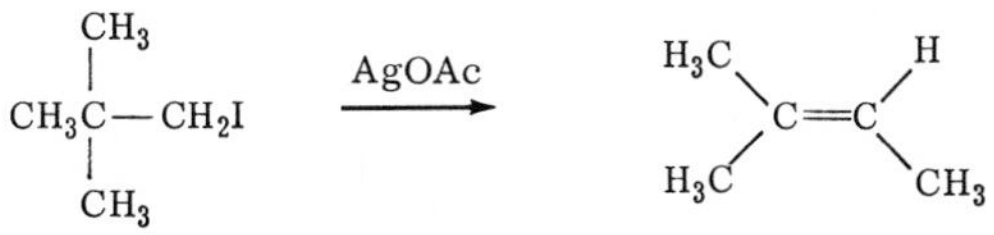

---

[4]H. O. House and D. J. Reif, *J. Am. Chem. Soc.*, **79**, 6491 (1957).
[5]H. O. House and D. J. Reif, *J. Am. Chem. Soc.*, **77**, 6525 (1955).

(cont.)

(105.2)

$$\text{C}_6\text{H}_{11}-\text{CH}_2\overset{\text{O}}{\overset{||}{\text{C}}}\text{NH}_2 \quad \xrightarrow[\text{NaOH}]{\text{Br}_2} \quad \text{C}_6\text{H}_{11}-\text{CH}_2\text{NH}_2$$

(105.3)

$$\text{C}_6\text{H}_5-\underset{\overset{|}{\text{Cl}^*}}{\text{N}}-\text{COCH}_3 \quad \xrightarrow{\text{1HCl}} \quad \text{Cl}^{*/2}-\underset{}{\langle\text{aryl}\rangle}-\text{NH}\overset{\text{O}}{\overset{||}{\text{C}}}\text{CH}_3$$

* = radio label

ANSWER 105.   [See *Molecular Rearrangements* (P. de Mayo, ed.), Wiley-Interscience, New York, 1963.]

(105.1)

$$\underset{\text{H}_3\text{C}}{\overset{\text{H}_3\text{C}}{>}}\text{CHCH}_2\text{Cl} + \text{AlCl}_3 \;\rightarrow\; \underset{\text{H}_3\text{C}}{\overset{\text{H}_3\text{C}}{>}}\overset{\oplus}{\text{CH}-\text{CH}_2} + \text{AlCl}_4^{\ominus} \;\rightarrow\; \overset{\text{H}}{\underset{}{\text{CH}_2}}-\overset{\oplus}{\text{CHCH}_2\text{CH}_3}$$

$$\downarrow \text{AlCl}_4^{\ominus}$$

$$\text{ClCH}_2\text{CH}_2\text{CH}_2\text{CH}_3 \xleftarrow{\text{AlCl}_4^{\ominus}} \overset{\oplus}{\text{CH}_2}\text{CH}_2\text{CH}_2\text{CH}_3 \qquad \text{CH}_3\underset{\overset{|}{\text{Cl}}}{\text{CHCH}_2\text{CH}_3}$$

$$\underset{\overset{|}{\text{CH}_3}}{\text{CH}_3\overset{\text{CH}_3}{\overset{|}{\text{C}}}-\text{CH}_2\text{I}} + \overset{\oplus}{\text{Ag}} \;\rightarrow\; \underset{\overset{|}{\text{CH}_3}}{\text{CH}_3\overset{\text{CH}_3}{\overset{|}{\text{C}}}-\overset{\oplus}{\text{CH}_2}} + \text{AgI}\downarrow \;\rightarrow\; \underset{\overset{|}{\text{CH}_3}}{\text{CH}_3-\overset{\oplus}{\text{C}}-\overset{\text{CH}_3}{\overset{|}{\text{CH}_2}}}$$

$$\downarrow -\text{H}^{\oplus}$$

$$\underset{\text{H}_3\text{C}}{\overset{\text{H}_3\text{C}}{>}}\text{C}=\text{CHCH}_3$$

Both AlCl_3 and Ag^+ are capable of abstracting halide ions from alkyl halides to give carbonium ions which can undergo rearrangement. In both cases shown, the mechanisms given undoubtedly represent an oversimplification, since it may be questioned whether a full carbonium ion is generated before the rearrangements begin, or whether the loss of halide is assisted by the movement of methyl groups.

(105.2)   [P. A. S. Smith in *Molecular Rearrangements*, Vol. I (P. de Mayo, ed.), Wiley-Interscience, New York, 1963, p.457; see also pp. 528ff; Gould, p. 621.]

This is the Hofmann rearrangement. The mechanism is written as going through a distinct nitrene intermediate A, but it is quite probable that the loss of bromide is actually concerted with the rearrangement process. Since nitrenes, like carbenes, have only six electrons, they would be expected to show electron deficient properties even though electrically neutral.

(105.3)   [M. J. S. Dewar in *Molecular Rearrangements*, Vol. I (P. de Mayo, ed.), Wiley-Interscience, New York, 1963, p. 295; see also pp. 309f; Gould, pp. 650ff.]

This is the Orton rearrangement. This is not a rearrangement in the usual sense because it is known to be intermolecular. The N-chloroamide merely serves as a reagent which can generate Cl_2 by reaction with HCl. The Cl_2 produced then carries out an independent reaction with the acetanilide which is also formed, or with any other reactive molecules present. The freedom of the Cl_2 is demonstrated by the observation that as the amount of Cl^- increases, the fraction of Cl^* which appears in the ring decreases. This results from the rapid exchange

$$Cl^- + Cl-Cl^* \rightleftharpoons Cl-Cl + Cl^{*-}$$

which causes all the chlorine and chloride to be in equilibrium.[1]

There exist a number of analogous "rearrangements" of the general type

A = N, O, etc.
X = halogen, $-NO_2$, $-COR$

which are known or believed to involve separation into fragments which can then recombine. They are as follows:

(a)   Alkylaniline rearrangement[2]:

(b)   Nitrosoamine rearrangement[2]:

---

[1] F. A. Long and A. R. Olson, *J. Am. Chem. Soc.*, **58**, 2214 (1936).

[2] *Molecular Rearrangements* (P. de Mayo, ed.), Wiley-Interscience, New York, 1963, p. 310.

(c) Phenol ester rearrangement (Fries rearrangement)[3,4]:

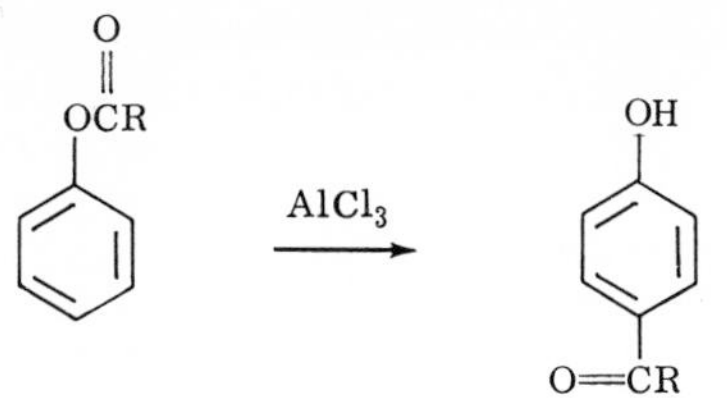

(d) Phenol ether rearrangements[5]:

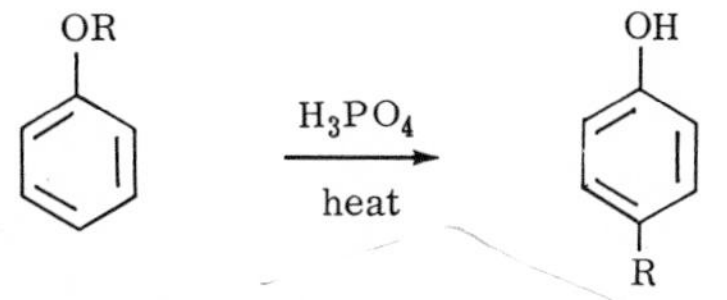

(e) The Jacobsen rearrangement[6]:

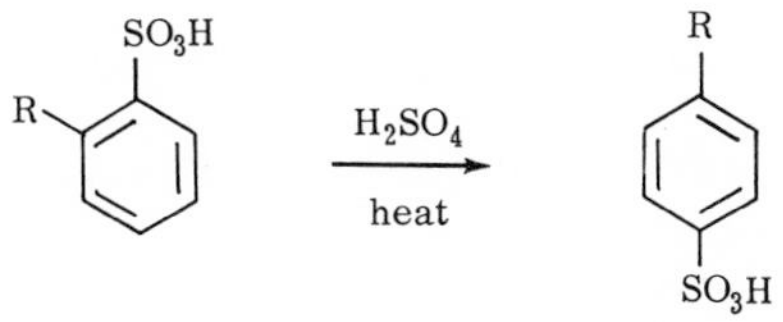

PROBLEM 106.   Suggest mechanisms for the following reactions:

(106.1)

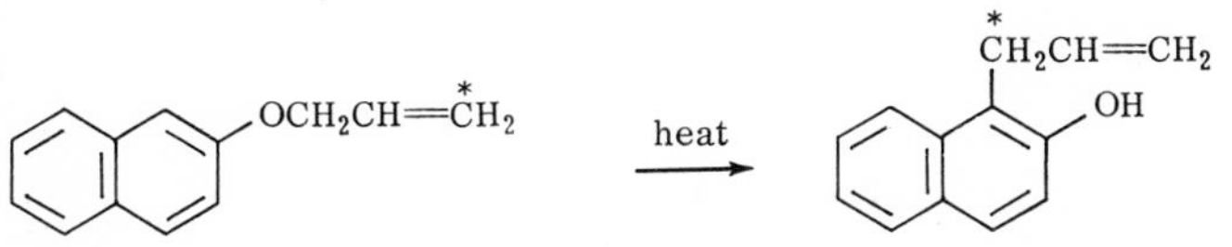

(* = labeled C)

(106.2)

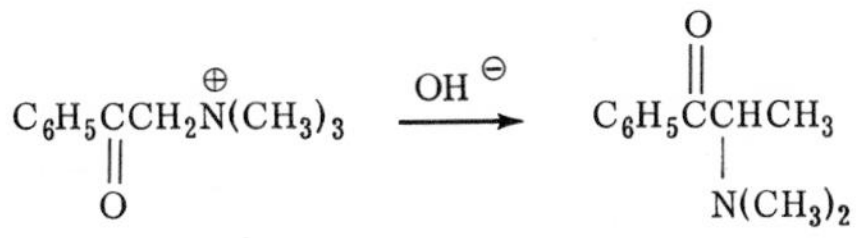

$$C_6H_5CCH_2N(CH_3)_3 \xrightarrow{\ \ OH^{\ominus}\ \ } C_6H_5CCHCH_3$$

[3] Ibid., pp. 318ff.

[4] A. H. Blatt in *Organic Reactions*, Vol. 1, Wiley, New York, 1942, p. 342.

[5] *Molecular Rearrangements* (P. de Mayo, ed.), Wiley-Interscience, New York, 1963, pp. 313ff.

[6] Ibid., pp 299ff.

ANSWER 106.   [*Molecular Rearrangements*, Vols. 1 and 2 (P. de Mayo, ed.),
Wiley-Interscience, New York, 1963.]

(106.1)   [S. J. Rhoads in *Molecular Rearrangements*, Vol. I (P. de Mayo, ed.), Wiley-
Interscience, New York, 1963, p. 655; see also pp. 660ff; Gould, pp. 644ff.

This is the Claisen rearrangement. This is one of a number of rearrangements involving the interchange of π- and σ-bonds in a six-membered cyclic
transition state. The exact mechanism is still a matter of disagreement, and the
reactions are perhaps best pictured as going through a transition state represented approximately by A, and leaving aside any questions of the direction of
electron movement while approaching this state.

A

In the example shown, the π-electron density of the 1,2-bond of naphthalene
is known to be greater than that of the 2,3-bond. The reaction leading to the
α-substituted products is consequently favored.

(106.2)   [H. E. Zimmerman in *Molecular Rearrangements*, Vol. I (P. de Mayo, ed.),
Wiley-Interscience, New York, 1963, p. 345; see also pp. 378ff; Gould, pp. 640ff

This is the Stevens rearrangement. The rearrangement is known to be intramolecular and to proceed with retention of configuration in the migrating
group, so a concerted mechanism is favored. Similar rearrangements are known
which involve initial anions less readily formed than the one shown, e.g., A → B,
but more drastic bases are required.

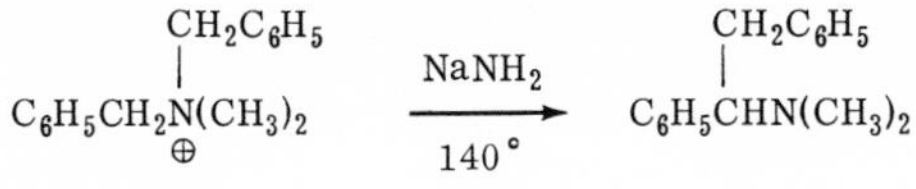

$$CH_2C_6H_5$$
$$|$$
$$C_6H_5CH_2\overset{\oplus}{N}(CH_3)_2 \quad \xrightarrow[140°]{NaNH_2} \quad C_6H_5\overset{|}{C}HN(CH_3)_2$$

A   B

PROBLEM 107.   Two plausible mechanisms, A and B, have been proposed for the Favorskii reaction. An experiment using an isotope tracer showed that in the case given the reaction must proceed by mechanism B. Devise an experiment using isotope labeling to choose between the two mechanisms.

A

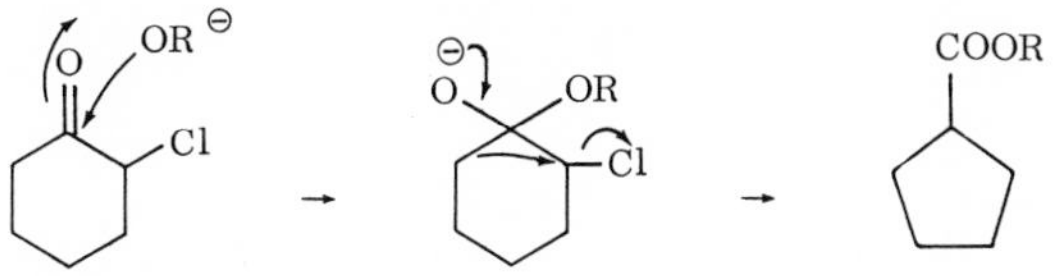

B

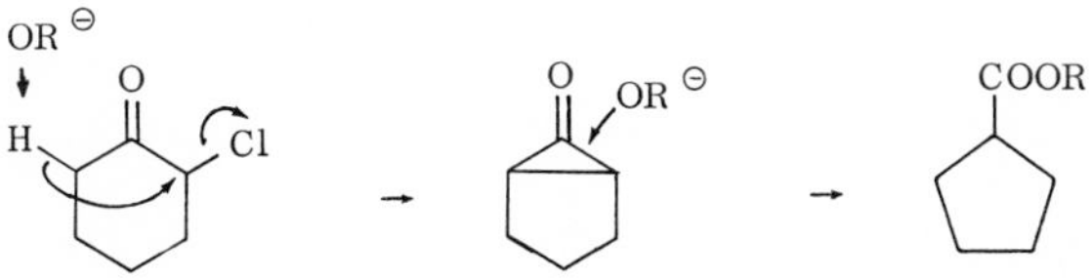

ANSWER 107.   [R. B. Loftfield, *J. Am. Chem. Soc.*, **73**, 4707 (1951).]

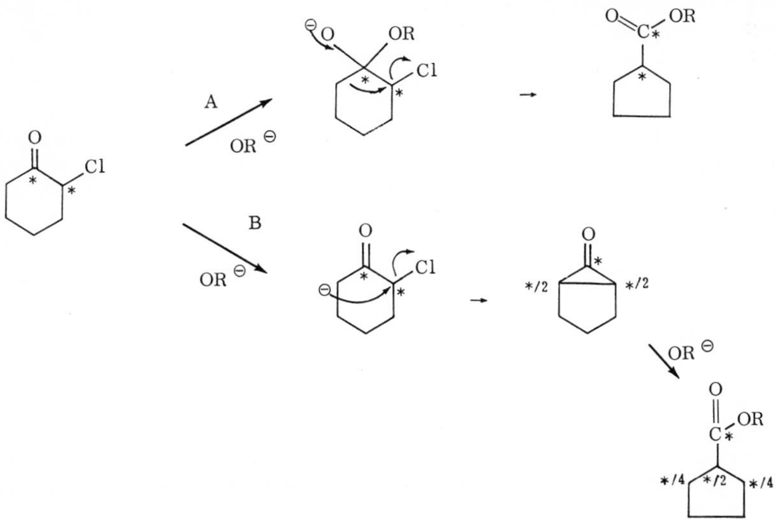

A number of mechanisms have been proposed for the Favorskii reaction,[1] but most of them require the halogen-bearing carbon to remain α to the carbonyl group (path A). That this is not the case was shown by the experimental results, which gave

completely in agreement with path B.

The carboxyl group could be confirmed to arise from the ketone carbon by

Another mechanism which had been proposed[2,3] and which could lead to the equilibrium observed involved the exchange of the halogen from the α to α' positions, followed by slower rearrangement via path A.

---

[1] For a recent review of this reaction, see A. S. Kende, *Organic Reactions*, Vol. II, Wiley, New York, 1960, p. 261.

[2] G. Richard, *Compt. Rend.*, **200**, 1944 (1935).

[3] W. D. McPhee and E. Klingsberg, *J. Am. Chem. Soc.*, **66**, 1132 (1944).

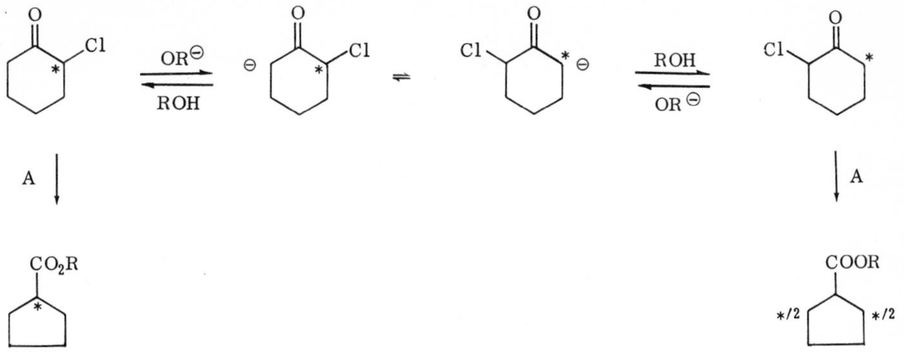

When the reaction was stopped at ca. 50% completion, however, and the recovered α-halo ketone degraded, no scrambling of the label was found. Thus there cannot be a fast equilibrium preceding a slow rearrangement step.

The cyclopropanone mechanism appears to explain the great majority of Favorskii rearrangements, but there are cases known in which it cannot be operative (no α'-H,[4] or steric[5] factors). For these reactions one of the other mechanisms must act.

PROBLEM 108.   Predict the products in the Favorskii reactions of the α-halo-ketones (108.1 and 108.2).

(108.1)

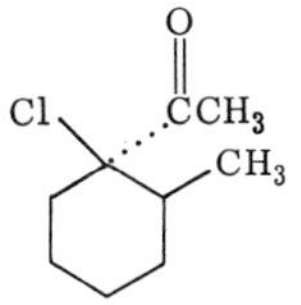

(108.2)

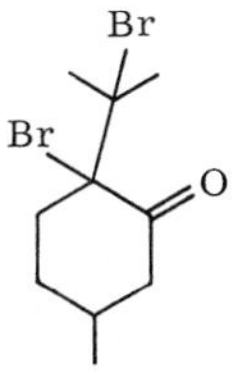

---

[4] B. Tchoubar and O. Sackur, *Compt. Rend.*, **208**, 1020 (1939).
[5] A. C. Cope and E. S. Graham, *J. Am. Chem. Soc.*, **73**, 4702 (1951).

ANSWER 108.   [See A. S. Kende in *Organic Reactions,* Vol. 11, Wiley, New York, 1960, p. 261.]

(108.1)   [G. Stork and I. J. Borowitz, *J. Am. Chem. Soc.,* **82,** 4307 (1960).]

The generally accepted mechanism for the Favorskii reaction involves internal displacement of the halogen to form a cyclopropanone.[1] This opens under base attack to give the most stable anion (prim > sec > tert).

(108.2)   [O. Wallach, *Ann.,* **327,** 125 (1903); **414,** 233 (1918).]

In this case the concerted loss of Br⁻ allows the opening of the cyclopropanone to occur in the direction opposite to that suggested by the stabilities of the isolated carbanions.

PROBLEM 109.   When the peroxy ester, A, in which the carbonyl oxygen is labeled with O^{18}, was subjected to the following series of reactions, virtually all the O^{18} was found in the benzyl alcohol, D. The rearrangement A → B is a heterolytic reaction, for the rate of rearrangement is greatly increased by transferring the reaction from nonpolar to polar solvents. Suggest a mechanism for

---

[1]R. B. Loftfield, *J. Am. Chem. Soc.,* **73,** 4707 (1951).

(cont.)

the rearrangement. Would a p-nitro or p-methoxyl substituent, added to the benzoate group in A, cause a greater increase in the rate of rearrangement?

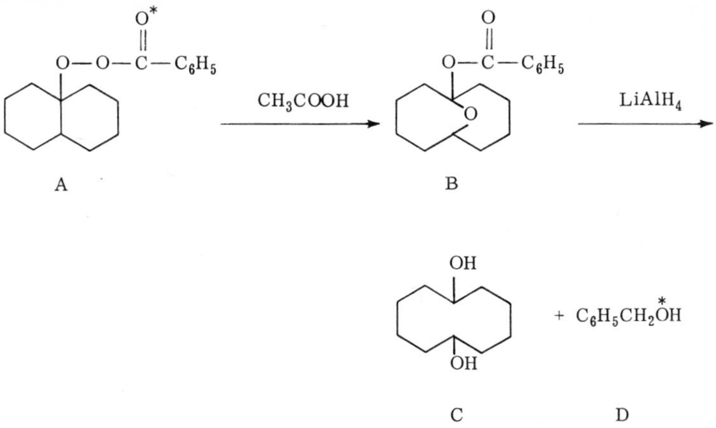

A → B →

+ $C_6H_5CH_2\overset{*}{O}H$

C D

ANSWER 109. [D. B. Denney and D. G. Denney, *J. Am. Chem. Soc.*, **79**, 4806 (1957).]

The gross reaction resembles the Wagner-Meerwein rearrangement[1] and may be written

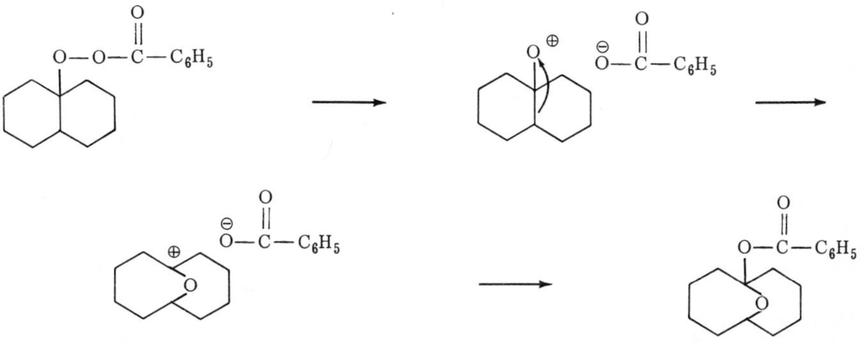

It has been found by studies with competing ions[2,3] not to involve dissociation into two independent charged species. Instead a concerted rearrangement, or the formation of a tight ion pair, has been suggested as the mechanism.

---

[1] Gould, pp. 584ff; see also Y. Pocker in *Molecular Rearrangements*, Vol. I (P. de Mayo, ed.), Wiley-Interscience, New York, 1963, p. 1.
[2] P. D. Bartlett and J. L. Kice, *J. Am. Chem. Soc.*, **75**, 5591 (1953).
[3] H. L. Goering and A. C. Olson, *J. Am. Chem. Soc.*, **75**, 5853 (1953).

Three arrangements (a, b, or c) would appear possible for the transition state:

The dotted lines may represent partial covalent bonds or electrostatic interactions between oriented partial changes.

Of these transition states,

The observation that LiAlH$_4$ reduction of the ester yields benzyl alcohol containing all the label indicates that the path followed corresponds to (a); i.e., the carbonyl group retains its identity during the rearrangement. This may arise either
from a concerted reaction or from the intermediate formation of a very tight ion
pair in which the ester oxygen is closer to the developing carbonium ion than is
the carbonyl oxygen, and which collapses so rapidly that they do not have a chance
to interchange positions.

  Since the transition state involves the formation, partly or completely, of the
anion of a carboxylic acid, it is to be expected that its stability would increase
with the stability of this anion. Thus the introduction of electron-withdrawing
groups, e.g., —NO$_2$, into the aromatic ring should increase the rate of reaction.
This has been observed.[4]

PROBLEM 110.   Suggest mechanisms for the following steroid reactions:

---

[4]R. Criegee and R. Kaspar, Ann., **560**, 127 (1948).

ANSWER 110.   [See N. L. Wendler in *Molecular Rearrangements*, Vol. II
(P. de Mayo, ed.), Wiley-Interscience, New York, 1963, pp.
1114ff.]

These acyloin rearrangements are part of a large set of complicated and in-
completely understood reactions relating the ketols of the normal and D-homo
steroids. The mechanism proposed for the Al(O-t-Bu)$_3$ catalyzed reaction of A
envisions a bridged complex linking the two oxygen atoms and holding them as
shown in C.

The fact that the carbonyl group is oriented down in C by the complex bridge determined the orientation of the substituents in the product.

On the other hand, the rearrangement in the KOH-catalyzed reaction is assumed to proceed from the anion of A. In this case, the O$^-$ and C=O are expected to take up an antiparallel orientation because of the repulsion of the two
oxygen atoms (D).

Again the orientation of the intermediate determines the stereochemistry of the
product.

What is not explained by the above mechanisms, and is still unclear, is the
directing power which determines whether migration of bond a or b will occur.
A number of explanations, electronic and steric, have been advanced, but none
appears to satisfy all the known facts. Among other problems, it has been found
that equilibration can occur among the various rearrangement products, and so
the observed products may represent in some cases varying degrees of kinetic
and thermodynamic control.

Similar mechanisms can be used to account for the products from B, subject
to the same reservation. Thus

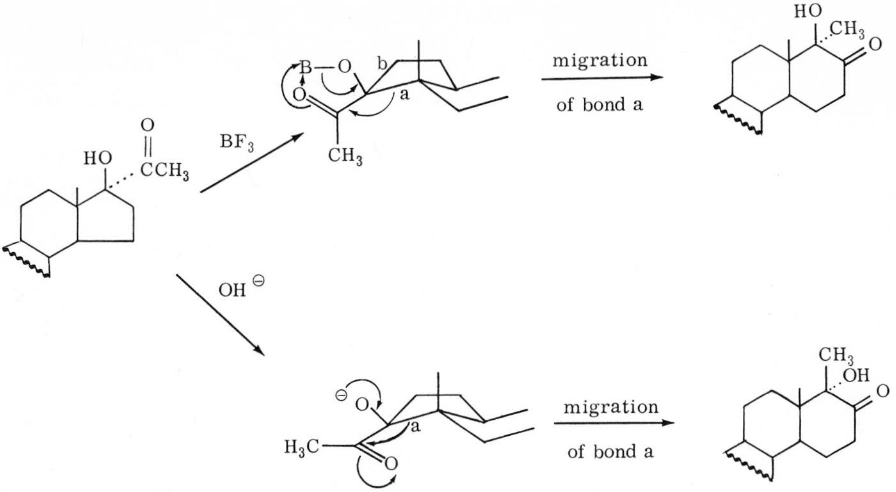

Note that in this case bond a migrates with both reagents.

PROBLEM 111.   Suggest a mechanism for the following reaction:

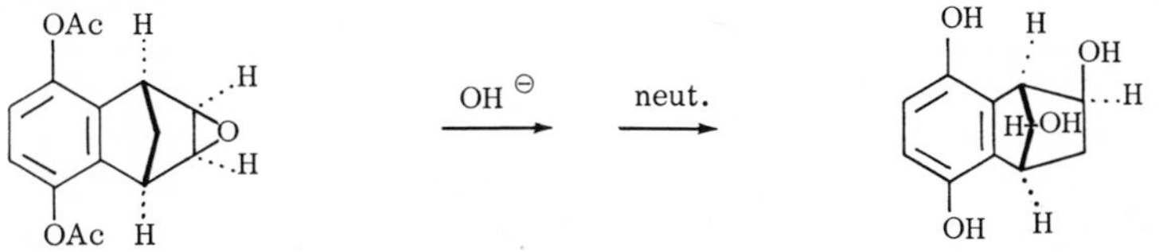

ANSWER 111.   [J. Meinwald and G. A. Wiley, *J. Am. Chem. Soc.*, **80**, 3667 (1958).]

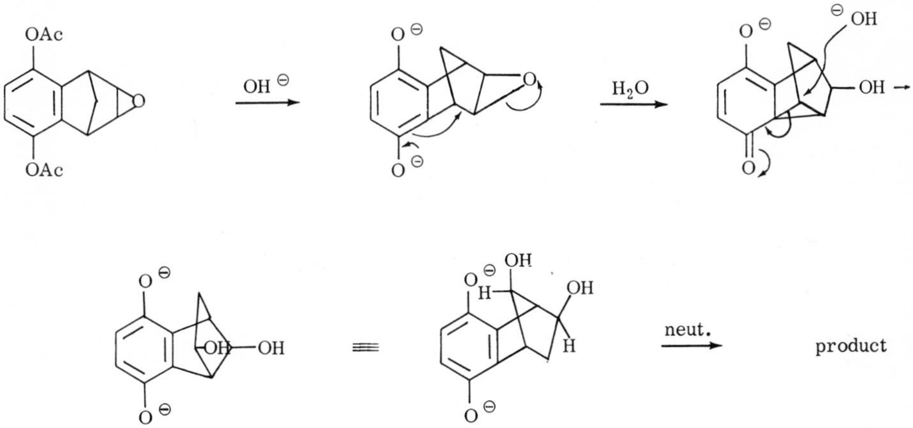

The mechanism shown has been suggested to account for the abnormally facile base-catalyzed ring opening of the epoxide. Normally, exo-norbornane systems are extremely inert to nucleophilic attack under basic conditions.

PROBLEM 112.   Suggest mechanisms for the following rearrangement reactions:

(112.1)

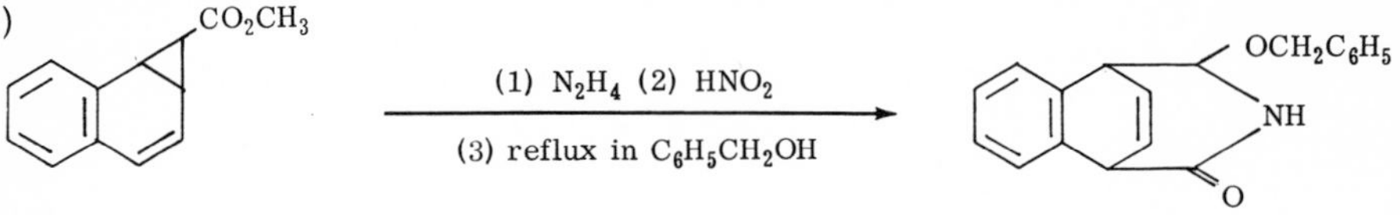

$$\xrightarrow[\text{(3) reflux in } C_6H_5CH_2OH]{\text{(1) } N_2H_4 \text{ (2) } HNO_2}$$

(112.2)

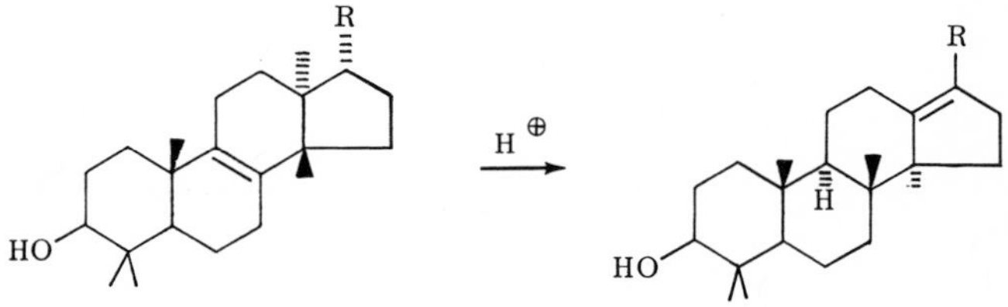

(112.3)

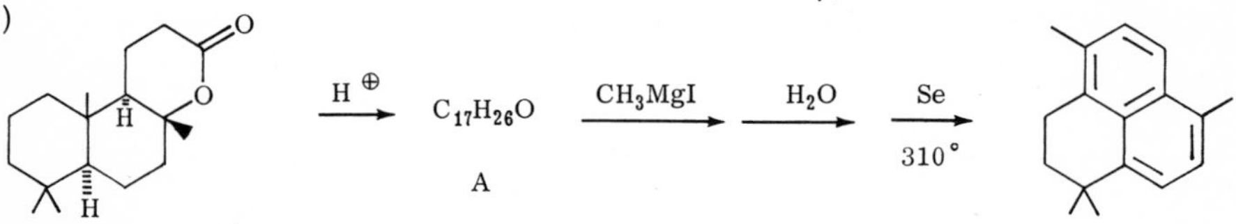

ANSWER 112.

(112.1)   [W. von E. Doering and M. J. Goldstein, *Tetrahedron*, **5**, 53 (1959).]

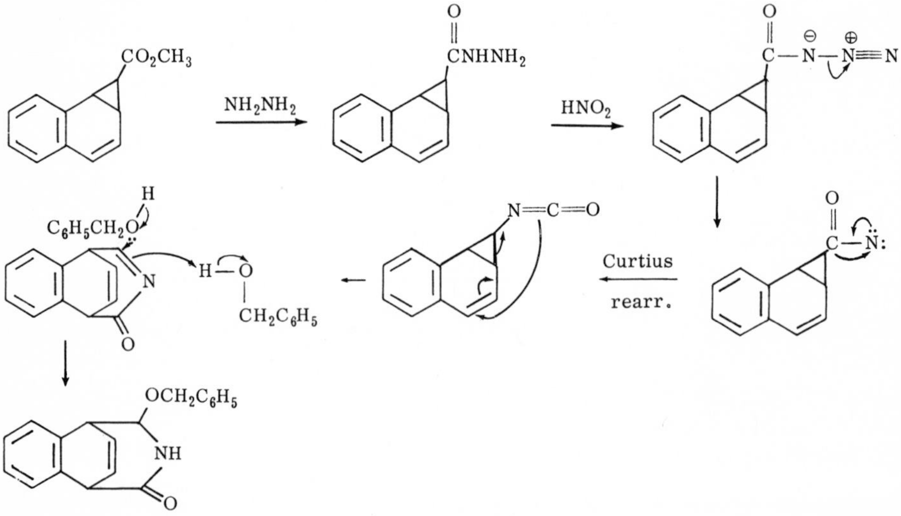

The reaction sequence is normal through the Curtius rearrangement,[1] but the rearrangement of the isocyanate is quite unusual. The question of the exact mechanism of the bridging process is still open and is complicated by the uncertainty as to the stereochemistry of the isocyanate. If it is cis (A), a concerted reaction is very feasible, but if it is trans (B, as some evidence indicates), then discrete cleavage, rotation, and recombination steps appear to be required.

A   B

(112.2)   [D. Arigoni, R. Viterbo, M. Dunnenberger, O. Jeger, and L. Ruzicka, *Helv. Chim. Acta*, **37**, 2306 (1954).]

euphol

Although the rearrangement is shown in steps, such reactions are often assumed to involve concerted 1, 2-migrations of alternately trans-diaxial groups,[2] beginning in this case with proton addition from the less hindered rear side. The importance of the orientation of the migrating substituents may be seen by comparing the behavior of lanosterol, which has the opposite C/D trans fusion.

---

[1] See P. A. S. Smith in *Molecular Rearrangements*, Vol. I (P. de Mayo, ed.), Wiley-Interscience, New York, 1963, pp. 528–568.

[2] See J. F. King and P. de Mayo in *Molecular Rearrangements*, Vol. II (P. de Mayo, ed.), Wiley-Interscience, New York, 1963, pp. 813ff.

lanosterol

(112.3)   [G. Büchi, W. S. Saar, and A. Eschenmoser, *Experientia,* **13**, 136 (1956).]

        This rearrangement also involves a series of 1,2-migrations of alternately
trans-diaxial groups and is followed by acylation of the intermediate alkene.

PROBLEM 113.   Suggest mechanisms for the following rearrangement reactions:

(113.1)

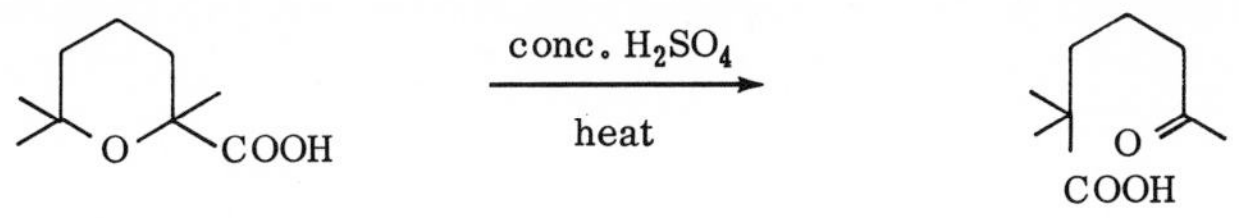

(113.2)

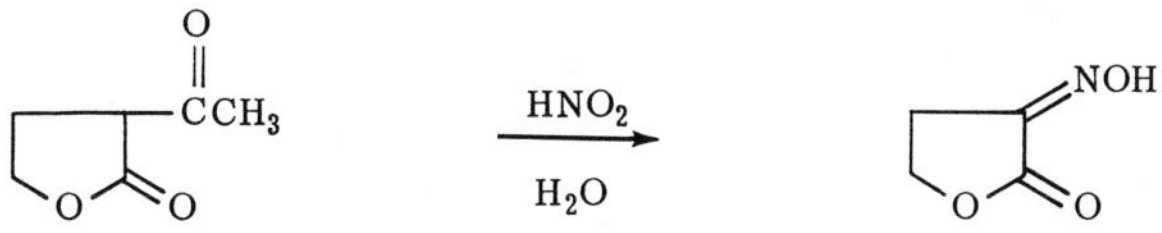

(113.3)

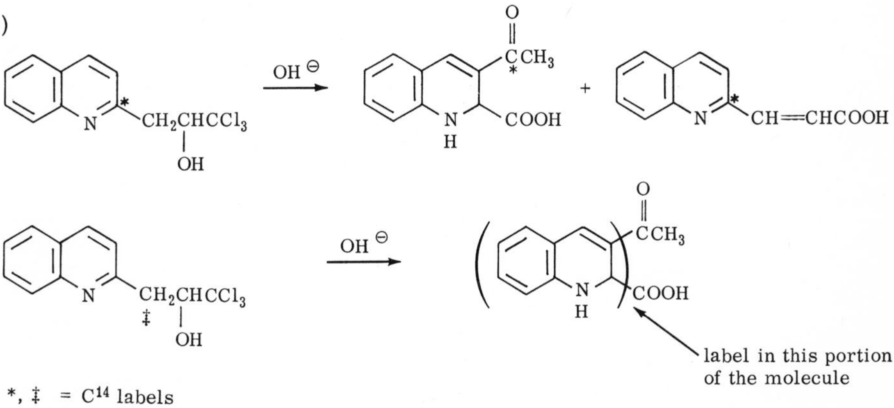

*, ‡ = C^{14} labels

ANSWER 113.

(113.1)   [J. Meinwald, H. C. Hwang, D. Christensen, and A. P. Wolf, *J. Am. Chem. Soc.*, **82**, 483 (1960).]

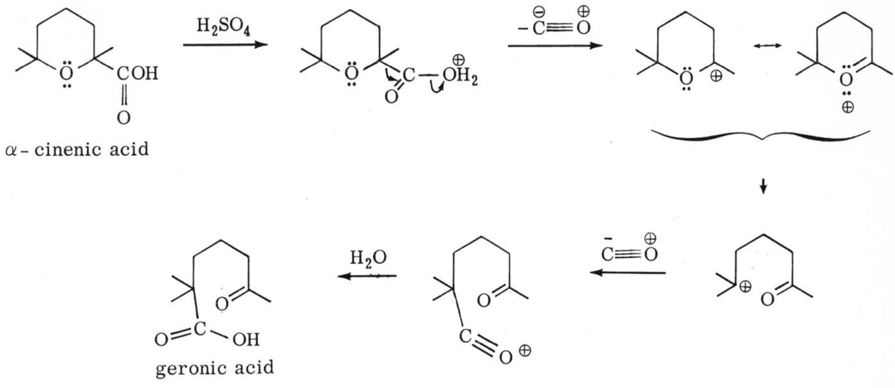

α – cinenic acid

geronic acid

The rearrangement shown is an unusual one, and for a long time its mechanism was unclear. Originally, it was thought that long-range methyl migration was involved, but this was disproved when tracer studies[1] showed that the reaction required a formal carboxyl migration. This was considered to be concerted and intramolecular,[1,2] until it was found that CO was liberated during the reaction and that added $C^{14}O$ could be incorporated into the resulting geronic acid. On this basis, the above mechanism has been proposed. The driving force for the reaction is presumably the relief of the steric interaction between the 2,6-substituents of the α-cinenic acid.

A side product of the same reaction is the lactone B. The mechanism shown has been proposed[3] to account for its formation. This reaction, which does not require any skeletal rearrangement, does not involve exchange of the —COOH group with added $C^{14}O$.

(113.2)   [A. E. Lanzilotti and M. J. Weiss, *J. Org. Chem.*, **24**, 1003 (1959).]

---

[1] J. Meinwald, *J. Am. Chem. Soc.*, **77**, 1617 (1955).
[2] J. Meinwald and C. C. Cornwall, **77**, 5991 (1955).
[3] J. Meinwald and H. C. Hwang, *J. Am. Chem. Soc.*, **79**, 2910 (1957).

The reaction is a general one for the cleavage of β-dicarbonyl compounds and the replacement of an acyl group by an oximano group.[4] In this case, the intermediate B has been isolated, although it has not been proved that the reaction involves an intramolecular rearrangement. Earlier suggestions had proposed the direct hydrolysis of A, with the formation of the oxime anion, and these may still be correct when the reaction is carried out under the more common basic conditions (RONO, RO$^-$).

It has been suggested[5] that a very similar reaction, the thermal decomposition of N-nitrosoamides, involves a similar rearrangement as its first step.

$$R-N\underset{\displaystyle\|O}{\overset{\displaystyle N=O}{\underset{}{-}}CCH_3} \quad \xrightarrow{\Delta} \quad R-N\overset{\displaystyle N-O-CCH_3}{\underset{\displaystyle \qquad O}{}}$$

(113.3)   [W. G. Dauben and C. W. Vaughan, Jr., *J. Am. Chem. Soc.*, **75**, 4651 (1953).]

---

[4] See O. Tonster in *Organic Reactions*, Vol. 7, Wiley, New York, 1953, p. 336.
[5] For a discussion and leading references, see A. Streitwieser, Jr., and W. D. Schaeffer, *J. Am. Chem. Soc.*, **79**, 2893 (1957).

The above is the better of the two proposed mechanisms which account for the observed distribution of the labeled carbons. No evidence exists of its correctness, but analogies do exist for the various steps.

It has been suggested that the unrearranged product can arise by an alternative mode of closure of the intermediate A; thus

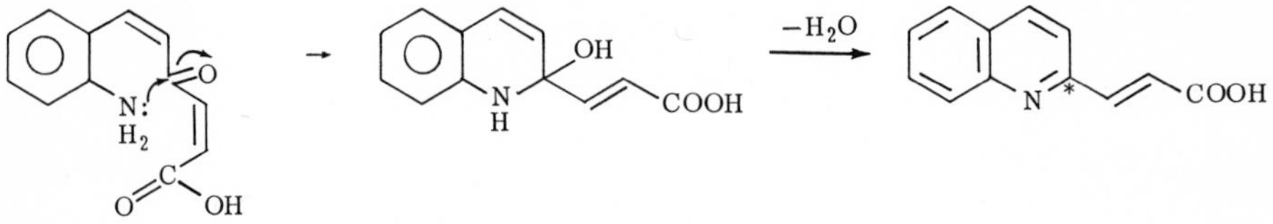

but there is certainly no evidence to favor this route over direct hydrolysis of the trichloromethyl group and base-catalyzed dehydration, which gives the same product.

PROBLEM 114.   Suggest mechanisms for the following reactions:

(114.1)

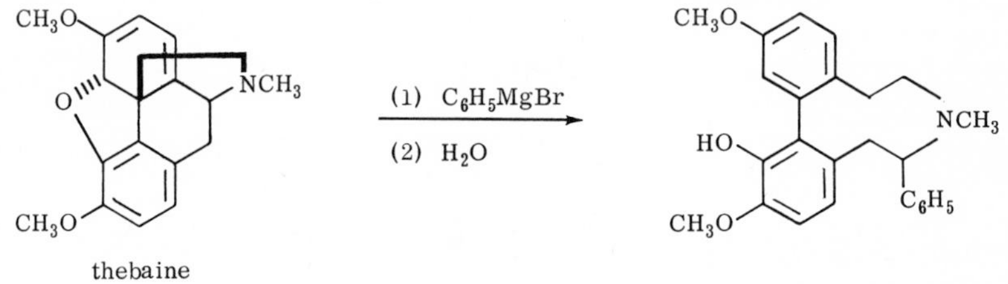

thebaine

(114.2)

thebaine $\xrightarrow{\text{dil. HCl}}$ $\xrightarrow{\text{neut.}}$

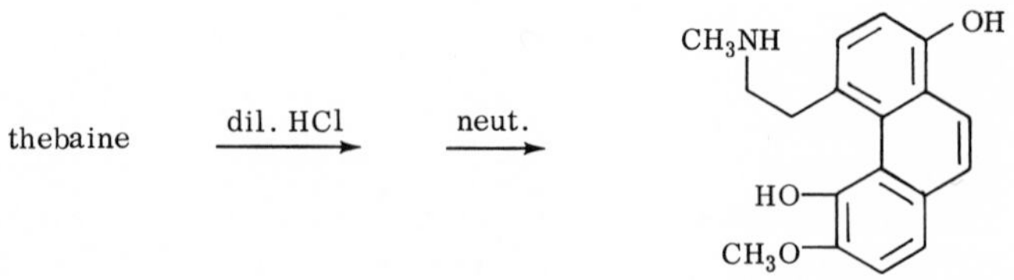

(cont.)

(114.3)

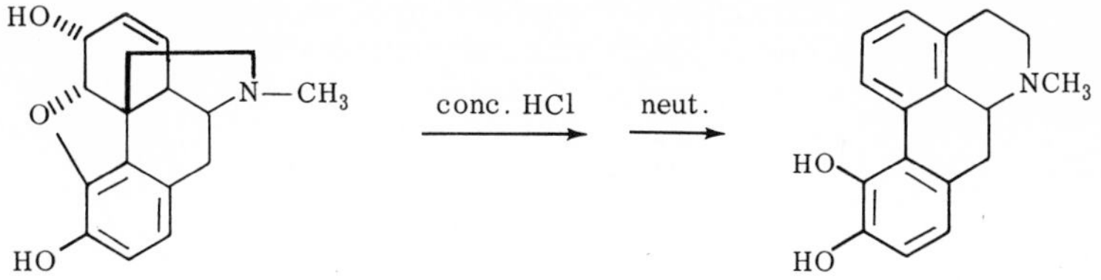

morphine

ANSWER 114.

(114.1)   [See G. Stork, *J. Am. Chem. Soc.*, **74**, 768 (1952).]

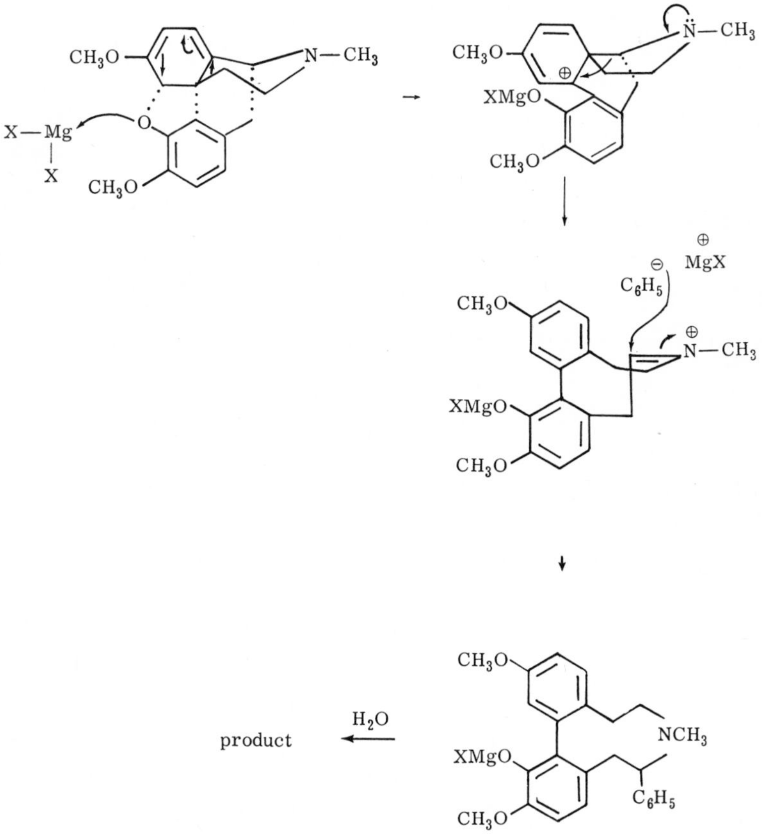

(114.2)   [See G. Stork in *The Alkaloids*, Vol. II (R. H. F. Manske and H. L. Holmes, eds.), Academic Press, New York, 1952, p. 197.]

thebenine

(114.3)   [See G. Stork, op. cit., p. 195.]

A completely analogous reaction occurs with thebaine to give morpho-thebaine (A).

A

The difference between the reactions in concentrated and dilute acids arises because in strong acid the nitrogen is entirely present in the protonated form and is unable to supply the electrons needed for the mechanism shown in part 114.2.

PROBLEM 115.   Suggest mechanisms for the following rearrangements:

(115.1)

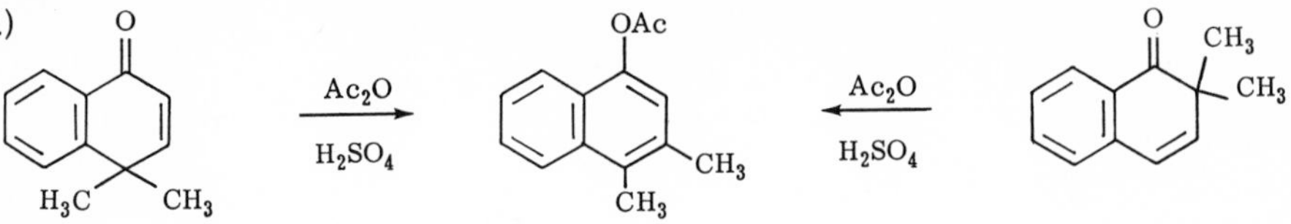

(115.2)

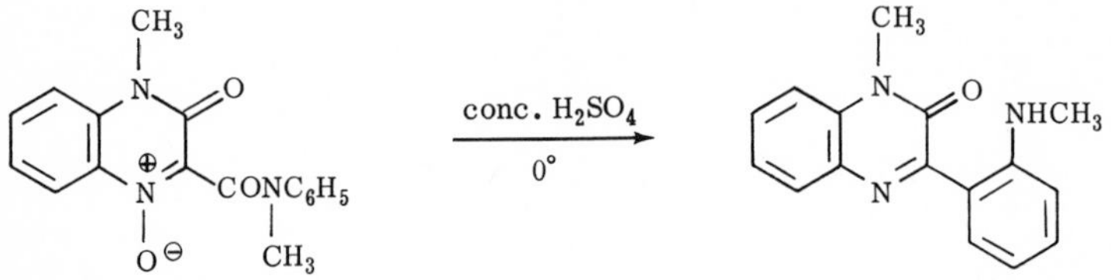

ANSWER 115.

(115.1)   [R. T. Arnold, J. S. Buckley, Jr., and J. Richter, *J. Am. Chem. Soc.*, **69**, 2322 (1947); E. N. Marvell and A. O. Geiszler, *J. Am. Chem. Soc.*, **74**, 1259 (1952); E. N. Marvell and J. L. Stephenson, *J. Am. Chem. Soc.*, **77**, 5177 (1955).]

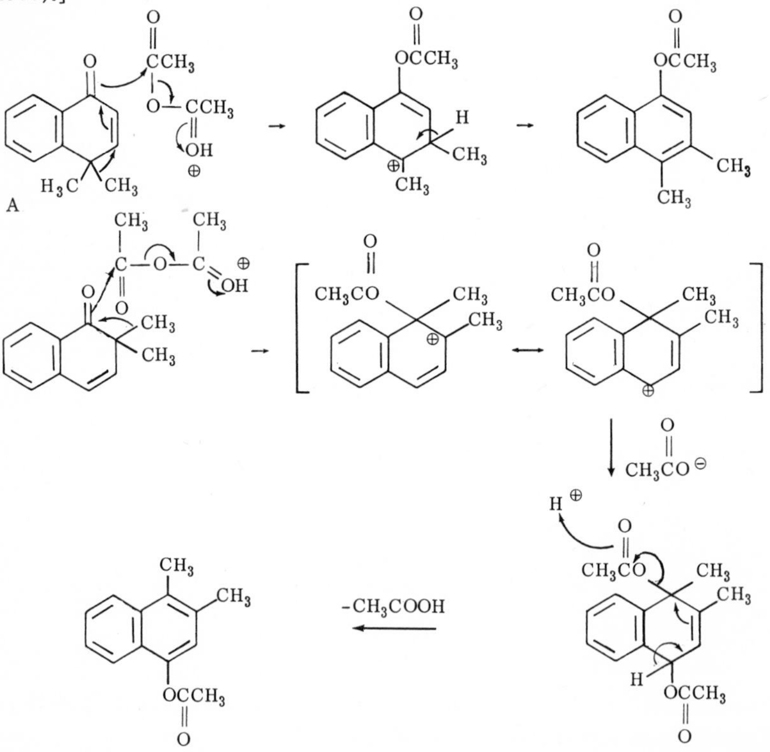

The first reaction is a normal dienone-phenol rearrangement. The second is an abnormal variant, probably caused by the high energy associated with the resonance form C, which would lead to normal rearrangement, but at the cost of losing the benzene resonance of the unsubstituted ring during the process.

C

(115.2)   [M. S. Habib and C. W. Rees, *Chem. Ind. (London)*, **1959**, 367.]

The reaction shows the behavior of an electrophilic substitution on the activated phenyl ring, and appears to be intramolecular.

PROBLEM 116. Suggest a mechanism for the following reaction:

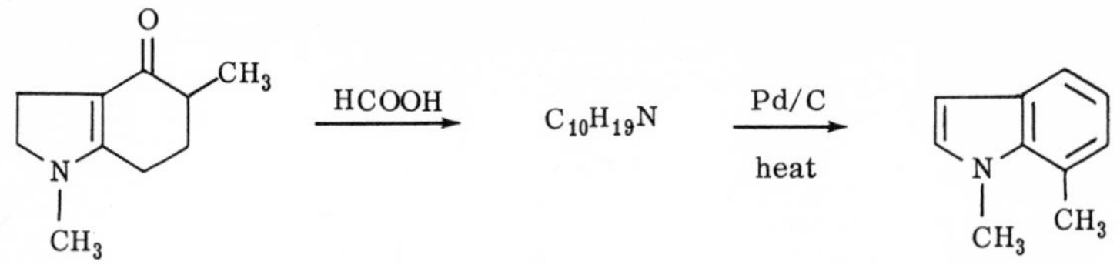
O
CH3
N
CH3
HCOOH
C10H19N
Pd/C
heat
N
CH3
CH3

ANSWER 116. [O. Cervinka, *Chem. Ind. (London)*, **1959**, 1129.]

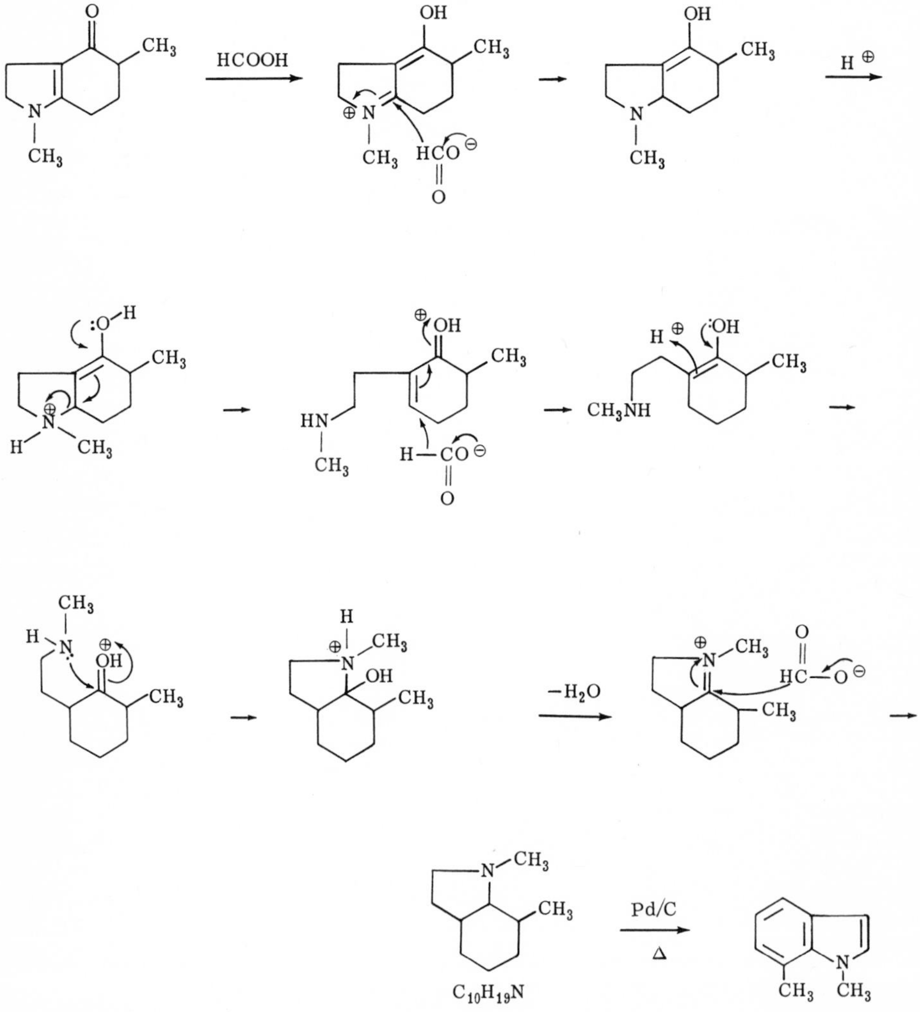
HCOOH
H ⊕
−H2O
Pd/C
Δ
C10H19N

The formic acid reduction of enamines is a general reaction (see the Leuckart reaction)[1] and has been studied by deuterium labeling,[2] with the results shown below. In the above case, the amino group is β to the carbonyl and is readily eliminated, opening the way to further reactions.

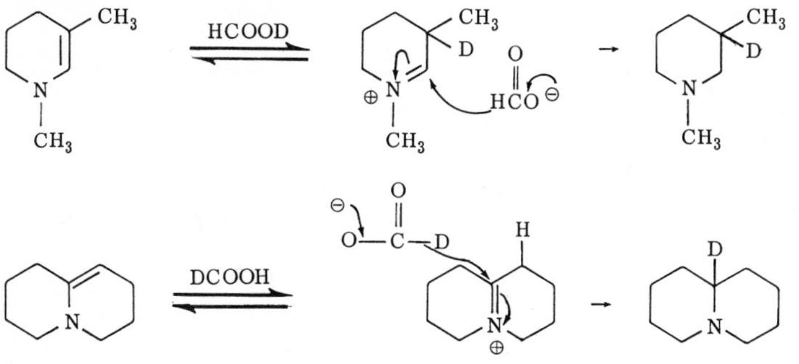
CH3
HCOOD
CH3
D
O
HCO ⊖
⊕ N
N
CH3
CH3
CH3
D
N
CH3
O
⊖
O—C—D
H
D
DCOOH
N
N
⊕
N

PROBLEM 117. Deduce structures for the products:

(117.1)

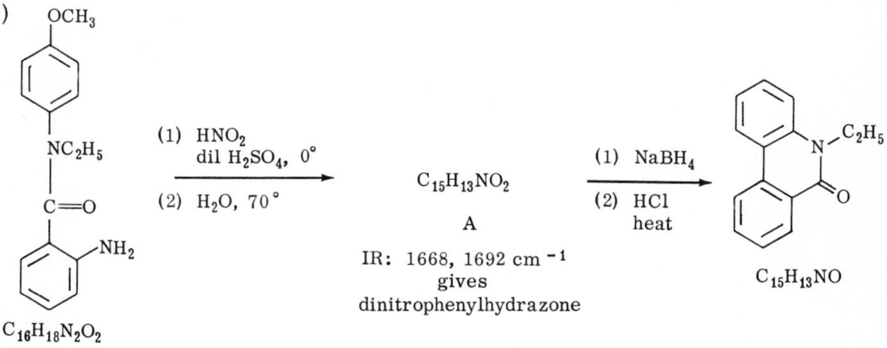
OCH3
NC2H5
C=O
NH2
C16H18N2O2
(1) HNO2
dil H2SO4, 0°
(2) H2O, 70°
C15H13NO2
A
IR: 1668, 1692 cm -1
gives
dinitrophenylhydrazone
(1) NaBH4
(2) HCl
heat
N
C2H5
O
C15H13NO

(117.2)

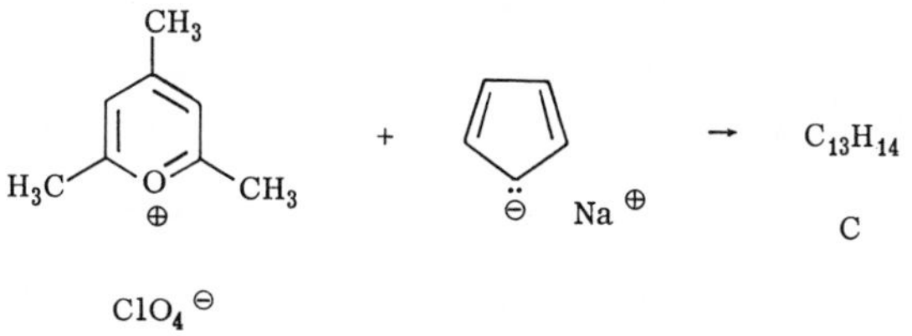
CH3
H3C
O
⊕
CH3
ClO4 ⊖
+
⊖
Na ⊕
C13H14
C

---

[1] M. L. Moore in *Organic Reactions*, Vol. 5, Wiley, New York, 1949, p. 301.
[2] N. J. Leonard and R. R. Sauers, *J. Am. Chem. Soc.*, **79**, 6210 (1957).

ANSWER 117.

(117. 1)   [D. H. Hey, J. A. Leonard, T. M. Moyneban, and C. W. Rees, *J. Chem. Soc.*, **1961**, 232.]

The decomposition of the diazonium intermediate normally gives the phenan-
thridone directly (Pschorr phenanthrene synthesis),[1] e.g., B can by synthesized,

but in this case the electron-donating powers of the —OCH_3 so favor para substitution that the spiro compound A is formed.

A can also be subjected to the dienone-phenol rearrangement,[2] although requiring unusually vigorous conditions, and gives

(117.2)   [K. Hafner, *Angew. Chem.*, **69**, 393 (1957); K. Hafner and H. Kaiser, *Ann.*,
618, 140 (1958).]

4,6,8-trimethylazulene

[1] See D. F. DeTar in *Organic Reactions*, Vol. 10, Wiley, New York, 1957, p. 409.
[2] R. B. Woodward and T. Singh, *J. Am. Chem. Soc.*, **72**, 494 (1950).

This reaction is based on the Ziegler-Hafner synthesis of azulenes,[3] an entirely analogous sequence of reactions starting from N-alkylated pyridines. Thus[4]

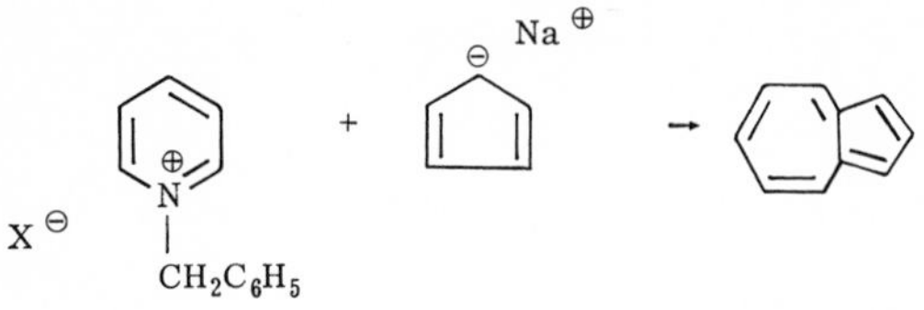

azulene

a blue, aromatic hydrocarbon

PROBLEM 118.   Suggest mechanisms for the following rearrangements:

(118.1)

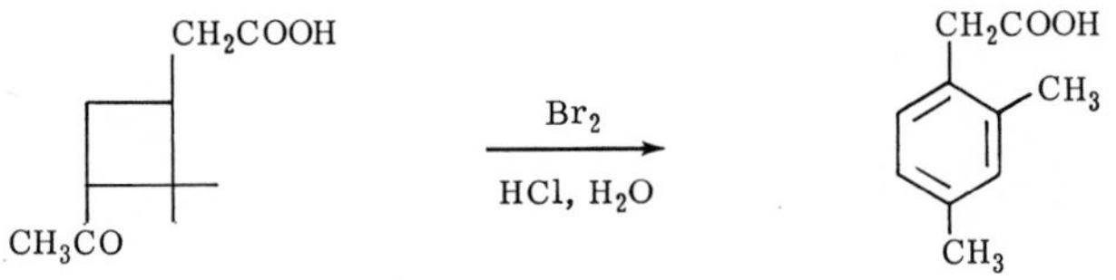

(118.2)

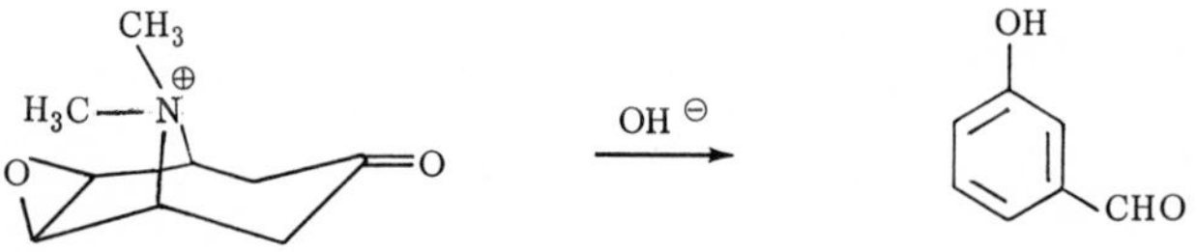

(118.3)

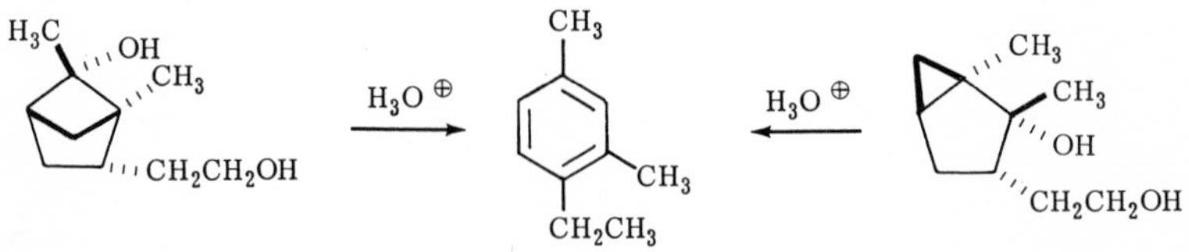

---

[3] K. Ziegler and K. Hafner, *Angew. Chem.*, **67**, 301 (1955); K. Hafner, *Angew. Chem.*, **70**, 419 (1958).

[4] See for a discussion D. H. Reid, *Chem. Soc.*, *(London) Spec. Publ.*, **12**, 69 (1958), or E. Heilbronner, and W. Keller-Schierlein; and E. Heilbronner in *Non-Benzenoid Aromatic Compounds* (D. Ginsburg, ed.), Wiley-Interscience, New York, 1959, pp. 171-338.

ANSWER 118.

(118. 1)   (C. L. Arcus and G. J. Bennett, *J. Chem. Soc.*, **1958**, 3180.)

This mechanism is an amplified version of that originally proposed. The acid-catalyzed ring opening of pinonic acid to the lactone A has been demonstrated,[1] but although A gives 2,4-dimethylphenylacetic acid on acidic bromination, its rate of formation is too slow for it to be a possible intermediate in the sequence shown.

The cyclization of B is quite similar to that observed for the α- and β-methylheptenones and a number of related cases[2]:

[1] C. L. Arcus and G. J. Bennett, *J. Chem. Soc.*, **1955**, 2627.

[2] J. Meinwald and J. A. Yankeelov, Jr., *J. Am. Chem. Soc.*, **80**, 5266 (1958).

β – heptenone   α – heptenone

(118.2)   [J. Meinwald and O. L. Chapman, *J. Am. Chem. Soc.*, **81**, 5800 (1959).]

A

The above mechanism has been proposed to account for the observed trans-formation. Although the outlines are probably correct, it is not necessary that the steps follow in the order shown. Thus it is possible that the opening of the nitrogen bridge occurs first, before the epoxide opening and formation of the cyclopropane ring in A. Another possibility would be the complete elimination of the nitrogen, leading to B, which then undergoes hydration and epoxide open-ing.

γ-tropolone

For the last mechanism to hold, it would be necessary for the cyclopropane formation to be faster than the alternative opening of the epoxide to give γ-tropolone, since it has been shown that this is stable under the reaction conditions.

(118.3)   [G. Büchi and I. M. Goldman, *J. Am. Chem. Soc.*, **79**, 4741 (1957).]

It is suggested that the dehydration of either tertiary alcohol leads to the same nonclassical carbonium ion C. This collapses, with the relief of much strain, to give the approximately planar ion D, following which reasonable processes lead to the observed product.

It is not mandatory to invoke nonclassical ions, however, to account for this reaction sequence. An alternative route using only classical ions could be

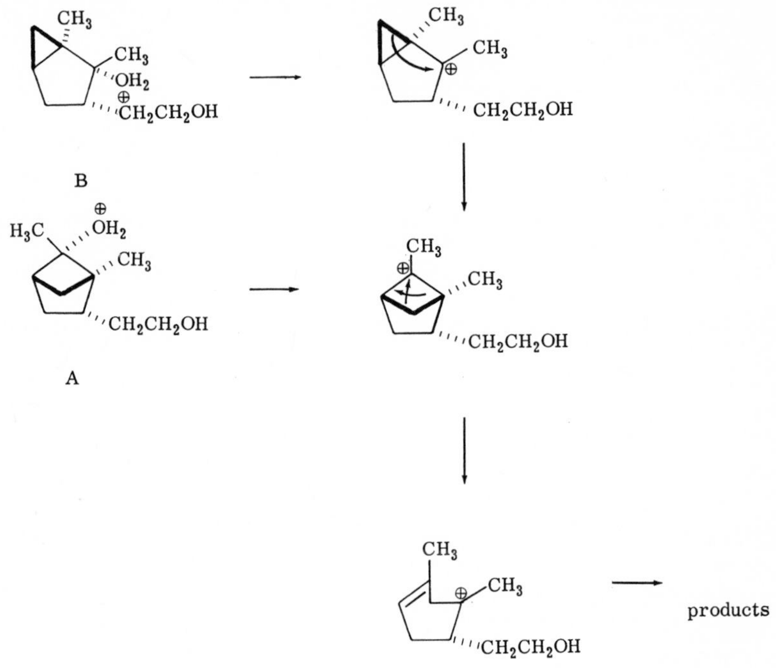

PROBLEM 119.   Suggest a reasonable path for the following reaction:

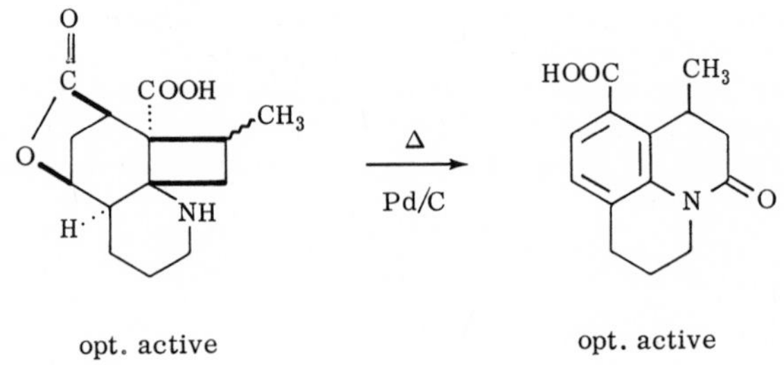

opt. active   opt. active

ANSWER 119.   [K. Wiesner, Z. Valenta, W. A. Ayer, L. R. Fowler, and J. E. Francis, *Tetrahedron*, **4**, 87 (1958).]

This proposed mechanism depends on two reverse Mannich reactions[1] (1 → 2, 4 → 5) to open the cyclobutane rings. In the presence of the dehydrogenation catalyst, the various tautomerizations are not unreasonable, and lead, at least formally, to the product. It should be noted that at no time is the asymmetric center adjacent to the methyl group affected, as is required by the observed optical activity of the product.

---

[1] See F. F. Blicke in *Organic Reactions*, Vol. 1, Wiley, New York, 1942, p. 304.

PROBLEM 120.   Suggest possible routes for the following reactions:

(120.1)

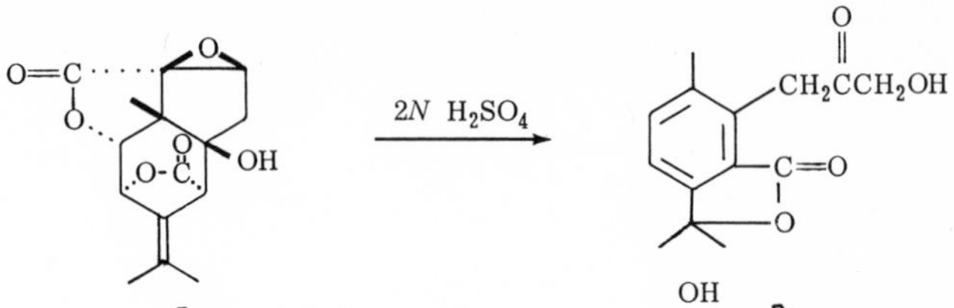

$2N$ H$_2$SO$_4$

(120.2)

py·HCl

218°

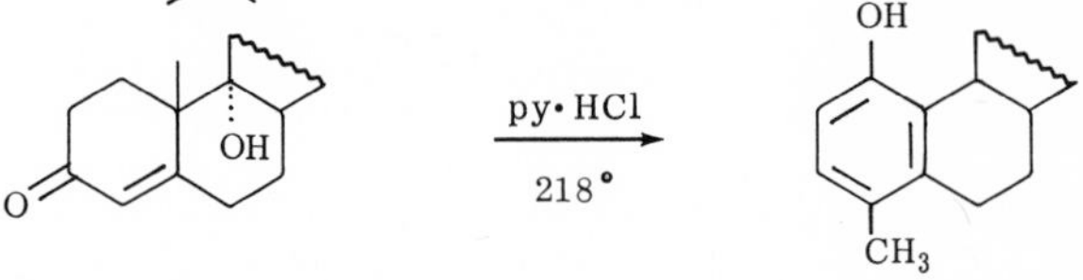

ANSWER 120.

(120.1)   [J. S. E. Holker, A. Robertson, J. H. Taylor, K. U. Holker, and W. R. N. Williamson, *J. Chem. Soc.*, **1958**, 2987.]

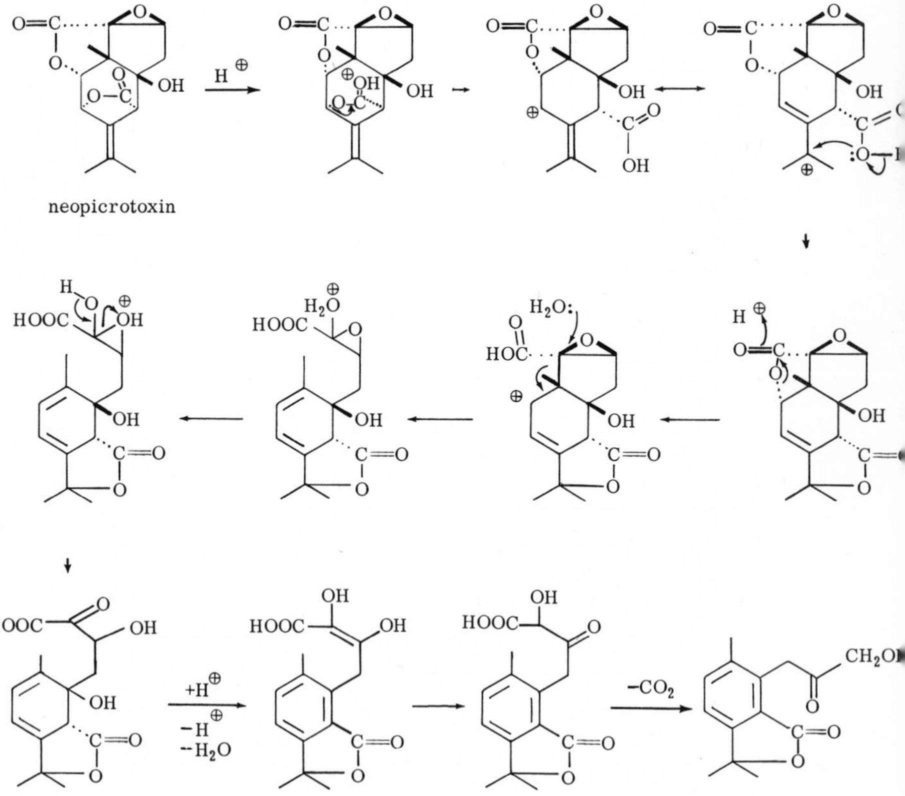

neopicrotoxin

picrotonol

This route differs in details from that originally proposed, but appears more reasonable.

It may be noted that, under the same conditions,

picrotoxinin   picrotoxic acid

the difference apparently being due to the absence of an allylic ester group.

(120.2)   [L. J. Chinn and R. M. Dodson, *J. Org. Chem.*, **24**, 879 (1959).]

The B-ring is opened by a vinylogous retro-aldol reaction, then reclosed by aldolization, following rotation of the A-ring around the 5,6-bond.

PROBLEM 121.   Suggest an explanation for the fact that at temperatures which lead to the following equilibria, complete stereochemical integrity (including optical activity) is maintained.

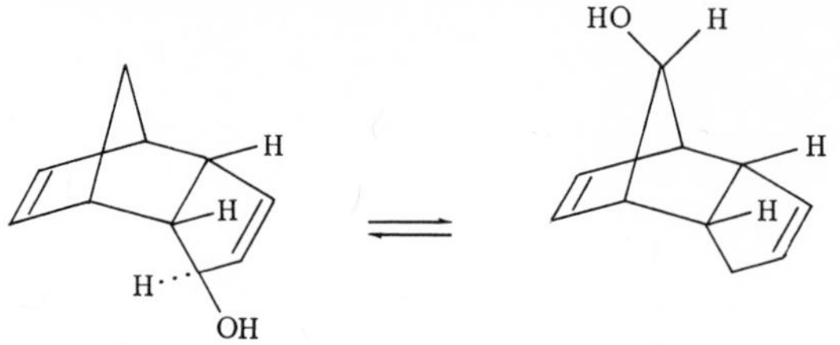

1   3

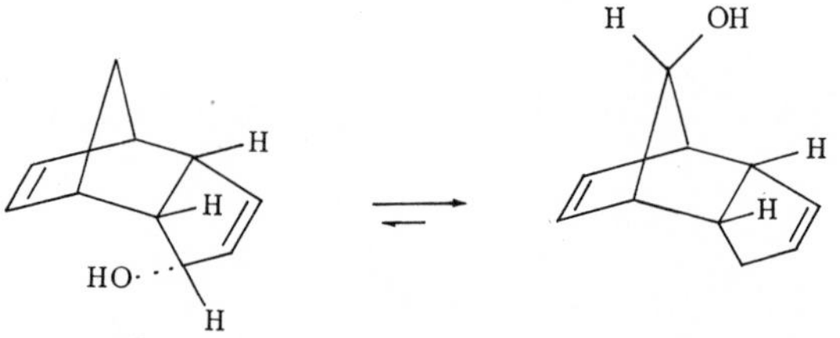

2   4

ANSWER 121.   [R. B. Woodward and T. J. Katz, *Tetrahedron*, **5**, 70 (1957).] The rearrangement cannot be explained by complete reversal of the Diels-Alder condensation to give cyclopentadiene and hydroxycyclopentadiene, followed by recombination to give the products. Under these conditions loss of optical activity and the formation of an equilibrated mixture of **3** and **4** would be expected. Instead, the two cyclopentene rings must remain joined by at least one bond in order to maintain the stereochemistry.

It has been proposed that the isomerizations occur by simultaneous cleavage of the bond ab in the dicyclopentadiene skeleton (A) and the formation of a new bond between atoms c and f.

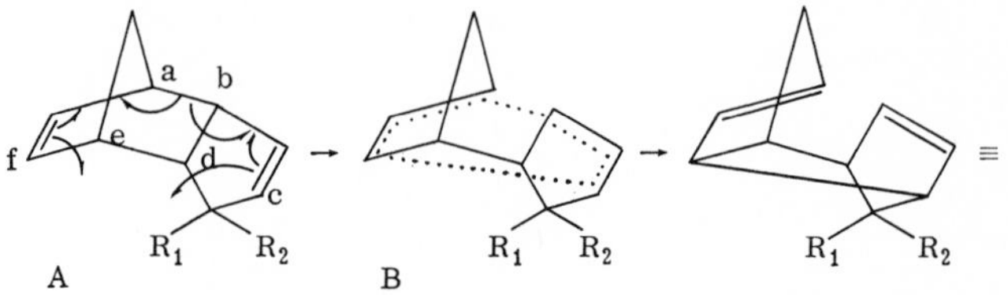

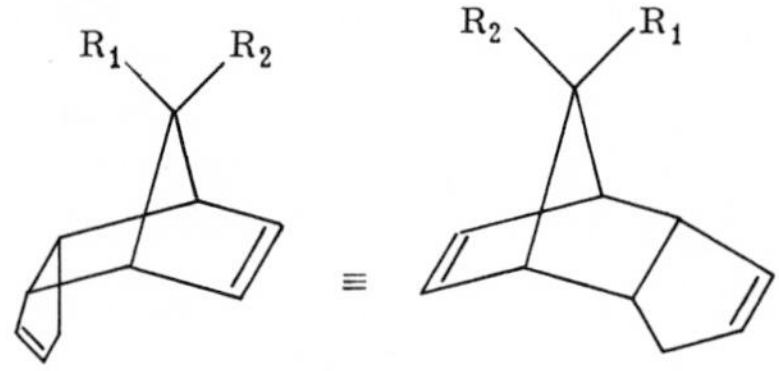

On this basis it has been suggested that the Diels-Alder reaction proceeds in two stages, first by the formation of the bond de, leading to an intermediate at least similar to B, and then by collapse of this intermediate to products.

It has been pointed out,[1] however, that this stereospecific rearrangement is formally equivalent to the Cope rearrangement,[2] and the transition state involved need not be that occurring in the Diels-Alder reaction. Indeed, other evidence[1,3] suggests that there is probably a whole range of possible transition states for various reactions, differing widely in the extent of bond formations.

PROBLEM 122.   Deduce structures for the following products:

(122.1)

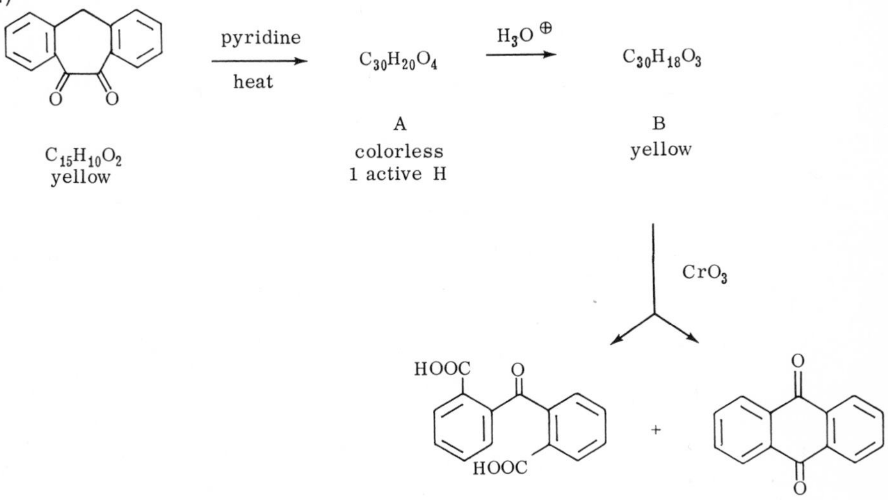

$$C_{15}H_{10}O_2 \text{ yellow} \xrightarrow[\text{heat}]{\text{pyridine}} C_{30}H_{20}O_4 \xrightarrow{H_3O^{\oplus}} C_{30}H_{18}O_3$$

A
colorless
1 active H

B
yellow

CrO₃ → HOOC ... + anthraquinone

(122.2)

$$(C_6H_5)_3C-CH_2\overset{O}{\overset{\|}{C}}OAg \xrightarrow[CCl_4]{Br_2} C_{21}H_{15}O_2Br$$

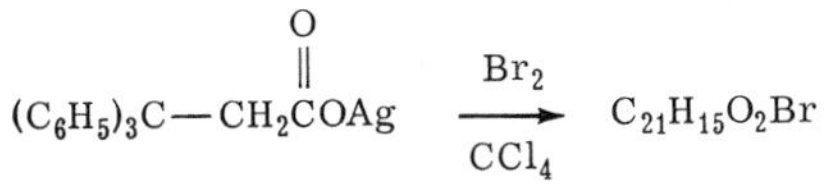

[1] J. A. Berson and A. Remanick, *J. Am. Chem. Soc.*, **83**, 4947 (1961).

[2] See S. J. Rhoads in *Molecular Rearrangements*, Vol. I (P. de Mayo, ed.), Wiley-Interscience, New York, 1963, pp. 684ff.

[3] S. Seltzer, *J. Am. Chem. Soc.*, **85**, 1360 (1963); M. J. Goldstein and G. L. Thayer, Jr., *J. Am. Chem. Soc.*, **87**, 1925, 1933 (1965).

ANSWER 122.
(122. 1)   [J. Rigaudy and L. Nedelec, *Bull. Soc. Chim. France,* **1959,** 643.]

The lack of color in A indicates that the α-diketone system is not present as such, and has led to the suggestion that the equilibrium favors the bridged structure A'.

(122.2)   [J. W. Wilt and D. D. Oathoudt, *J. Org. Chem.*, **23**, 218 (1958); J. W. Wilt and J. L. Finnerty, *J. Org. Chem.*, **26**, 2173 (1961).]

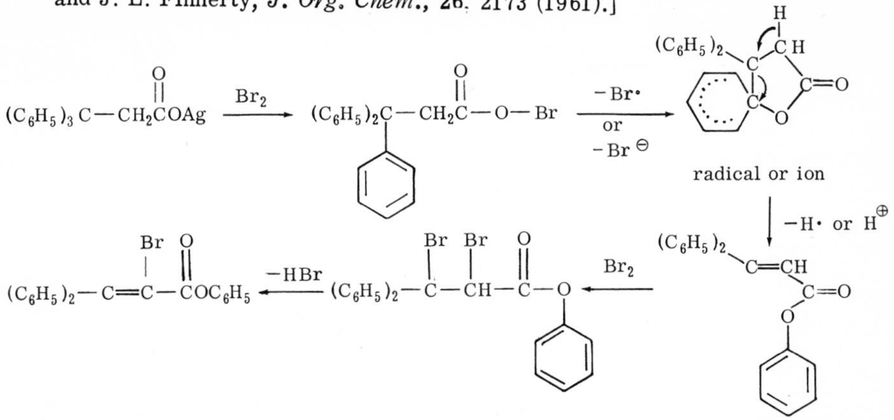

The normal reaction between Br_2 and the silver salt of an acid is the Huns-diecker reaction,[1] which replaces the —COOH by —Br. The mechanism may be radical or ionic (or both in different cases). The example shown involves an ab-normal variation. An analogous reaction is found in the Kolbe electrolysis[2] of the same acid and occurs[3] as follows:

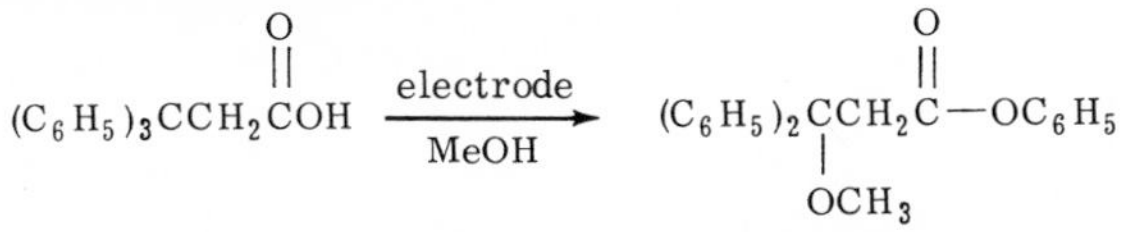

This reaction is ordinarily assumed to go by a radical path.

PROBLEM 123.   Deduce structures for the following reaction products and suggest a reasonable mechanism for the formation of **1**.

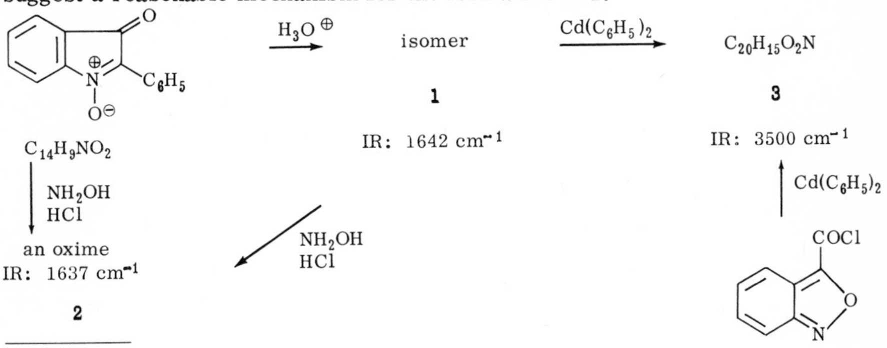

[1] R. G. Johnson and R. K. Ingham, *Chem. Rev.*, **56**, 219 (1956).
[2] M. J. Allen, *Organic Electrode Processes*, Chapman and Hall, London, 1958, pp. 95–115.
[3] E. C. Koogman and H. Breederweld, *Rec. Trav. Chim.*, **76**, 297 (1957).

ANSWER 123.   [J. L. Pinkus, T. Cohen, M. Sundaralingam, and G. A. Jeffrey, *Proc. Chem. Soc.,* 1960, 70.]

The structures of **1** and **3** can be deduced from the alternative synthesis from the acid chloride A. The formation of a tertiary alcohol by reaction with diphenylcadmium is unexpected, and can only be attributed to the use of a large excess of the organometallic reagent and perhaps too vigorous conditions. The original intent was to prepare **1** from A as an independent synthesis.

The structure of **1** was actually proved, however, by an X-ray crystallographic analysis before this chemical evidence was available.

That the oxime **2** has a structure corresponding to the rearranged isomer is suggested both by the improbability that **1** would revert to starting material under acid conditions and by the low frequency of the C═N bond, similar to the C═O frequency of **1**.

PROBLEM 124.   Deduce structures for the following reaction products:

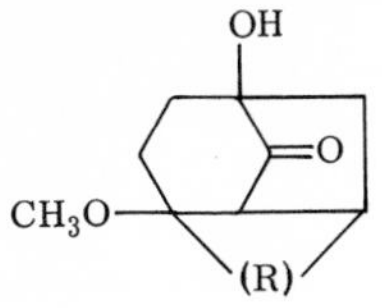

$$\xrightarrow{\text{OH}^{\ominus}} \quad C_9H_{12}O_3R \quad \xrightarrow[\text{(1 mole)}]{\text{HIO}_4} \quad C_8H_8O_3R$$

1   **2**   **3**

IR: 1754 cm^{-1}

UV: 250 mμ (10,000)
IR: 1730, 1695 cm^{-1}

$C_9H_{12}O_3R$

$\downarrow$ CrO$_3$

$C_9H_{12}O_4R$ $\xrightarrow{\text{CH}_2\text{N}_2}$ $C_{10}H_{14}O_4R$

(1) CH$_3$OH, CH$_3$ONa
(2) OH$^{\ominus}$, H$_2$O, then neutral

4   **5**

IR: 1736, 1706 cm^{-1}

ANSWER 124.   [K. Wiesner, F. Bickelhaput, D. R. Babin, and M. Gotz,
Tetrahedron, **9**, 254 (1960).]

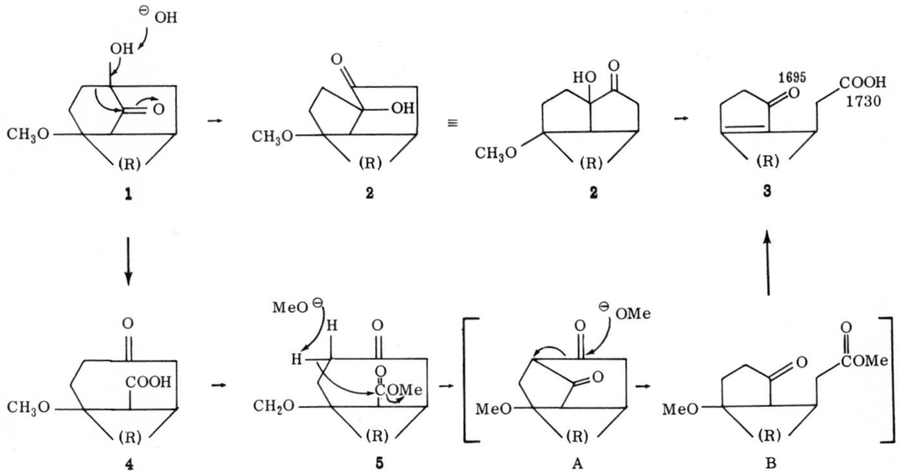

The UV spectrum of **3** indicates the presence of an $\alpha\beta$-unsaturated ketone. Although the wavelength is quite long for a conjugated cyclopentenone,[1] there are precedents. The IR band suggests a cyclopentenone rather than a cyclohexenone.[2]

The reaction sequence **4 → 5 → 3** involves a Dieckmann condensation to give the diketone A, which then reopens by a reverse Dieckmann reaction on the original keto group to give B. Apparently, the ether group of **5** cannot be eliminated, although β to the ester, because such an elimination would produce a strained-bridgehead double bond (Bredt's rule).[3] In B, however, a simple non-bridged system is present, and elimination occurs easily.

PROBLEM 125. Deduce structures and configurations for the products **3 → 5** and **7→10**:

---

[1] Cyclopentenones usually absorb at ca. 8 to 10 mμ shorter wavelengths than similarly substituted cyclohexenones. See H. S. French, *J. Am. Chem. Soc.,* **74,** 514 (1952).

[2] Nakanishi, p. 42.

[3] See F. S. Fawcett, *Chem. Rev.,* **47,** 219 (1950).

ANSWER 125.   [N. L. Wendler, *Tetrahedron,* **11**, 213 (1960); N. L. Wendler
and D. Taub, *J. Am. Chem. Soc.,* **82**, 2836 (1960).]

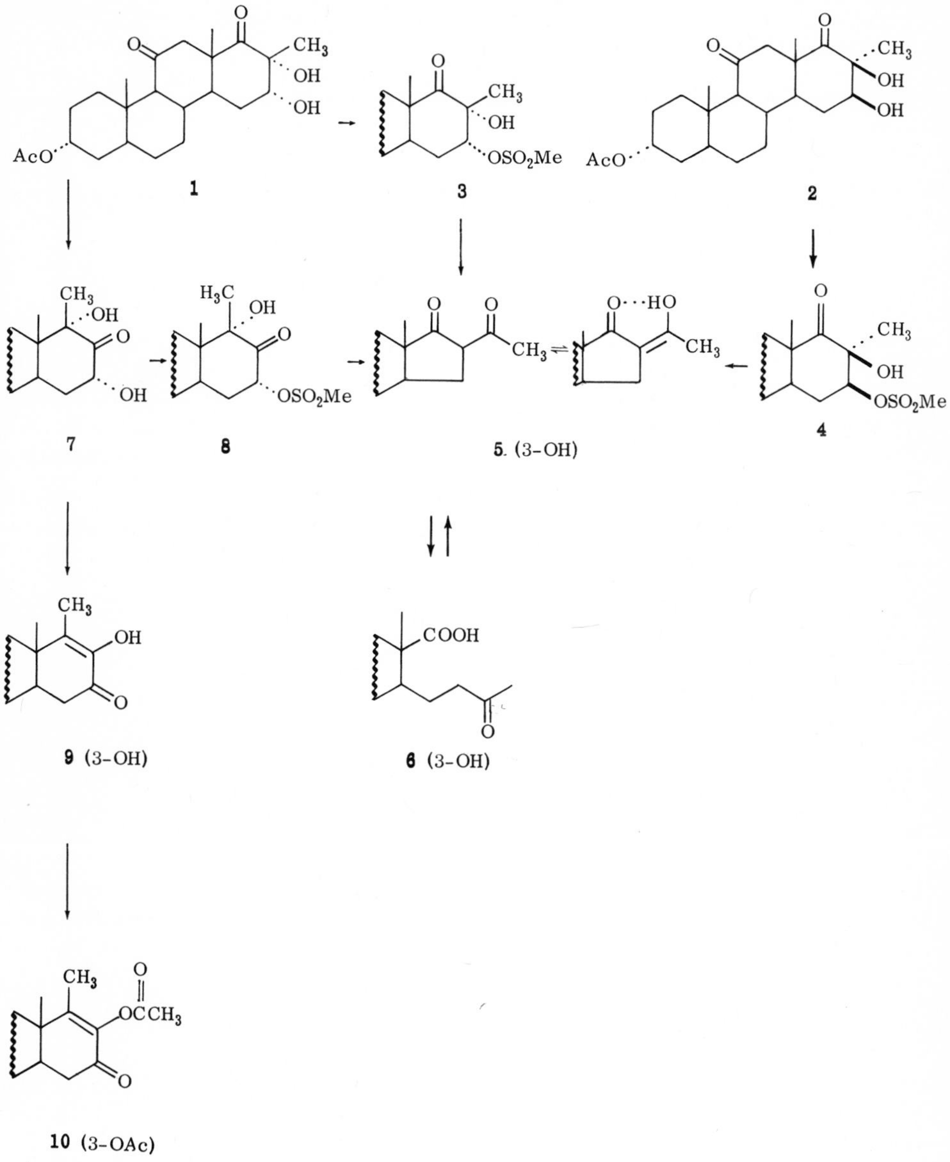

1

3

2

7

8

5. (3–OH)

4

9 (3–OH)

6 (3–OH)

10 (3–OAc)

The structure of **5** is suggested by its reversible relationship with **6**. The formation from the mesylates **3** and **4** may be visualized as

It is suggested that the formation of **5** from both **3** and **4** is evidence that **3** exists in the boat form whereas **4** is a chair, but the argument is not compelling.

The IR spectra of **3** and **4** can be interpreted as 3571, 3448 (OH), 1730 and 1250 (OAc), 1712 (C=O), and 1370 and 1176 cm^{-1} (RSO$_2$O—).

The transformation **1** → **7** may be interpreted most simply as a base-catalyzed methyl migration. Thus

which leads to the stereochemistry shown. There is no direct evidence for methyl migration, however, and in other cases similar rearrangements have been shown to involve shifts of ring bonds rather than methyls.[1]

The subsequent conversion of **7** → **9** is simply

leading to the diosphenol product.

The reaction of the mesylate **8** to the diketone **5** involves, at least formally, a methyl rearrangement which is the reverse of that in **1** → **7**. A reasonable, if unproved, intermediate along this path would be **3**, which then rearranges normally to give **5**.

It is suggested that the various back-and-forth migrations are driven by the tendency of the system to find products such as **9** and **5** which are converted in base to stable anions.

---

[1] R. B. Turner, M. Perelman, and K. T. Park, Jr., *J. Am. Chem. Soc.*, **79**, 1108 (1957).

CHAPTER 8

RADICAL AND PHOTOCHEMICAL REACTIONS

Radical reactions have tended to be neglected in most introductory courses in organic chemistry, and as a result, many students are relatively unfamiliar with them. Good discussions, however, are to be found in Gould and Hine.

Photochemistry has been developed largely in the last decade, and any attempt to discuss it generally is complicated by the disagreements among those most active in the field over the mechanisms actually involved in the observed reactions. The problems of describing photoexcited states in terms of structures which appear meaningful to most organic chemists are considerable; and it is often necessary to choose between simple descriptions which probably distort reality, and more complex ones which do not have much intuitive content.

Radical reactions:
(1) C. Walling, *Free Radicals in Solution*, Wiley, New York, 1957. The most comprehensive book on the subject. Particular attention is given to polymerization processes.
(2) G. Sosnovsky, *Free Radical Reactions in Preparative Organic Chemistry*, Macmillan, New York, 1964. Particular emphasis on the preparative aspects of free radicals. An excellent list of references for supplementary reading.
(3) W. A. Pryor, *Free Radicals*, McGraw-Hill, New York, 1966. An excellent introduction to the preparation, properties and reactions of free radicals. Problems with references.

Photochemical reactions:
(1) P. de Mayo in *Advances in Organic Chemistry*, Vol. 2, Wiley-Interscience, New York, 1960, pp. 367-425. A general introduction to the photochemistry of simple systems.
(2) P. de Mayo and S. T. Reid, *Quart. Rev.*, **15**, 393 (1961). Photorearrangement reactions.

(3) O. L. Chapman in *Advances in Photochemistry,* Vol. 1, Wiley-Interscience, New York, 1963, pp. 323-420. More on photorearrangements. Other, more specialized topics are also covered in the several volumes of this series.

(4) H. E. Zimmerman and D. I. Schuster, *J. Am. Chem. Soc.,* **84**, 4527 (1962); for more recent references see H. E. Zimmerman and J. W. Wilson, *J. Am. Chem. Soc.,* **86**, 4036 (1964).

(5) G. S. Hammond, J. Saltiel, A. A. Lamola, N. J. Turro, J. S. Bradshaw, D. O. Cowan, R. C. Counsell, V. Vogt, and C. Dalton, *J. Am. Chem. Soc.,* **86**, 3197 (1964).

(6) N. J. Turro, *Molecular Photochemistry*, Benjamin, New York, 1965. A gen eral introduction to the theory and results of organic photochemistry.

(7) R. O. Kan, *Organic Photochemistry*, McGraw-Hill, New York, 1966. Less theoretical than the preceding work, it is more concerned with the practical aspects of photochemical transformations.

(8) J. G. Calvert and J. N. Pitts, Jr., *Photochemistry*, Wiley, New York, 1966. An extensive and excellent survey covering physical theory, organic appli- cations, and experimental methods.

PROBLEM 126.   Deduce the labeling of the reaction product:

$$* = C^{14}$$

ANSWER 126.   [For an extensive review of N-bromosuccinimide chemistry, see L. Horner and E. H. Wenkelmann, *Angew. Chem.,* **71**, 349 (1959).

Usually NBS reacts with an olefin by a radical-chain mechanism to give an allylic bromide. For a long time this chain was thought to involve the succini- mide radical as a carrier, but recent work indicates that the NBS reacts with HBr to provide a steady low concentration of Br_2, which is the true brominat- ing agent.[1]

---

[1] See H. O. House, *Modern Synthetic Reactions,* Benjamin, New York, 1965, pp. 159–161.

In the present case, the symmetry of the molecule causes a number of positions to become equivalent, provided the radical intermediate is really "free" and that its formation and halogenation are independent.

If all four products are equally probable, the distribution of the label in the final product will be

Note that this represents an average over a very large number of molecules, most of which are unlabeled (the actual C^{14} concentration is very low) and almost none of which contain more than one radiocarbon.

The double labeling in the starting cyclohexene arises because it is not possible to distinguish the two carbon atoms at the ends of a symmetric double bond. Thus

PROBLEM 127.   Suggest mechanisms for the following reactions:

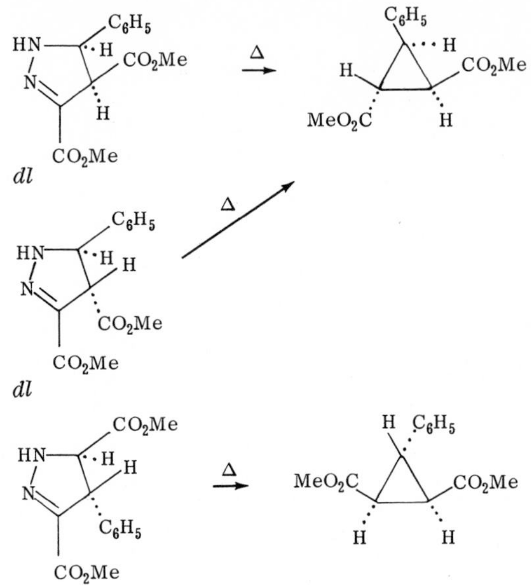

ANSWER 127.   [W. M. Jones, *J. Am. Chem. Soc.*, 80, 6687 (1958); **81**, 5153 (1959).]

The general mechanism for this reaction has been suggested to be

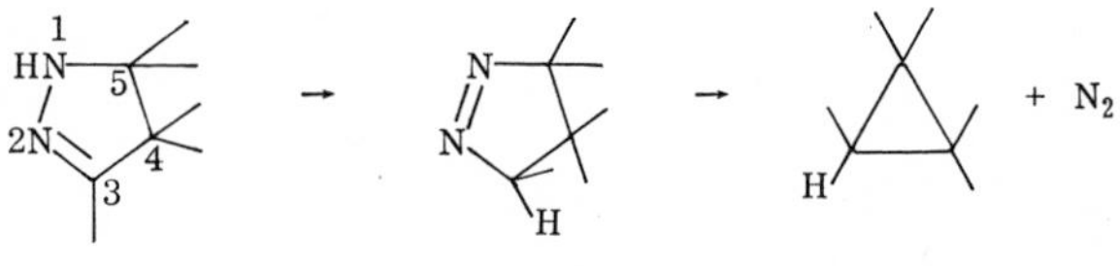

in which the first step is the slow[1] conversion of a 2-pyrazoline into a 1-pyrazoline, and the second is the rapid, stereospecific extrusion of N_2 and the formation of the cyclopropane. It has also been suggested that the preliminary tautomerism yields the more stable 1-pyrazoline, i.e., the one in which the 3 and 4 substituents are trans. The arrangement so achieved is preserved in the final cyclopropane.

---

[1] W. M. Jones, *J. Am. Chem. Soc.*, **82**, 3136 (1960).

Thus

PROBLEM 128.   Suggest a mechanism for the following transformation:

ANSWER 128.   [G. A. Schmidt and G. S. Fisher, *J. Am. Chem. Soc.*, **76**, 5426 (1954).]

The following mechanism has been suggested.

pinane hydroperoxide   + HO·

The yield of the ketone is increased by the presence of pinane to serve as a source of H atoms.

PROBLEM 129.   Suggest an explanation for the effects of sodium acetate and sulfuric acid on the following reaction:

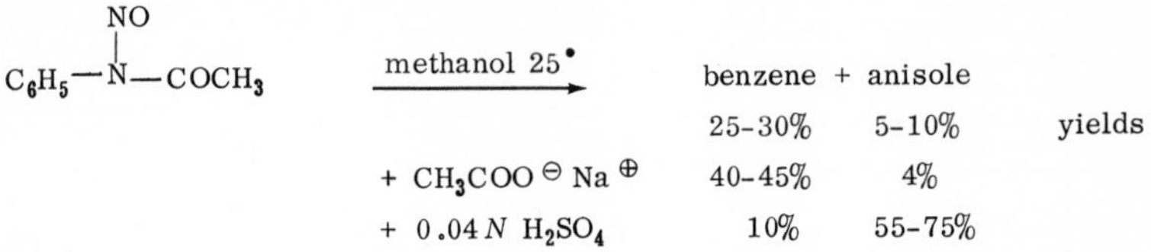

$$C_6H_5-\overset{\overset{NO}{|}}{N}-COCH_3 \xrightarrow{\text{methanol } 25°}$$

	benzene	+ anisole	
	25-30%	5-10%	yields
+ CH$_3$COO$^{\ominus}$ Na$^{\oplus}$	40-45%	4%	
+ 0.04N H$_2$SO$_4$	10%	55-75%	

ANSWER 129.   [D. F. DeTar, *J. Am. Chem. Soc.,* **73**, 1446 (1951).]

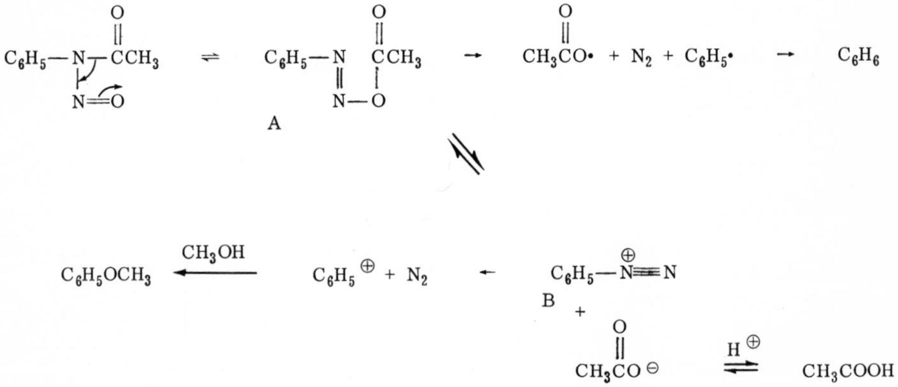

The initial rearrangement of the N-nitrosoacetanilide to the diazoacetate A is the slow step in the reaction.[1,2] It is proposed that A can decompose to give phenyl radicals which abstract hydrogen from the solvent and give benzene. A also exists in equilibrium with the ionized diazonium salt B, however, and this decomposes more slowly to give phenyl carbonium ions which react with solvent to form anisole. Addition of acid to the medium shifts the equilibrium toward B by removing the acetate ion also formed, and thus increases the yield of anisole at the expense of benzene. Added acetate, on the other hand, increases the concentration of A and has the opposite effect.

---

[1] R. Huisgen and G. Harold, *Ann.,* 562, 137 (1949).
[2] D. H. Hey, J. Stuart-Webb, and G. H. Williams, *J. Chem. Soc.,* **1952**, 4657.

PROBLEM 130.   Suggest routes for the following reactions:

(130.1)

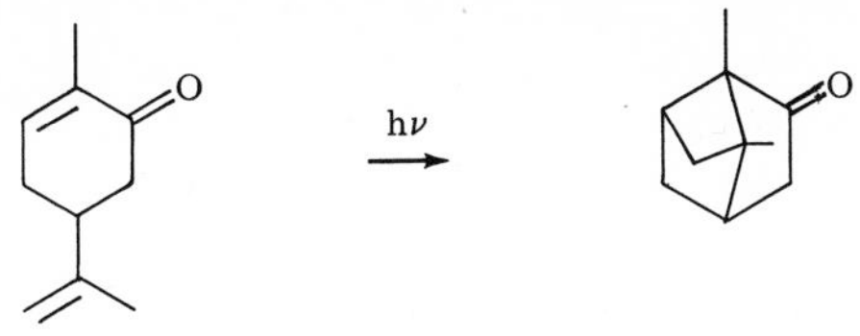

(130.2)

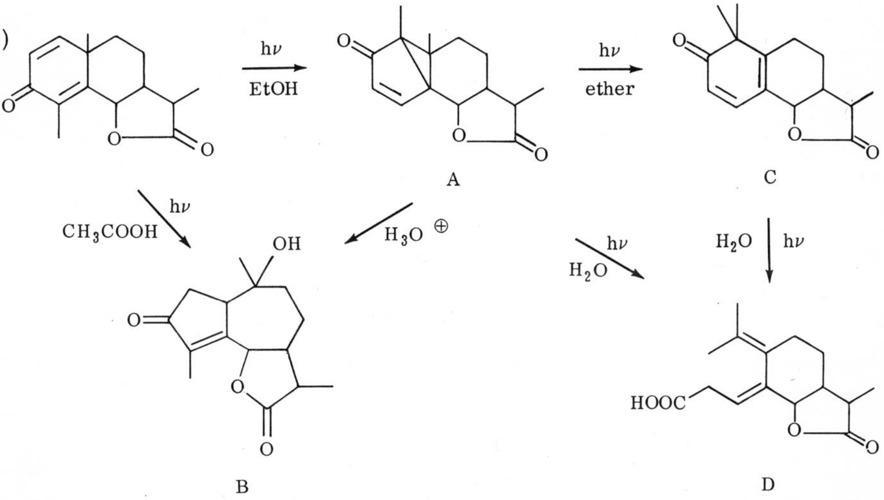

ANSWER 130.

(130.1)   [G. Büchi and I. M. Goldman, *J. Am. Chem. Soc.*, **79**, 4741 (1957).]

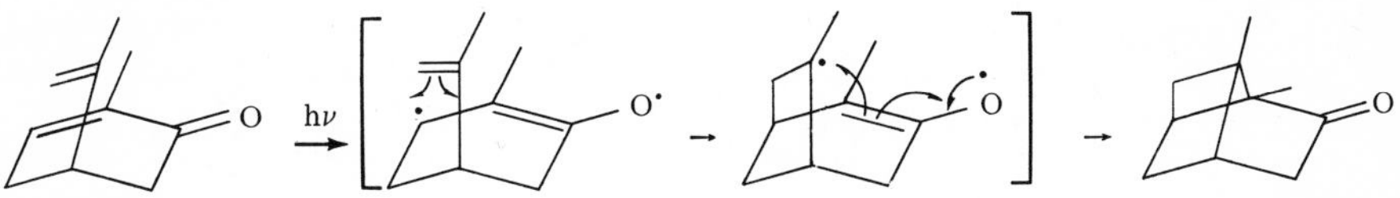

The reaction is shown formally as a radical one, using single-barbed arrows[1] to indicate one electron shifts.

---

[1] H. Budzikiewicz, C. Djerassi, and D. H. Williams, *Interpretation of Mass Spectra of Organic Compounds*, Holden-Day, San Francisco, 1964, Introduction.

(130.2)   [D. H. R. Barton, P. de Mayo, and M. Shafiq, *J. Chem. Soc.*, 1958, 140; O. L. Chapman and L. F. Englert, *J. Am. Chem. Soc.*, **85**, 3028 (1963).]

This reaction is described above in terms of separated charges, because of the resemblance of the steps to more conventional carbonium rearrangements.[1] It is probable, however, that these ions, if present, arise from radical-like precursors formed by the primary photochemical excitation.[2]

Various mechanisms have been proposed for the photorearrangement of santonin and similar 1,4-cyclohexadienones. In particular the direct 1,3-migration of a bond is attractive, but is ruled out here since it would lead to a cyclopropane *trans* fused to the B ring.[2] Other studies[3] have shown that even where this restriction does not hold, the "slither" mechanism of two 1,2-shifts is preferred over the 1,3-shift.

Additional support for the intermediacy of **1** is given by the fact that while lumisantonin (A) goes to isophotosantonic lactone (B) on acid treatment, *irradiation* of santonin under mildly acidic conditions which do not cause the transformation also produces B. Thus an intermediate (**1**) which can be directly converted to B is favored.

---

[1] D. H. R. Barton, R. de Mayo, and M. Shafiq, *J. Chem. Soc.*, **1960**, 1.

[2] H. E. Zimmerman and D. I. Schuster, *J. Am. Chem. Soc.*, **84**, 4527 (1962).

[3] H. E. Zimmerman and D. S. Crumrine, *ibid*, **90**, 5612 (1968); T. M. Brennan and R. K. Hill, *ibid*, **90**, 5614 (1968).

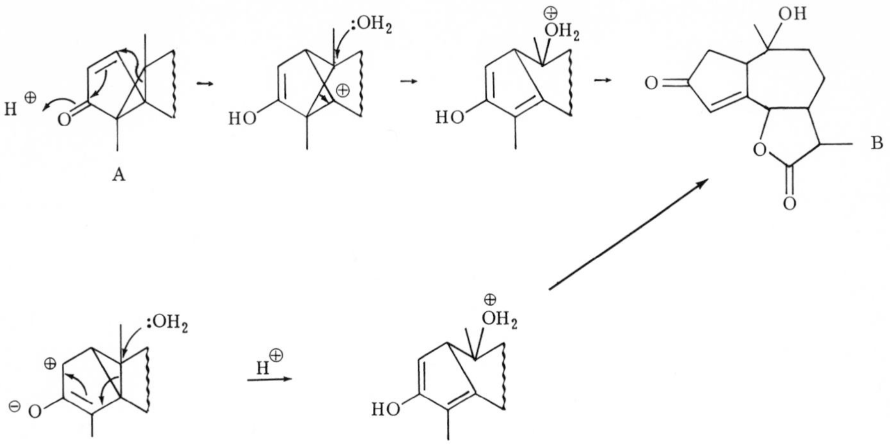

Photoisomerization of lumisantonin in ether leads to C, which is in photo-induced equilibrium with the ketene **2**.[2] In the absence of water C is favored, but in its presence reaction leading to D occurs.

PROBLEM 131.   Suggest mechanisms for the following reactions:

(131.1)

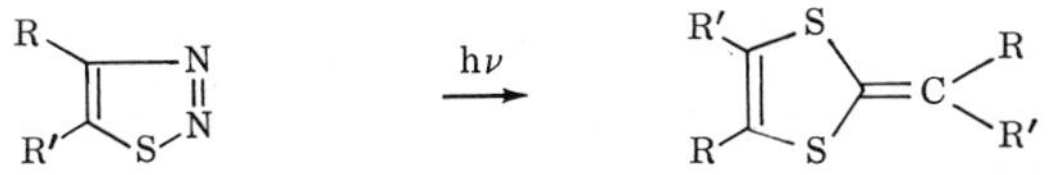

(131.2)

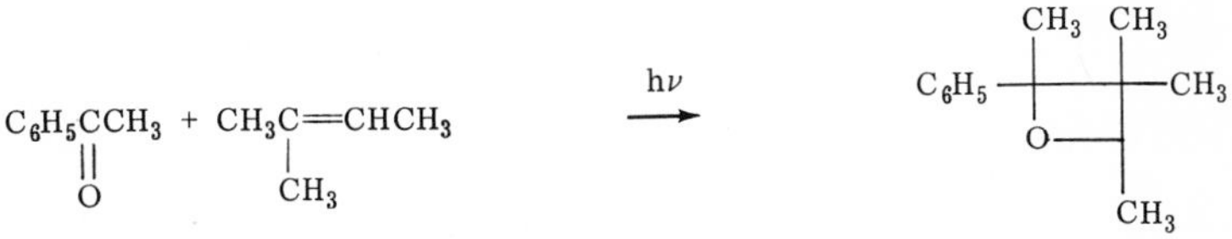

_____

[2] But for evidence of the inaccuracy of this representation see H. E. Zimmerman, R. C. Hahn, H. Morrison, and M. C. Wani, *J. Am. Chem. Soc.*, **87**, 1138 (1965).

ANSWER 131.

(131.1)   [W. Kirmse and L. Harner, *Ann.*, **614**, 4 (1958); W. Kirmse, *Angew. Chem.*, **71**, 537 (1959).]

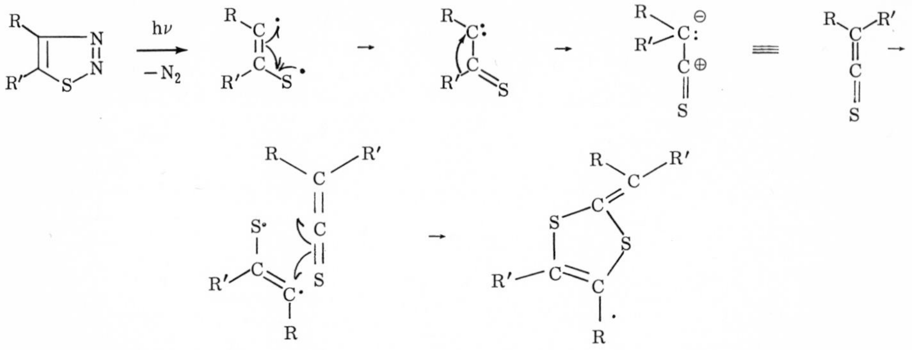

The starting 1,2,3-thiodiazole is formally equivalent to a diazoketone, and the first part of the reaction is the same as the photocatalyzed Wolff rearrangement.[1]

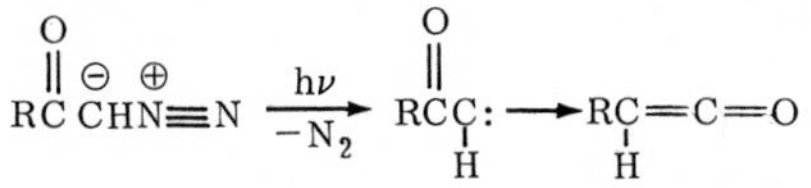

(131.2)   [G. Büchi, G. G. Inman, and E. S. Lapinsky, *J. Am. Chem. Soc.*, **76**, 4327 (1954).]

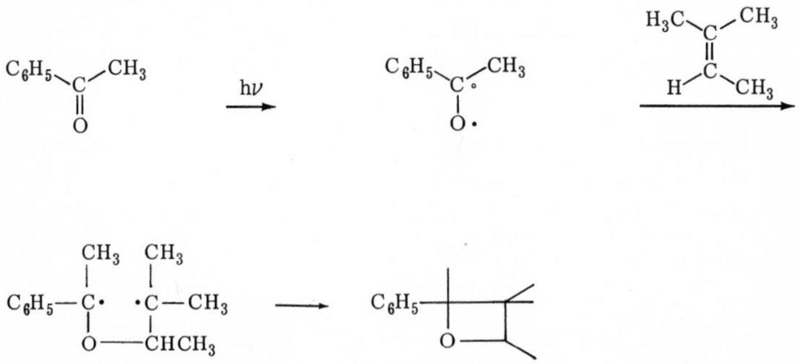

1

---

[1] W. Kirmse and L. Harner, op. cit.

The observed products correspond to the formation of the most stable intermediate **1** by the addition of the photoexcited triplet (diradical) state of acetophenone
to the alkene.

PROBLEM 132. Predict the products:

(132.1)

           $h\nu$ →

(132.2)

           $h\nu$ →

(132.3)

     +   EtOCN₃ $h\nu$ →

(132.4)

     OAc $h\nu$ →
     OAc

ANSWER 132.

(132.1)   [F. E. Blacet and A. Miller, *J. Am. Chem. Soc.*, **79**, 4327 (1957); R. Srinivasan, *J. Am. Chem. Soc.*, **81**, 1546, 2601, 2604 (1959).]
This reaction gives a number of products, among which the major ones are

                                               CO

(132.2)   [S. Cremer and R. Srinivasan, *Tetrahedron Letters*, **21**, 24 (1960).]
     The major products were CO and 1,5-hexadiene (**1**), but a small amount
(5%) of the desired bicyclo[2,2,0]-hexane (**2**) was formed.

                1   **2**

(132.3)   [K. Hafner and C. Konig, *Angew. Chem.*, **75**, 89 (1963); W. Lwowski, T. J. Maricich, and T. W. Mattingly, Jr., *J. Am. Chem. Soc.*, **85**, 1200 (1963).]

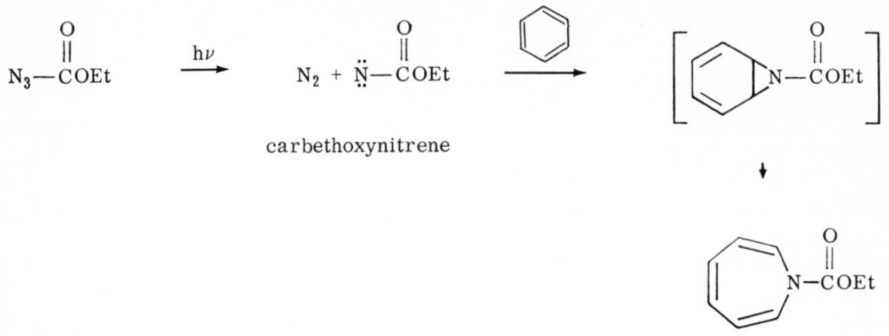

carbethoxynitrene

(132.4)   [D. H. R. Barton, *Helv. Chim. Acta,* **42**, 2604 (1959).]

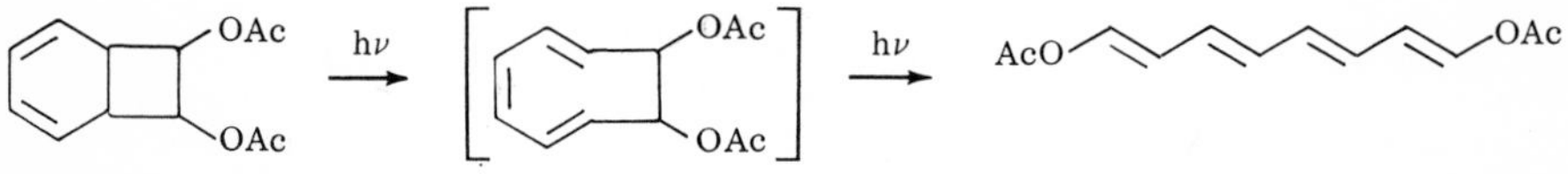

PROBLEM 133.   The photolysis of suitably substituted organic nitrites brings about an intramolecular exchange of the nitroso group and a hydrogen attached to a δ-carbon atom. This reaction provides a route to the selective introduction of an oxygen function at the nonactivated carbon atom.

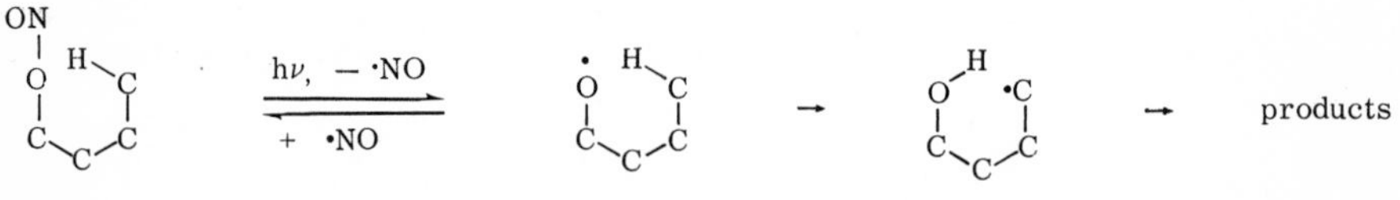

(133.1)   The photolysis of the nitrite of n-octanol, followed by heating, gave an oxime. Write the structure of the oxime.

$$CH_3(CH_2)_6CH_2ONO \xrightarrow[\text{(2) heat}]{\text{(1) } h\nu \text{ in hexane}} \text{oxime}$$

(cont.)

(**133.2**) The photolysis of the nitrite (**1**) gave three oximes, (**2**), (**3**), and (**4**); of these the oxime (**2**), on treatment with sodium nitrite-acetic acid, afforded (**5**). Give the structure of (**2**), and then explain the formation of (**3**), (**4**), and (**5**).

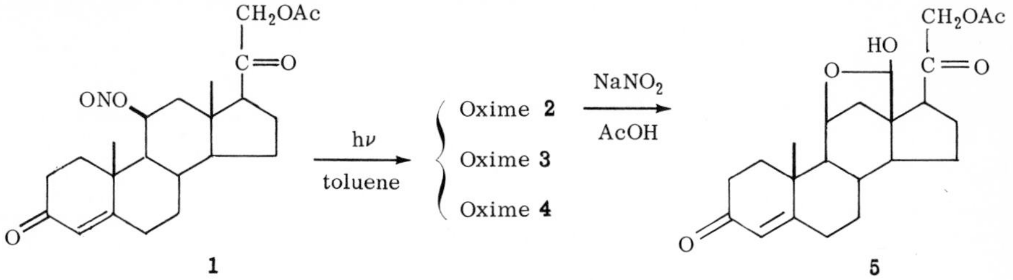

1 **5**

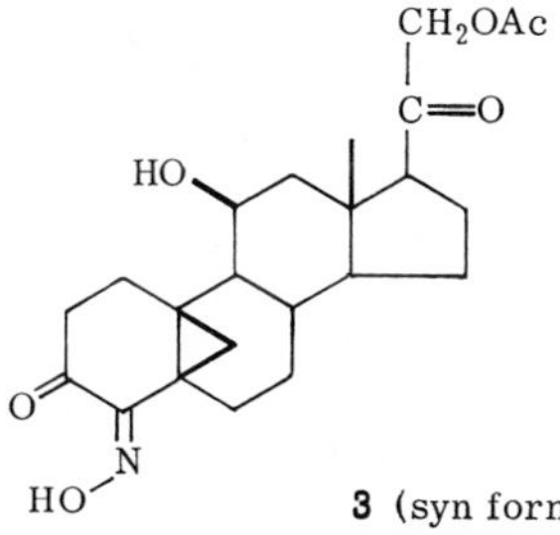

3 (syn form)

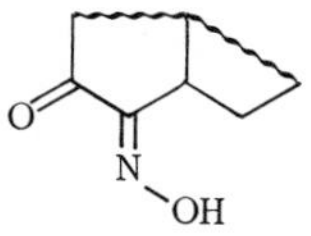

4 (anti form)

(**133.3**) In some cases, the intermediate produced by photolysis of the nitrite takes a different reaction course. Shown below are two such cases. Explain these results.

(a)

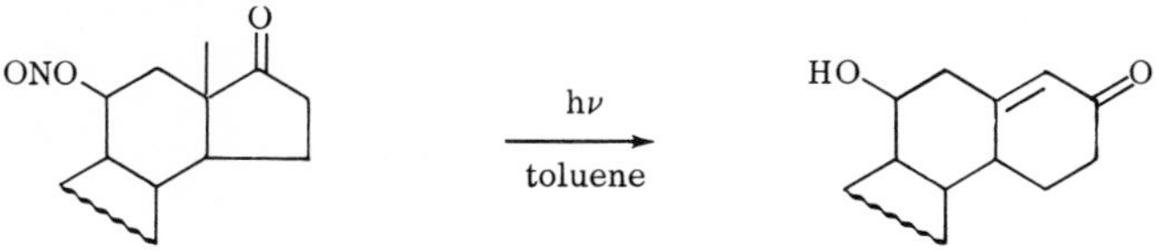

(b)

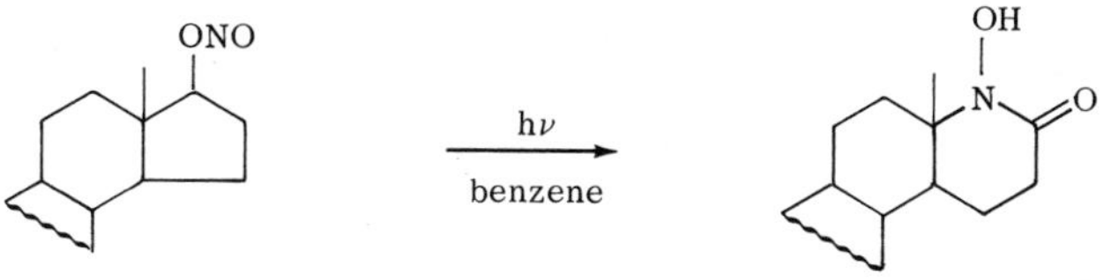

ANSWER 133.   [For a general review, see A. L. Nussbaum and C. H. Robinson, *Tetrahedron*, **17**, 35 (1962); for studies on the mechanism, see M. Akhtar and M. M. Pechet, *J. Am. Chem. Soc.*, **86**, 265 (1964).]

(133.1)   [P. Kabasakalian and E. R. Townley, *J. Am. Chem. Soc.*, **84**, 2711 (1962).]

The dimeric product, characteristic of primary and secondary nitroso compounds, can be isolated from the photolysis mixture, but rearranges on standing or heating to the isomeric oxime.

(133.2)   [D. H. R. Barton and J. M. Beaton, *J. Am. Chem. Soc.*, **82**, 2641 (1960); **83**, 4083 (1961).]

The use of this photolytic reaction allowed a remarkable four-step synthesis of the important hormone aldosterone (as the acetate) in 15% yield from the readily available corticosterone acetate. The importance of this result can be judged from the fact that the natural supplies were so limited that the structure analysis of aldosterone had to be carried out on only 56 mg.[1]

3) (a) [H. Reimann, A. S. Capomaggi, T. Strauss, E. P. Oliveto, and D. H. R. Barton, *J. Am. Chem. Soc.*, **83**, 4481 (1961).]

The rearrangement (A → B → C) is written in steps, but could just as well be concerted (A → C). Presumably, the rearrangement occurs because the ability of the carbonyl group to stabilize a lone electron (as in B) provides an energetically reasonable path to a product in which the strain present in the steroid ring system is relieved.

(b) [C. H. Robinson, O. Gnoj, A. Mitchell, R. Wayne, E. Townley, P. Kabasakalian, E. P. Oliveto, and D. H. R. Barton, *J. Am. Chem. Soc.*, **83**, 1771 (1961).]

---

[1] L. F. Fieser and M. Fieser, *Steroids*, Reinhold, New York, 1959, pp. 703ff.

The above mechanism has been advanced to account for the formation of the hydroxamic acid. In some cases, two isomers, presumably differing in the configuration of the C_{13} methyl group, have been isolated.

No general theory has been presented, however, to predict which of the various possible reaction paths will be followed in a specific case.

PROBLEM 134.   Deduce the structure of the isomer.

NMR of the isomer (τ, CCl_4, s = singlet, d = doublet, t = triplet) 8.94(6H) s, 8.3 ~ 8.7(6H) broad, 7.96(3H)s, 6.84(2H)d (J = 7.1cps), 5.49(1H)d (J = 2.6), 5.04(1H)d (J = 2.6), 4.67(1H)t (J = 7.1).

ANSWER 134.   [P. de Mayo, J. B. Stothers, and R. W. Yip, *Can. J. Chem.*, **39**, 2135 (1961).]

The NMR spectrum suggests the presence of the following groups.[1]

$$\tau = 8.94 \ldots$$

$$8.3 \sim 8.7 \ldots -(CH_2)_3-$$

$$7.96 \ldots CH_3-C= \quad \text{or} \quad CH_3C-$$
$$\qquad\qquad\qquad\qquad\qquad\qquad \underset{O}{\overset{\|}{}}$$

$$4.67 \ldots H-C=, \quad 6.84 \ldots -CH_2-\underset{\underset{O}{\|}}{C}-, \quad -CH_2C=C$$

$$5.49, 5.04 \ldots \overset{H}{\underset{H}{>}}C=C \quad \text{or} \quad -HC-CH= \quad \text{(the small coupling constant, J,}$$
$$\qquad\qquad\qquad\qquad\qquad\qquad\qquad\quad \underset{O-}{|} \qquad \text{favors the former structure)}$$

The structure (A) having a cyclopropane ring had been proposed for the isomer,[2] but the NMR evidence favors a dienone structure (B).

---

[1] See Jackman, Chap. 4.
[2] G. Büchi and N. C. Yang, *J. Am. Chem. Soc.*, **79**, 2318 (1957).

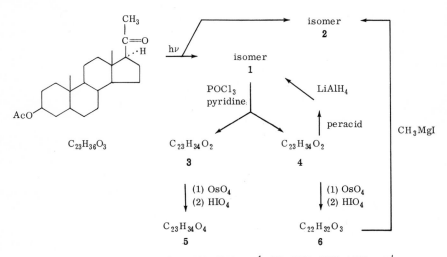

The hydrogen transfer shown here appears to be a general phenomenon in systems having this geometry. Thus

PROBLEM 135.   Deduce structures for the following reaction products:

IR: 2760, 1728, 1709, 1256 cm^{-1} IR: 1778, 1735, 1245 cm^{-1}
has reducing properties

(*cont.*)

Along with **1** and **2**, the following is also formed in the photochemical reaction.

AcO

ANSWER 135.   [P. Buchschacher, M. Cereghetti, H. Wehrli, K. Shaffner, and
O. Jeger, *Helv. Chim. Acta,* **42**, 2122 (1959); M. Cereghetti, H.
Wehrli, K. Schaffner, and O. Jeger, *Helv. Chim. Acta,* **43**, 354
(1960).]

The reducing properties of **5**, coupled with the IR data[1] (2760, 1709 cm^{-1}) suggest the presence of a $-$CHO group, and the sequence

$$-CH\!\!=\!\!C- \quad \rightarrow \quad -CHO \quad O\!\!=\!\!C-$$

for **3** $\rightarrow$ **5**. The analogous reactions leading to loss of the elements of formaldehyde in **4** $\rightarrow$ **6** allow expansion to

$$\underset{-CH_2-C-}{\overset{\overset{\displaystyle CH_2}{\|}}{}}$$

for **4** and suggest

$$\underset{\underset{OH}{|}}{\overset{\overset{\displaystyle CH_3}{|}}{-CH_2-C-}}$$

for **1**.

Since the empirical formula requires a pentacyclic system in **1**, **3**, and **4**, consideration of the structure of the starting material leads to the two possible isomeric structures.

The stereochemistry of **1** and **2** follows from the addition reactions of their unsaturated derivatives **4** and **6**. These may be represented

R = CH$_2$ or O

and it would be expected that addition would occur more easily from the relatively unhindered back (α) side than from the front over the cyclopentane ring. Thus

6 $\xrightarrow{\text{CH}_3\text{MgI}}$ **2**

4 $\xrightarrow{\text{peracid}}$ $\xrightarrow{\text{LiAlH}_4}$ **1**

---

[1] Nakanishi, p. 42.

both results being consistent with the suggestion.

The mechanism proposed, although subject to the usual reservations about representation of reactions in electronically excited states, is

An alternative path, leading to the side product, is

Many analogies are known for the last step in this sequence, both in irradiation[2] and in mass spectral studies.[3] Likewise it has been found that other irradiated ketones can attack methylene groups, both intramolecularly[4,5] and intermolecularly.[4]

PROBLEM 136.   Deduce the structures of the products A and B and suggest a consistent mechanism for their formation (see Table 8-1).

Table 8-1
Spectral Data

	A	B
IR:	1689 cm^{-1}	1700 cm^{-1}
UV:	226 mμ (6400)	223 mμ (9700)
NMR:	τ 8.60 (3H, s)	τ 7.94 (3H, s)
	6.95 (1H)	6.68 (1H)
	6.45 (3H, s)	6.42 (1H)
	5.07 (1H)	6.33 (3H, s)
	4.34 (1H, d = 6.0 cps)	4.91 (1H)
	2.55 (1H, d = 6.0 cps)	4.25 (1H)

---

[2] See T. W. Martin, Jr., and J. N. Pitts, Jr., *J. Am. Chem. Soc.,* **77**, 5465 (1955) and references cited there.

[3] See K. Biemann, *Mass Spectrometry,* McGraw-Hill, New York, 1962, pp. 119ff.

[4] N. C. Yang and D.-D. H. Yang, *J. Am. Chem. Soc.,* **80**, 2913 (1958).

[5] M. Bernard and N. C. Yang, *Proc. Chem. Soc.,* **1958**, 302.

$$C_9H_{10}O_2 \xrightarrow[\text{MeOH}]{h\nu} \text{A} \quad C_9H_{10}O_2 \xrightarrow[\text{or } H_3O^{\oplus}]{h\nu, H_2O}$$

↓ 420°

$$C_9H_{10}O_2 \xrightarrow[\text{MeOH}]{h\nu} \text{B} \quad C_9H_{10}O_2 \xrightarrow[\text{or } H_3O^{\oplus}]{h\nu, H_2O}$$

ANSWER 136. [W. G. Dauben, K. Koch, O. L. Chapman, and S. L. Smith, *J. Am. Chem. Soc.*, **83**, 1768 (1961); *J. Am. Chem. Soc.*, **85**, 2616 (1963).]

A   B

The structures of A and B are suggested by their hydrolysis products and can be deduced by an analysis of the NMR spectra. The thermal rearrangement of A to the corresponding tropone is common for these compounds.

The formation of these products involves a deep-seated photoisomerization for which the following mechanism has been proposed:

where the intermediates within the brackets represent photoexcited states. In accord with this mechanism, it has been found that

as would be predicted.

The UV spectra of these compounds also reflect the $\pi - \pi$ interaction which
is required for the rearrangement and which presumably arises from the geometry of the ring system. Both products absorb at wavelengths which are long for
cyclopentenones, probably because of extended conjugation in the excited states.

The final step in the sequences is hydration of the enol ether (light- or acid-
catalyzed), followed by a reverse aldol or reverse Claisen cleavage.

CHAPTER **9**

OXIDATION-REDUCTION REACTIONS

1. H. O. House, *Modern Synthetic Reactions,* Benjamin, New York, 1965, pp. 1-133. An excellent survey of practical oxidation and reduction reactions of all kinds.
2. R. Stewart, *Oxidation Mechanisms: Applications to Organic Chemistry,* Benjamin, New York, 1964. An introduction to the extremely complex field of oxidation mechanisms.
3. N. G. Gaylord, *Reduction with Complex Metal Hydrides,* Wiley-Interscience, New York, 1956. An exhaustive survey of early metal hydride reductions; it lacks some of the more recent developments (see Ref. 1).
4. V. M. Micovic and M. L. Mihailovic, *Lithium Aluminum Hydride in Organic Chemistry,* Serbian Academy of Sciences, Belgrade, 1955. A smaller but extremely good survey.
5. P. S. Bailey, *Chem. Rev.,* **58**, 925 (1958). A review on ozonolysis.
6. K. T. Potts in *Elucidation of Structures by Physical and Chemical Methods,* Part Two (K. W. Bentley, ed.), Wiley-Interscience, New York, 1963, pp. 823-873; K. W. Bentley, ibid., pp. 875-906. Surveys of oxidative methods for cleavage of single and double carbon-carbon bonds.

PROBLEM 137. Arrange the following cholestanols in order of decreasing ease of oxidation by chromic acid.

(cont.)

1   2   3

4   5

ANSWER 137.   [L. F. Fieser and M. Fieser, *Steroids*, Reinhold, New York, 1959, p. 218.]

Rates of oxidation **5** > **4** > **2** > **1** > **3**. The rate-determining step in chromate oxidations involves breaking the C — H bond α to the — OH being oxidized.[1] During this process the hydroxyl moves from its original position toward that occupied by the carbonyl oxygen in the product. This motion can reduce the steric interactions between axial alcohols and neighboring axial groups. The relief of strain which occurs makes the transition state relatively more stable with respect to the starting material and increases the rate of the reaction. As a first approximation, the greater the original strain, as measured in terms of the number of 1:3 interactions, the greater the "steric acceleration" of the process. This is demonstrated by the examples given in Table 9-1.

Table 9-1

Compound	1:3 interactions OH (ax)-CH$_3$ (ax)	1:3 interactions OH (ax)-H (ax)	Relative rates of oxidation by Cr^{VI}
5 (11β-OH)	2	1	60
4 (4β-OH)	1	2	35
2 (2β-OH)	1	1	20
1 (1α-OH)	0	3	13
3 (3α-OH)	0	2	3

[1]See R. Stewart, *Oxidation Mechanisms: Applications to Organic Chemistry*, Benjamin, New York, 1964, Chap. IV.

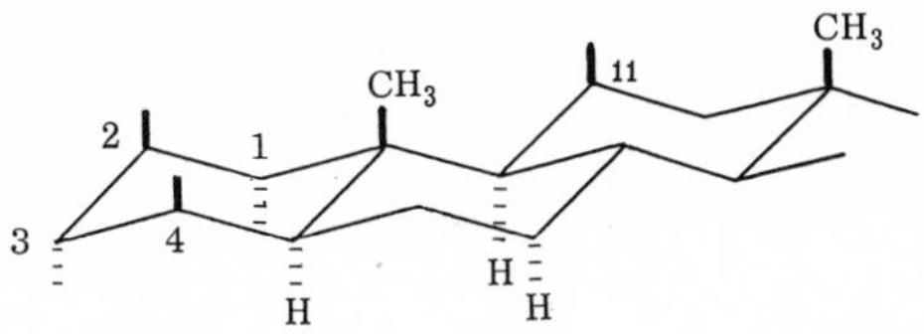

PROBLEM 138.   Suggest mechanisms for the following oxidation reactions:

(138.1)

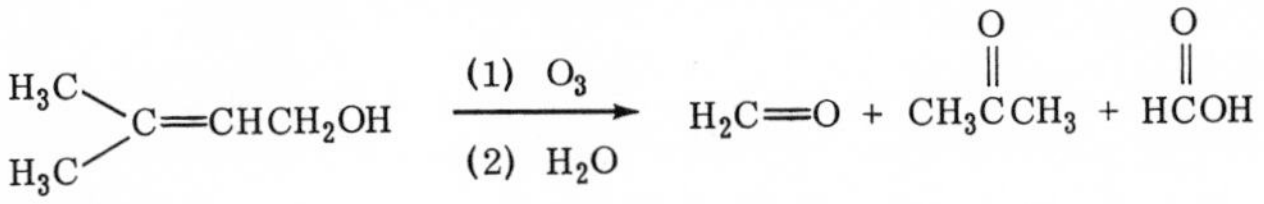

$$\underset{H_3C}{\overset{H_3C}{>}}C=CHCH_2OH \xrightarrow[\text{(2) } H_2O]{\text{(1) } O_3} H_2C=O + CH_3\overset{O}{\overset{\|}{C}}CH_3 + H\overset{O}{\overset{\|}{C}}OH$$

(138.2)

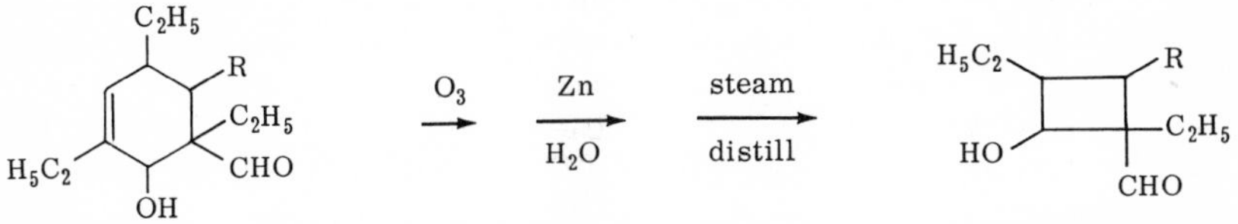

ANSWER 138.   [For an extensive review of ozonolytic reactions, see P.S. Bailey, *Chem. Rev.*, **58**, 925 (1958).]

(138. 1) [Bailey, op. cit., pp. 947ff.]
    It has been suggested that the abnormal products which sometimes appear in the ozonolysis of compounds having the part structure A arise by rearrangement.[1]

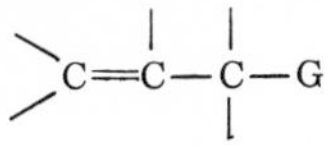

$$\underset{/}{\overset{\diagdown}{>}}C=C-\overset{|}{\underset{|}{C}}-G \qquad \text{(G = oxygen, nitrogen, sulfur)}$$

A

Thus

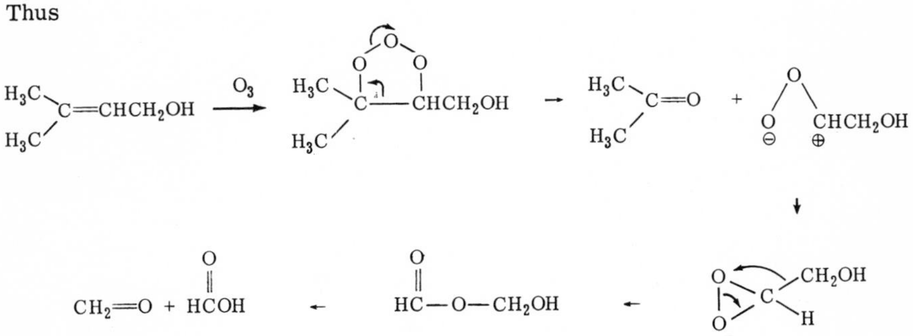

[1]W. G. Young, A. C. McKinnis, I. D. Webb, and J. D. Roberts, *J. Am. Chem. Soc.*, **68**, 293 (1946).

In many cases, however, including the one shown, an alternative and simpler path involving a normal ozonide is also possible,[2] i.e.,

A final possibility, particularly in aqueous solution, is the hydrolysis of the intermediate ozonide to normal products, followed by further oxidation by O_2, O_3, or H_2O_2.

It is probable that all these mechanisms are operative in certain cases, the choice among them depending on the exact structural features involved.

(138.2)   [A. T. Nielsen, *J. Am. Chem. Soc.*, **79**, 2518 (1957).]

---

[2]D. H. R. Barton and E. Seoane, *J. Chem. Soc.*, **1956**, 4150.

That the path of the ozonolysis is not as straightforward as shown is suggested by the observation that the 2-ketobutanal is not found as such, but rather as HCOOH, $CH_3 CH_2 COOH$, and $CH_3 CH_2 C \overset{O}{\underset{}{\diagdown}} H$. Thus it must be formed (if it is actually an intermediate) while the reaction is under oxidizing rather than reducing conditions. It is possible by the mechanisms given in the first answer to account for the formation of formic and propionic acids directly, but the propionaldehyde is more difficult.

PROBLEM 139.   Suggest mechanisms for the following oxidation reactions:

(139.1)

$$(1) \ O_3 \ (CHCl_3)$$
$$(2) \ H_2O$$

$+ \ CH_3COOH$

(139.2)

$\xrightarrow{O_3}$

$C_6H_5\overset{O}{\underset{\|}{C}}CHO \ + \ C_6H_5COOH$

ANSWER 139.   [For a review of ozonolysis, see P. S. Bailey, *Chem. Rev.*, **58**, 925 (1958).]

(139.1)   [D. H. R. Barton, P. de Mayo, and M. Shafiq, *J. Chem. Soc.*, **1957**, 929.]

If the crude ozonide is worked up by hydrogenation, the triketone (A) is obtained. Its isolation shows that the conversion of the original carbonyl group to a carboxyl function occurs during the hydrolysis of the ozonide and not during its formation, as would be predicted by another mechanism proposed for such abnormal ozonolyses.[1]

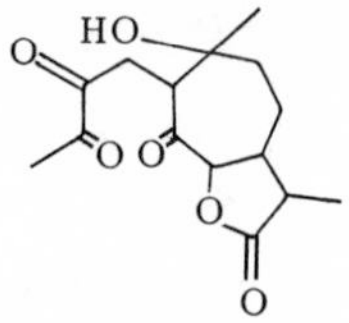

A

(139.2)   [P. S. Bailey and H. O. Colomb, Jr., *J. Am. Chem. Soc.*, **79**, 4238 (1957).]

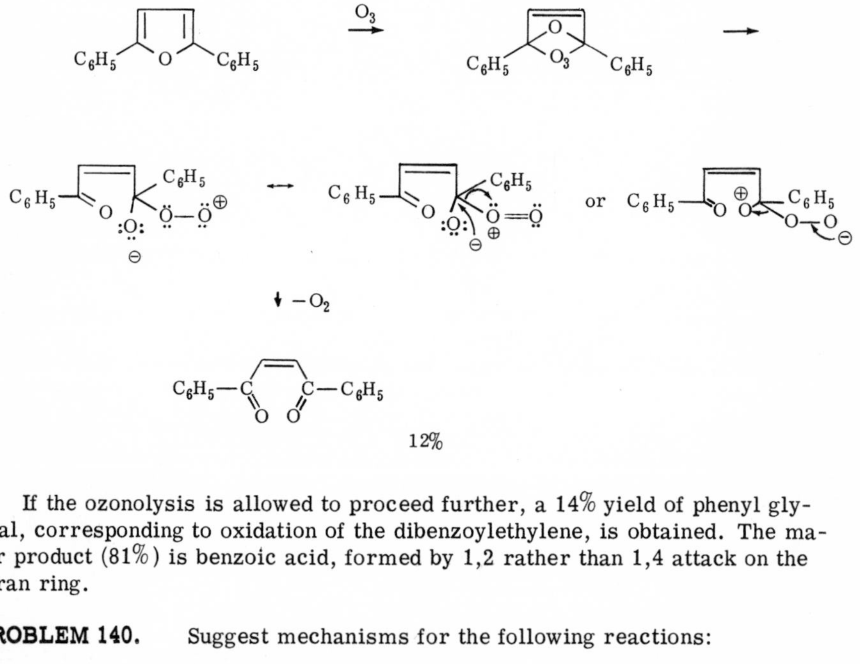

If the ozonolysis is allowed to proceed further, a 14% yield of phenyl glyoxal, corresponding to oxidation of the dibenzoylethylene, is obtained. The major product (81%) is benzoic acid, formed by 1,2 rather than 1,4 attack on the furan ring.

PROBLEM 140.   Suggest mechanisms for the following reactions:

(140.1)

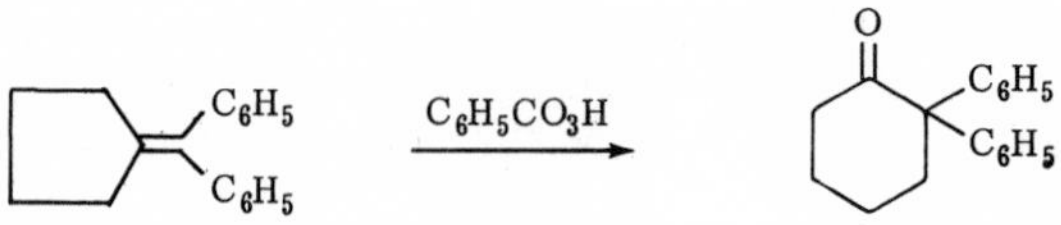

---

[1]See the answer to Problem 138 and Bailey, op. cit., pp. 947ff.

(cont.)

(140.2)

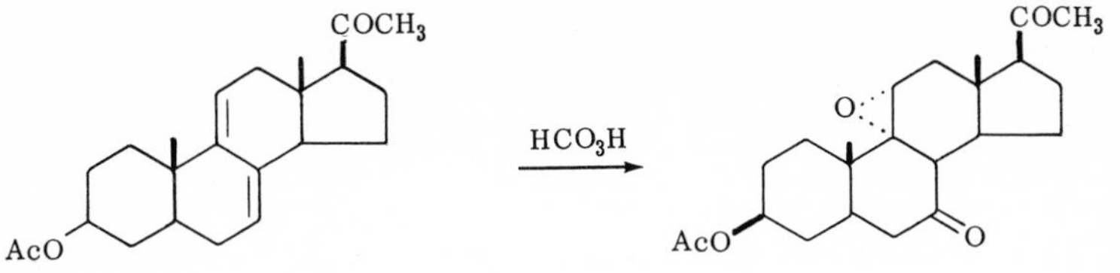

HCO_3H

ANSWER 140.

(140.1)　　[G. Cauquil and J. Rouzard, *Compt. Rend.*, **237**, 1720 (1953).]

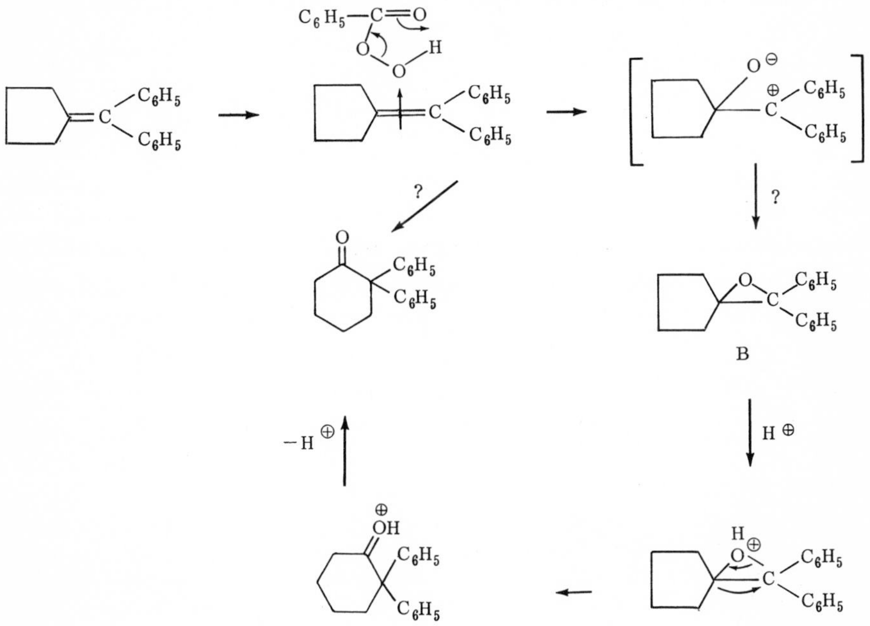

B

The reaction of peroxyacids with alkenes is suggested to involve the donation of :Ö through a π-complex A. In this case, the reaction may proceed normally to give the epoxide B, which rearranges very readily under the influence of traces of acid, or the complex itself may rearrange without ever forming B.

It is interesting to note that the rearrangement can be run in reverse as well.[1]

---

[1] R. E. Lyle, N. B. Martin, Jr., and H. L. Fielding, *J. Am. Chem. Soc.*, **75**, 4089 (1953).

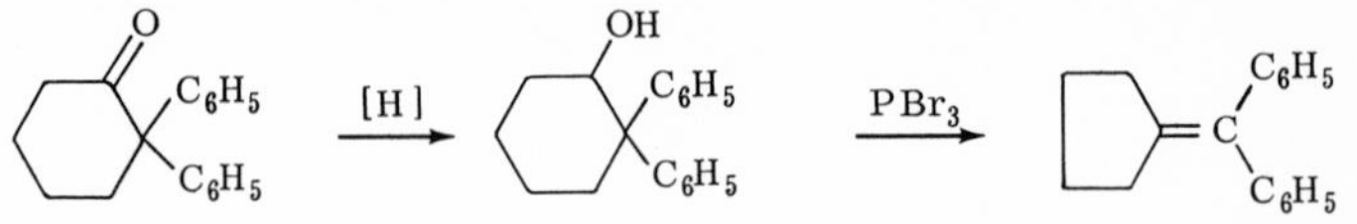

(140.2)   [C. Djerassi, O. Mancera, G. Stork, and G. Rosenkranz, *J. Am. Chem. Soc*
73, 4496 (1951).]

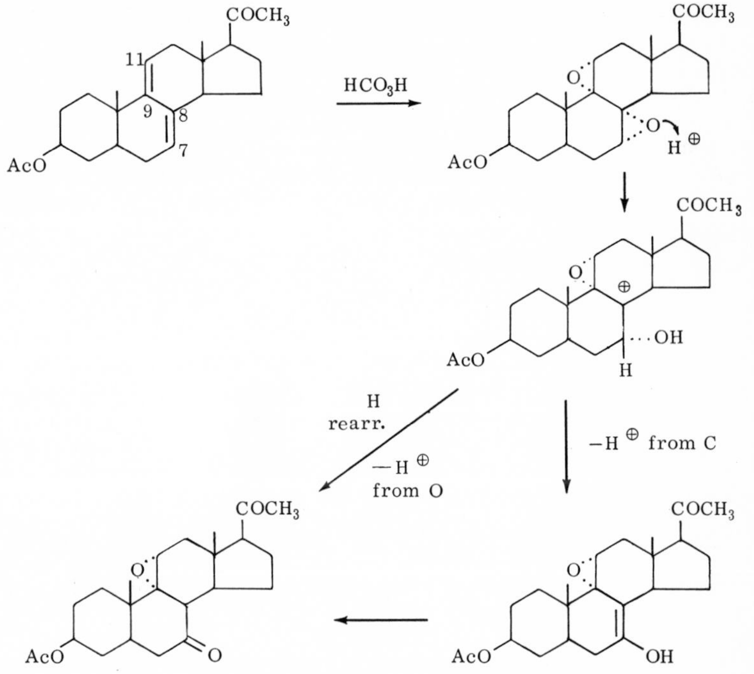

The epoxidation occurs from the less hindered α side.

PROBLEM 141.   Suggest mechanisms for the following reactions:

(141.1)

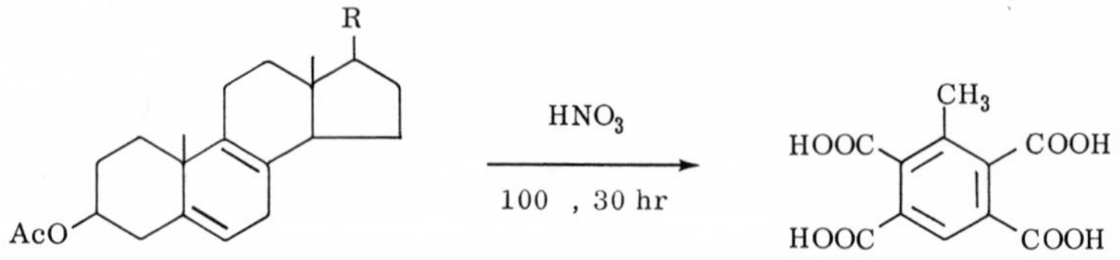

(c

(141.2)

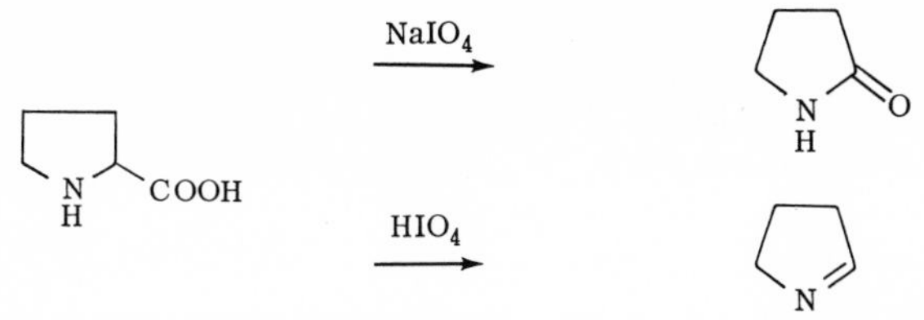

ANSWER 141.

141.1)   [K. Tsuda, K. Arima, and R. Hayatsu, *J. Am. Chem. Soc.*, **76**, 2933 (1954); see also A. W. Burgstahler, *J. Am. Chem. Soc.*, **79**, 6047 (1957).]

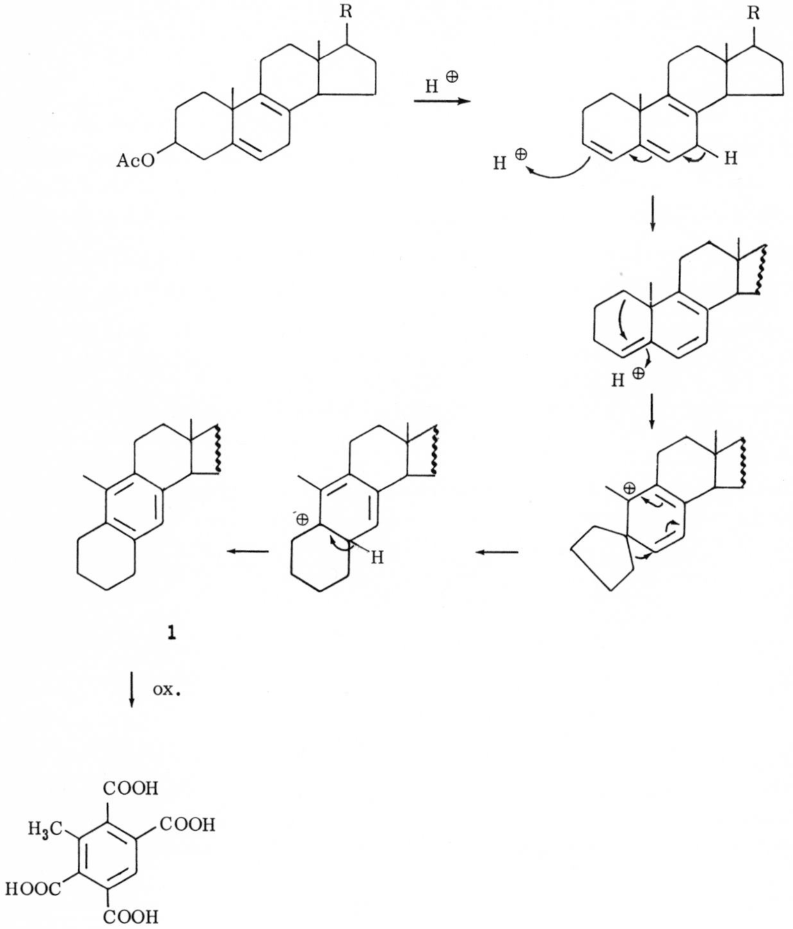

1

↓ ox.

This reaction (the anthrasteroid rearrangement) has been studied extensively by Nes and co-workers, particularly with reference to ergosterol and
$\Delta^{9\,(11)}$-dehydroergosterol.[1] It has been shown that these compounds rearrange
to products having the part structure 1 under mild acid conditions.

(141.2)   [P. D. Bragg and L. Hough, *J. Chem. Soc.*, **1958**, 4050.]

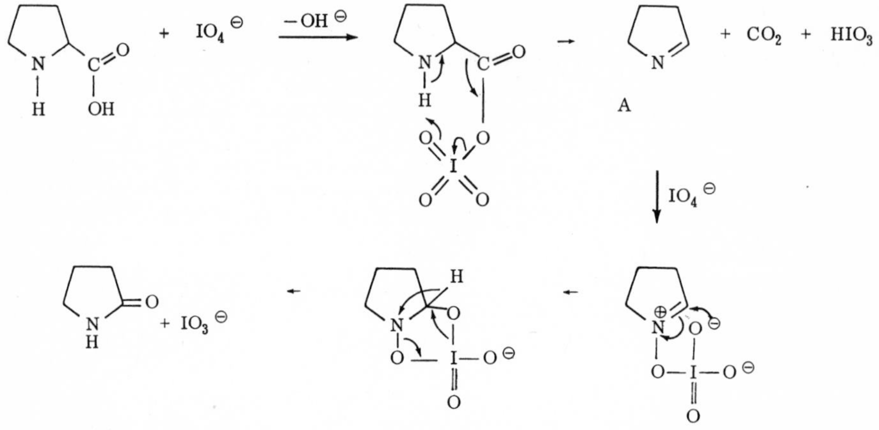

Periodic acid does not usually oxidize α-amino acids, but in this case it
causes oxidative decarboxylation. The mechanism is speculative, but accounts
for the fact that oxidation of Δ^1-pyrroline (A) occurs only in basic solution. In
acid the electron pair on nitrogen is tied up as the ammonium salt and is unavailable for reaction with periodate.

PROBLEM 142.   The reagents A and B give rise to isomeric diols in the
following reaction. Specify the configurations of the products.

Reagents:
A: Oxidation with OsO_4.
B: Treatment with I_2-AgOAc in HOAc, followed by heating with AgOAc and
    one equivalent of water, and finally hydrolysis with cold aqueous KOH.

---

[1]W. R. Nes and E. Mosettig, *J. Am. Chem. Soc.*, **76**, 3182 (1954).

ANSWER 142.   [R. B. Woodward and F. V. Brutcher, Jr., *J. Am. Chem. Soc.*,
          80, 209 (1958).]

A. OsO_4 attacks predominantly from the less hindered α (back) side and
gives the α-cis-diol.

B. The original reaction mixture can be considered as a source of IOAc or
$I^+ OAc^-$, which serves as an iodinating agent. Trans-addition of the elements of
IOAc, beginning with attack by I^+ or its equivalent from the back (α) side leads to
the trans-iodoacetate (**1**), which is formulated as the diaxial isomer by analogy
with other halogenations.[1] When **1** is heated with silver ion in acetic acid, it loses
iodide with neighboring group participation from the acetate. The resulting intermediate (**2**) reacts with water to form the cis-orthoacetate **3**, which decomposes
to give a mixture of two hydroxy acetates;[2] these on saponification give the β-cis-
diol.

---

[1]See L. F. Fieser and M. Fieser, *Steroids*, Reinhold, New York, 1959, pp. 38ff.
[2]Gould, pp. 563ff.

PROBLEM 143.   For the periodate oxidation of each of the following, account for the number of moles of oxidant consumed, and give the expected products.

(143.1)

$$
\begin{array}{l}
\text{CHO} \\
|\\
\text{HCOH} \\
|\\
\text{H}_3\text{COCH} \\
|\\
\text{HCOH} \\
|\\
\text{HCOH} \\
|\\
\text{CH}_2\text{OH}
\end{array}
\qquad
\begin{array}{l}
5° \quad 1\ \text{mole} \\
\\
30° \quad 3\ \text{moles}
\end{array}
$$

(143.2)

$$
\begin{array}{c}
\text{HOCH}_2\text{CHCOOH} \\
|\\
\text{NH}_2
\end{array}
\qquad 1\ \text{mole}
$$

(143.3)

3 moles

ANSWER 143.   [For general reviews of the periodate oxidation see E. L. Jackson in *Organic Reactions,* Vol. 2, Wiley, New York, 1944, p. 341; J. M. Bobbitt in *Advances in Carbohydrate Chemistry,* Vol. 11, Academic Press, New York, 1956, p. 1.]

Both periodic acid and lead tetraacetate are oxidants which are reasonably specific for the cleavage of C—C bonds between atoms bearing oxygen or amine substituents. Thus periodic acid cleaves

$$
\begin{array}{ccccc}
\overset{|}{-\text{C}}-\overset{|}{\text{C}}- &
\overset{|}{-\text{C}}-\overset{|}{\text{C}}- &
\overset{|}{-\text{C}}-\overset{|}{\text{C}}- &
\overset{|}{-\text{C}}-\text{C}- &
-\text{C}-\text{C}- \\
\underset{\text{OH}}{|}\ \underset{\text{OH}}{|} &
\underset{\text{NH}}{|}\ \underset{\text{OH}}{|} &
\underset{\text{NH}}{|}\ \underset{\text{NH}}{|} &
\underset{\text{OH}}{|}\ \underset{\text{O}}{\|} &
\underset{\text{O}}{\|}\ \underset{\text{O}}{\|}
\end{array}
$$

Lead tetraacetate oxidizes α-hydroxy acids and α-keto acids as well.

The reactions are usually considered to involve cyclic complexes of the form **1**, and to proceed more rapidly when the hydroxyl

$$
\begin{array}{ccc}
\begin{array}{l}
|\\
-\text{C}-\text{OH} \\
|\\
-\text{C}-\text{OH} \\
|
\end{array}
& \rightarrow &
\begin{array}{l}
|\\
-\text{C}-\text{O} \diagdown \quad \diagup \text{O}- \\
\qquad\qquad \text{X} \\
-\text{C}-\text{O} \diagup \quad \diagdown \text{O}- \\
|
\end{array}
& \rightarrow &
\begin{array}{l}
|\\
-\text{C}=\text{O} \\
\\
-\text{C}=\text{O} \\
|
\end{array}
\end{array}
$$

1   X = I, Pb

groups are cis rather than trans.[1]

---

[1] See R. Stewart, *Oxidation Mechanisms: Applications to Organic Chemistry,* Benjamin, New York, 1964, Chap. 7.

(143.1)   [G. W. Huffman, B. A. Lewis, F. Smith, and D. R. Spriestersbach, *J. Am. Chem. Soc.*, **77**, 4346 (1955).]

The starting carbohydrate exists in the cyclic form in solution. The first oxidation leads to a formate ester which is stable in the cold and which contains no free glycol groups. At higher temperatures the ester hydrolyzes and further oxidation occurs.

(143.2)   [B. H. Nicolet and L. A. Shinn, *J. Am. Chem. Soc.*, **61**, 1615 (1939).]

If the reaction mixture is allowed to stand for a day or so, a slower oxidation of the glyoxylic acid occurs, but this is easily differentiated from the rapid cleavage of the amino alcohol.

(143.3)   [M. L. Wolfrom and J. M. Bobbitt, *J. Am. Chem. Soc.*, **78**, 2489 (1956).]

The oxidation by periodate of methylene or methine groups activated by two α-carbonyl groups is a fairly common reaction. Cyclohexane-1,3-dione takes up 4 moles of periodate to give glutaric acid and CO_2. It is suggested that the reaction involves successive oxidation of the enol tautomers until the nonenolizable 1,2,3-trione is reached, and that cleavage then occurs.

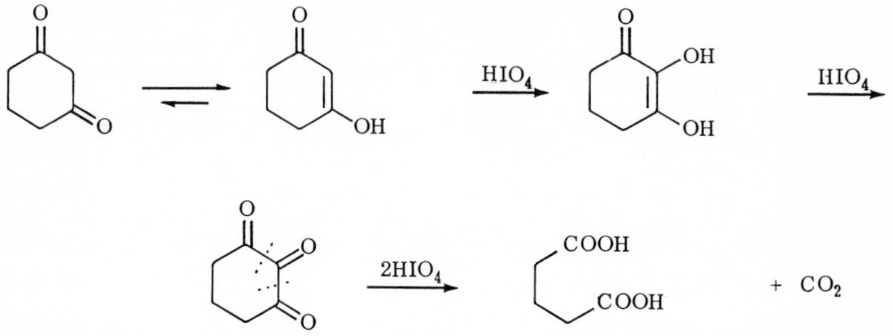

PROBLEM 144.   Suggest mechanisms for the following reactions:

(144.1)

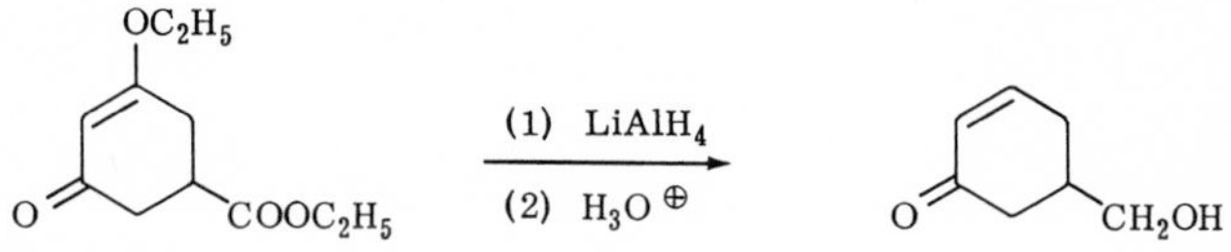

(144.2)

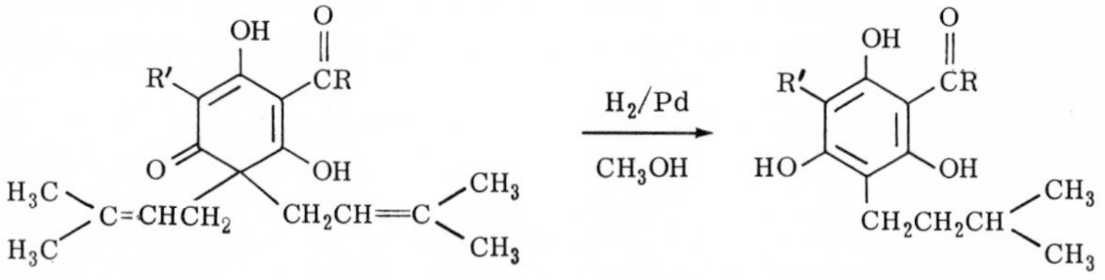

R,R′ = alkyl groups

(144.3)

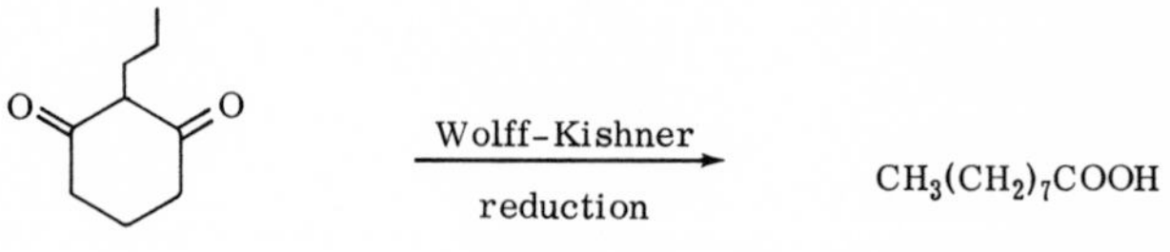

ANSWER 144.

(144.1)   [E. E. van Tamelen and G. T. Hildahl, *J. Am. Chem. Soc.*, **78**, 4405 (1956).]

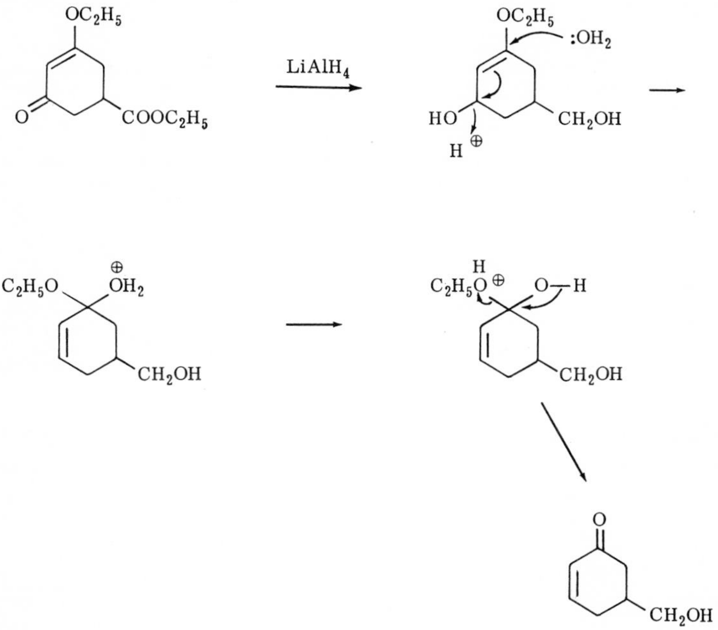

This conversion of the enol ethers of β-diketones to $\alpha\beta$-unsaturated ketones is quite general. One reaction which may actually involve hydrogenolysis of an enol ether, however, is[1]

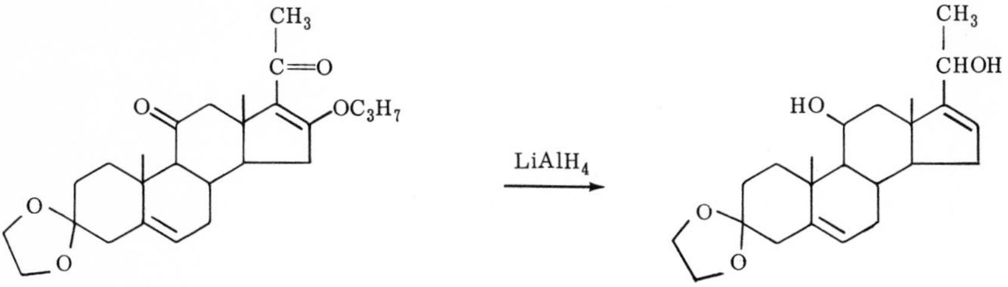

---

[1] G. E. Arth, G. I. Poos, and L. H. Sarett, *J. Am. Chem. Soc.*, **77**, 3834 (1955).

(144.2)   [W. Riedl and J. Nickl, *Ber.*, **89**, 1839 (1956).]

$$H^{\oplus}$$

A

$$H_2/Pd$$

The above mechanism is that originally proposed. It is supported by the observation that under acid conditions (MeOH—HCl) the starting material loses one isopentenyl side chain as isoprene, presumably by the route

$$H^{\oplus} \quad \text{other products}$$

$$+$$

$$\overset{\oplus}{CH_2}-CH=\overset{\overset{\displaystyle CH_3}{|}}{C}-CH_3 \quad \xrightarrow{-H^{\oplus}} \quad CH_2=CH-\overset{\overset{\displaystyle CH_3}{|}}{C}=CH_2$$

$$\updownarrow$$

$$CH_2=CH-\overset{\overset{\displaystyle CH_3}{|}}{\underset{\oplus}{C}}-CH_3$$

On the other hand, A is sure to be a poor representation of the true transition state, which presumably involves a molecule adsorbed on the catalyst and undergoing attack (homolytic? heterolytic?) by H_2 in some activated form.

(144. 3)   [H. Stetter and W. Diericks, *Ber.*, **85**, 61, 1061 (1952).]

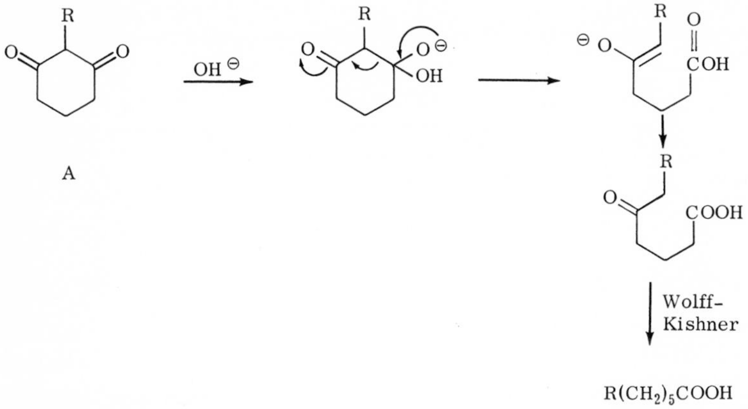

This is a generally useful synthetic method for lengthening a chain by six carbon atoms at once, since the starting material A can be prepared by the alkylation of the readily available cyclohexane-1,3-dione (dihydroresorcinol).

PROBLEM 145.   Suggest mechanisms for the following reactions:

(145.1)

(145.2) $(C_6H_5)_2C$—CHC_6H_5 $\xrightarrow[\text{AlCl}_3]{\text{LiAlD}_4}$ $\xrightarrow{\text{H}_2\text{O}}$ $(C_6H_5)_2CH$—$\overset{\text{OH}}{\underset{\text{D}}{\text{C}}}C_6H_5$

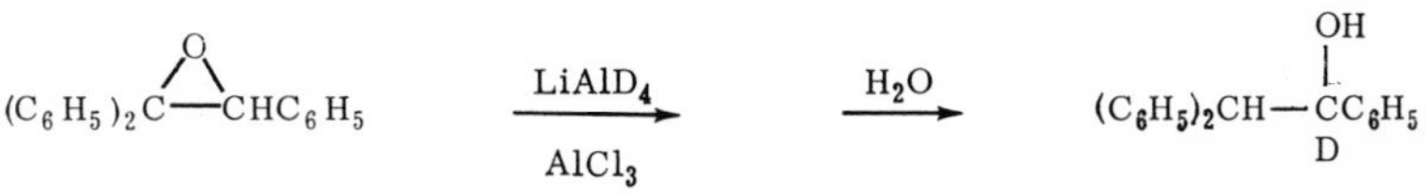

ANSWER 145.

(145.1)   [A. C. Cope, E. S. Graham, and D. J. Marshall, *J. Am. Chem. Soc.*, **76**, 6159 (1954).]

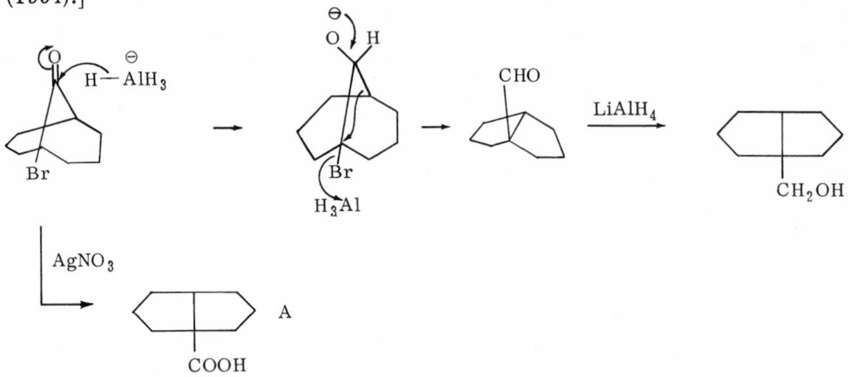

The reaction is formally very similar to a Favorskii rearrangement, and in fact the starting material reacts readily with silver nitrate to give the rearranged acid A.[1] The usual cyclopropanone mechanism[2] cannot be applied in this case, however, because of the nonacidity of the bridgehead α-hydrogen, so the "push-pull" route shown is preferred.

(145.2)   [E. L. Eliel and D. W. Delmonte, *J. Am. Chem. Soc.*, **80**, 1744 (1958).]

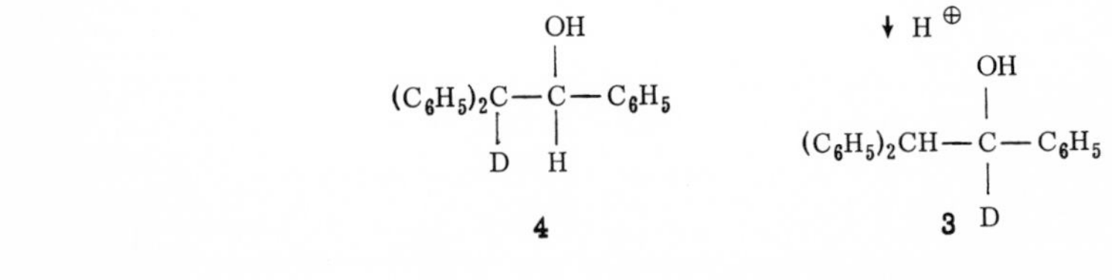

If the intermediate ion **1** were reduced directly by the LiAlD$_4$, the result would be **4**. Since **3** is actually found, the rearrangement to the ketone **2** (or its complexed equivalent) must be complete before the reduction occurs.

---

[1] A. C. Cope and E. S. Graham, *J. Am. Chem. Soc.*, **73**, 4702 (1951).

[2] R. B. Loftfield, *J. Am. Chem. Soc.*, **73**, 4707 (1951).

PROBLEM 146.   Suggest an explanation for the fact that the ratio of 2β—ol to 2α—ol, formed from the keto-steroid shown below, is largest by catalytic hydrogenation, less by NaBH₄ reduction, and least of all by LiAlH₄ reduction.

	2α – ol	2β – ol
cat. hydrog.	0	100 (%)
NaBH₄	16	71
LiAlH₄	37	52

ANSWER 146.   [W. G. Dauben, E. J. Blanz, Jr., J. Jiu, and R. A. Micheli, *J. Am. Chem. Soc.*, **78**, 3752 (1956).]

The effects of steric factors in determining the direction of reduction of carbonyl groups have been summarized as "product development control" and "steric approach control."[1] In the first, the tendency is for the reaction to proceed so as to give the most stable product configuration, and in the latter it is for the reducing agent to approach by the least hindered path, usually producing the unstable isomer of the product. Any actual case represents a balance between these two effects, but in general "product development" is effective for relatively unhindered ketones, whereas the "steric approach" becomes increasingly important for hindered ones.

In the case of 2-ketosteroids, the favored isomer is the equatorial 2α—ol, formed by axial approach of the reducing agent, whereas the easiest approach is equatorial and leads to the 2β—ol.

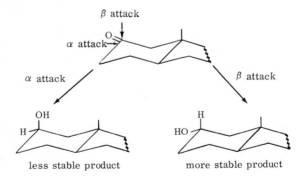

[1]W. G. Dauben, G. J. Forken, and D. S. Noyce, *J. Am. Chem. Soc.*, **78**, 2579 (1956).

One of the important factors in determining the direction of addition is the bulk of the hydride reagent. The larger the reagent, the more steric interactions will force it to approach by the easiest route. NaBH₄ in methanol generally behaves as if it were larger than LiAlH₄ in ether and gives, as in this case, more of the unstable isomer.

Catalytic hydrogenation, being a heterogeneous reaction on a surface, is not directly comparable with hydride reductions, but often behaves as if the catalyst were a very bulky reagent.

PROBLEM 147.   Suggest a reasonable path for the following oxidation reaction.

ANSWER 147.   [L. C. McKean and F. S. Spring, *J. Chem. Soc.*, **1954**, 1989; G. Brownlie and F. S. Spring, *J. Chem. Soc.*, **1956**, 1949.]

The above mechanism has been proposed[1] to account for this and some similar rearrangements. The suggested triketone intermediate A presumably arises by a series of allylic oxidations and rearrangements brought about by the SeO_2. The rearrangement may be driven by the stability gained by eliminating the unfavorable dipole-dipole interactions of the closely packed carbonyl groups.

The same lactone product is formed by the oxidation of systems B and C by CrO_3, presumably also through the triketone intermediate A.

PROBLEM 148.   Deduce structures for the following products, and suggest reasonable mechanisms for their formation:

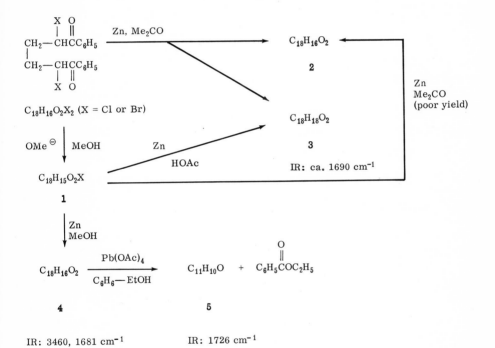

ANSWER 148.   [H. H. Wasserman and M. J. Gorbunoff, *J. Am. Chem. Soc.*, **80**, 4568 (1958); R. C. Fuson and M. W. Farlow, *J. Am. Chem. Soc.*, **56**, 1593 (1934).]

[1]See P. Yates and G. H. Stout, *J. Am. Chem. Soc.*, **76**, 5110 (1954), footnote 19a.

The reaction A → **1** is a base-catalyzed dehydrohalogenation. Possible routes are

The product B, although apparently probable, is not found from such reactions of α-haloketones and cannot be rationalized with the subsequent reactions, especially **4 → 5**. The formation of the epoxyketones is formally analogous to the Darzens glycidic ester synthesis.[1] Reduction leading to a keto alcohol (**4**) could occur with either C or D.

Of the two products, F would be expected to cleave readily with $Pb(OAc)_4$ to give ethyl benzoate and a product having the formula of **5**. Furthermore, the CO frequency of **4** fits an isolated benzoyl group better than one conjugated with an additional double bond[2] (E is known and absorbs at 1653 cm^{-1}).

Of the other reactions, A → **2** resembles the Reformatsky reaction,[3]

while A → **3** probably represents the analogous attack of Zn on both halogens and simple reduction without C—C bond formation.

Reaction **1 → 2** has been suggested to go

---

[1] See M. S. Newman and B. J. Magerlein in *Organic Reactions*, Vol. 5, Wiley, New York, 1949, p. 413.

[2] Nakanishi, p. 42.

[3] See R. L. Shriner in *Organic Reactions*, Vol. 1, Wiley, New York, 1942, p. 1.

whereas for **1** → **3** it has been proposed that the initial attack of Zn occurs α to the carbonyl

It is obvious that the reactions with zinc depend greatly on the solvent and probably on the vagaries of isolation. The intermediates are undoubtedly more complex than shown, particularly since reactions occur on the surface of the zinc. Note that the same intermediate stage is written in A → **2** and **1** → **3** and then continued to different products, suggesting that the mechanisms are far from complete.

PROBLEM 149.   In a study of a hypothetical biosynthetic scheme for the conversion of cinchonamine (**1**) to cinchonine (**2**), 2-methyltryptophan (**3**) was smoothly transformed to 4-acetylquinoline (**4**) in a single step (note that two equivalents of hypochlorite were employed). Give a mechanism for this conversion.

ANSWER 149.   [E. E. van Tamelen and V. B. Haarstad, *Tetrahedron Letters*, **1961**, 390.]

The various parts of this mechanism can be permuted in a number of ways without affecting the outcome.

CHAPTER 10

MISCELLANEOUS REACTIONS

PROBLEM 150. By what steps can one effect each of the following transformations?

(150.1)

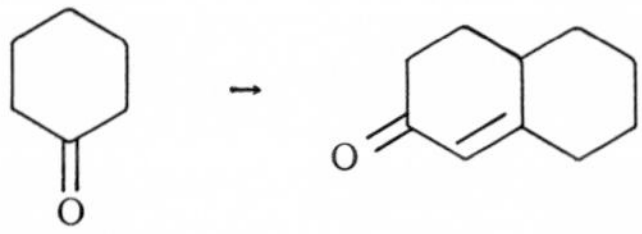

(150.2)   (a)

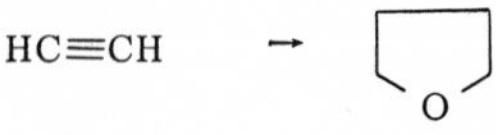

$$HC{\equiv}CH \quad \rightarrow$$

(b)

$$HC{\equiv}CH \quad \rightarrow$$

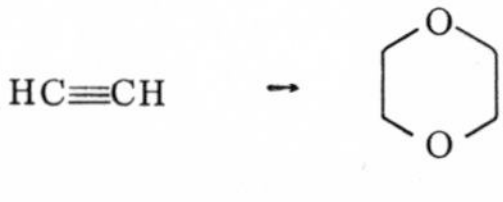

(150.3)

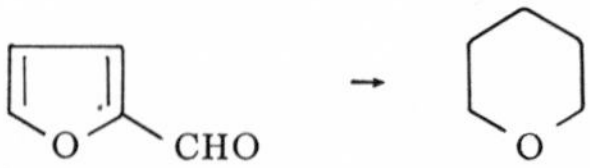

(150.4)

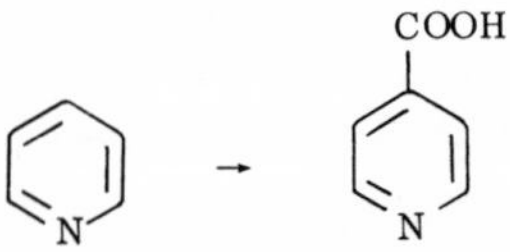

ANSWER 150.

(150.1)   [C. Mannich, W. Koch, and F. Borkowsky, *Ber.*, **70**, 355 (1937).]

1

EtOH,NaOEt aldol cond.

hydrol. $-CO_2$

$$CH_3\overset{O}{\overset{\|}{C}}CH_2-CH_2-NMe_2 \xrightarrow{CH_3I} CH_3\overset{O}{\overset{\|}{C}}CH_2CH_2\overset{\oplus}{N}Me_3 \; I^{\ominus} \xrightarrow{OEt^{\ominus}} CH_3\overset{O}{\overset{\|}{C}}CH=CH_2$$

2   **3**

This is an example of the Mannich synthesis.[1] A common modification[2] consists of quaternizing the intermediate amine **1** with methyl iodide, so as to obtain easier elimination.

The reaction is often run with the Mannich derivative of acetone (**2**) to give methyl vinyl ketone (**3**), which can condense with the second ketone, but with cyclohexanone further condensation occurs.

(150.2)   (a)   [W. Reppe et al., *Ann.*, **596**, 25, 39, 80 (1958).]

$$HC\equiv CH \xrightarrow{CH_2O} HOCH_2-C\equiv C-CH_2OH \xrightarrow{H_2/Ni} HOCH_2CH_2CH_2CH_2OH$$

$$\downarrow H^{\oplus}$$

(b)

$$HC\equiv CH \xrightarrow[\text{Lindlar catalyst}^3]{H_2} H_2C=CH_2 \xrightarrow{HOCl} HOCH_2CH_2Cl$$

$$\downarrow \text{base}$$

  $\xleftarrow{H^{\oplus}}$ H_2C—CH_2 (epoxide)

---

[1] See F. F. Blicke in *Organic Reactions*, Vol. 1, Wiley, New York, 1942, p. 303.
[2] E. C. du Feu, F. J. McQuillin, and R. Robinson, *J. Chem. Soc.*, **1937**, 53.
[3] H. Lindlar, *Helv. Chim. Acta*, **35**, 446 (1952).

This is only one of many possible routes.[4]

(150.3) [R. Paul, *Bull. Soc. Chim. France*, **53** (V), 1489 (1933); R. L. Sawyer and D. W. Andrus, *Org. Syn. Coll.*, **3**, 276 (1943).]

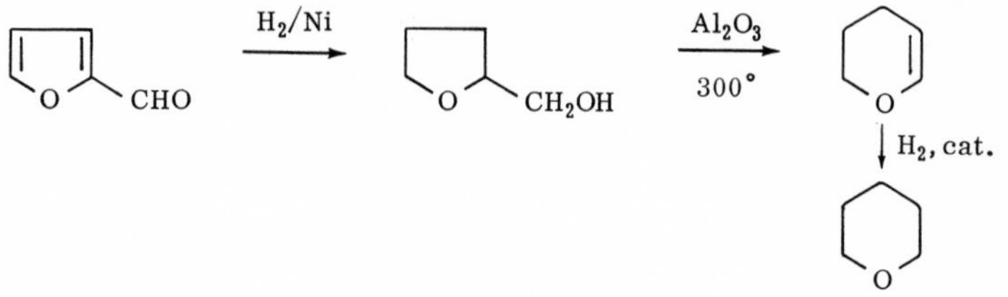

(150.4) [W. E. Feely and E. M. Beavers, *J. Am. Chem. Soc.*, **81**, 4004 (1959).]

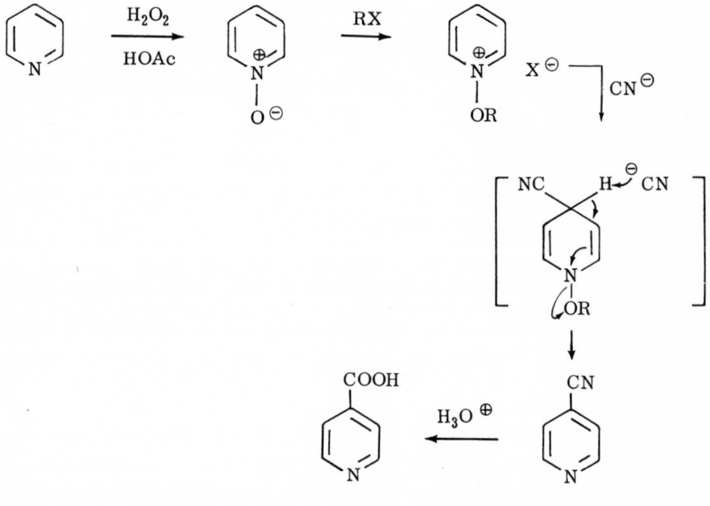

The yields from the substitution reaction are only fair (<50%) and both the 2- and 4-isomers may be obtained.

PROBLEM 151.   Suggest reagents which might be used for the following reactions. (Note: In part 1, each of the steps A, B, C, and D, involves multistage reactions.)   *(cont.)*

---

[4]See C. B. Kremer and L. K. Rochen in *Heterocyclic Compounds*, Vol. 6 (R. C. Elderfiel ed.), Wiley, New York, 1957, pp. 3ff.

(151.1)

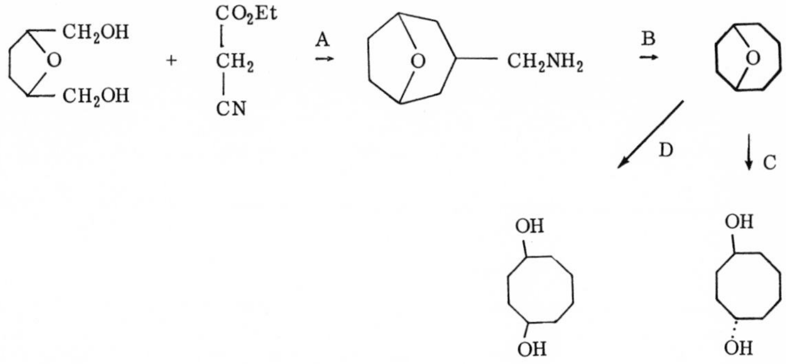

(151.2)

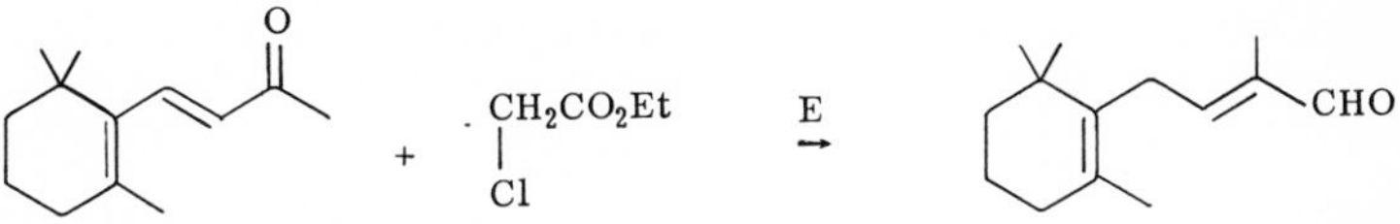

(151.3)

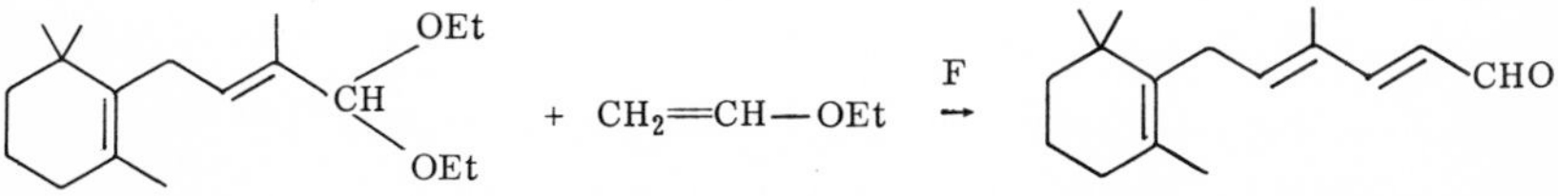

ANSWER 151.

(151.1) [A. C. Cope and B. C. Anderson, *J. Am. Chem. Soc.*, **78**, 149 (1956); **79**, 3892 (1957).]

A. The diol was tosylated with TsCl and then condensed with the nitrile at 110° in the presence of NaH (tetrahydrofuran solvent–autoclave) to give the cyanoester **1**.

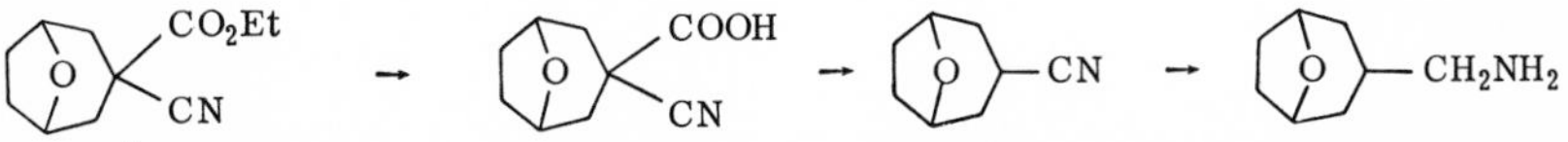

The cyanoester was hydrolyzed with aqueous NaOH, and the free acid decarboxylated by being heated, either above its melting point or in quinoline. The resulting nitrile was reduced by high-pressure hydrogenation over Raney nickel to give the product shown.

B. Deamination and ring enlargement was effected with nitrous acid[1] to give a mixture of products including the desired cyclooctanol **2**.

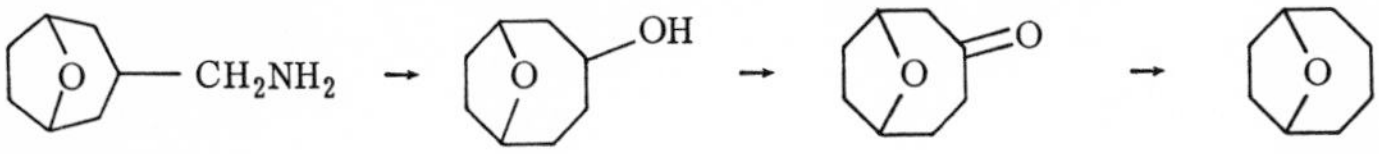

_____

[1]This is the Demjanov rearrangement; see P. A. S. Smith and D. R. Baer in *Organic Reactions*, Vol. 11, Wiley, New York, 1960, p. 157.

The alcohol was oxidized with NBS in aqueous acetone,[2] although other oxidants could undoubtedly have been used. The ketone was reduced to the 1,4-epoxy-cyclooctane by the Huang-Minlon modification of the Wolff-Kishner method[3] (hydrazine, KOH, diethylene glycol).

C. The trans-diol was obtained from the oxide by ring opening with acetic anhydride-BF$_3$ (poor yield), followed by hydrolysis with methanolic NaOH.

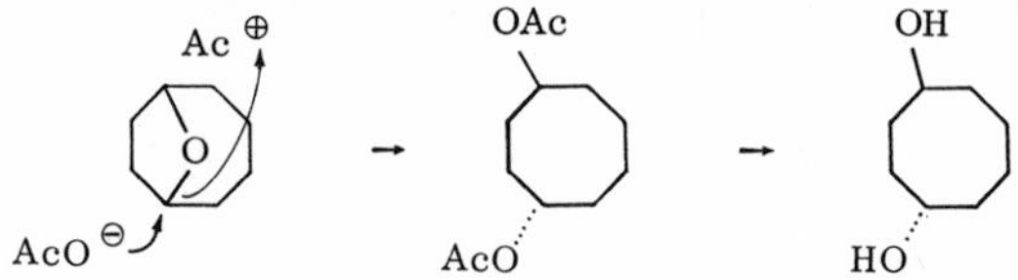

D. The cis-diol was obtained by opening the oxide bridge with acetyl bromide to give the trans-bromoacetate 3. Treatment with tetraethylammonium acetate led to displacement of the bromine with inversion, and the formation of the cis-diacetate. Hydrolysis with methanolic KOH gave the cis-diol.

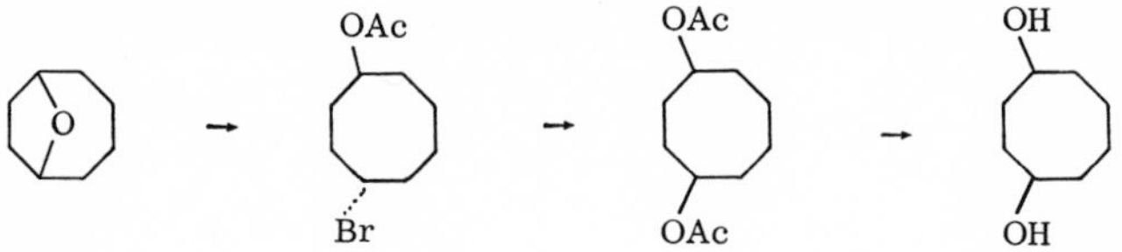

(151.2) [O. Isler, W. Huber, A. Ronco, and M. Kofler, *Helv. Chim. Acta,* **30,** 1911 (1947).]

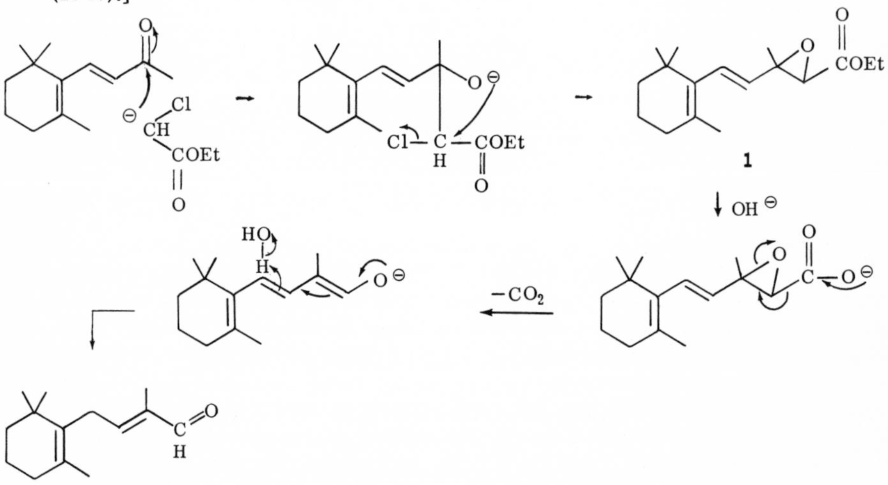

2

---

[2] R. Filler, *Chem. Rev.,* **63,** 21 (1963).

[3] D. Todd in *Organic Reactions,* Vol. 4, Wiley, New York, 1948, p. 378.

The fact that ethyl monochloroacetate is a component suggests that the Darzens reaction[4] is involved. A strong base such as potassium t-butoxide is used as a catalyst to produce the glycidic ester **1**. Hydrolysis with aqueous alkali is accompanied by decarboxylation and opening of the epoxide ring. The resulting enol is protonated to give the aldehyde product.

The series of reactions given is the first step in a practical synthesis of vitamin A. The position of the double bonds in **2** was in dispute for some time, but has been proved to be as shown.[5]

(151.3)   [O. Isler, H. Lindlar, M. Montavon, R. Ruegg, and P. Zeller, *Helv. Chim. Acta*, **39**, 249 (1956).]

A Lewis acid such as $ZnCl_2$ or BF_3 is used to catalyze the addition of ethyl vinyl ether to the $\alpha\beta$-unsaturated acetal. The reaction is run at low temperatures because under these conditions the starting material leads to the conjugated ion **1** and thence to the intermediate acetal **2**, whereas **2** is stable and does not undergo further reaction.

This reaction has proved to be a generally useful method of lengthening an unsaturated chain by two atoms.[6]

---

[4] M. S. Newman and B. J. Magerlein in *Organic Reactions*, Vol. 5, Wiley, New York, 1949, p. 413.

[5] G. W. H. Cheeseman, I. Heilbron, E. R. H. Jones, F. Sondheimer, and B. C. I. Weedon, *J. Chem. Soc.*, **1949**, 1516.

[6] See O. Isler and P. Schudel in *Advances in Organic Chemistry*, Vol. 4, Wiley-Interscience, New York, 1963, p. 128.

PROBLEM 152.   Give methods by which the following transformations can be effected:

(152.1)

(X = Br, OH, COOH, NO$_2$)

(152.2)

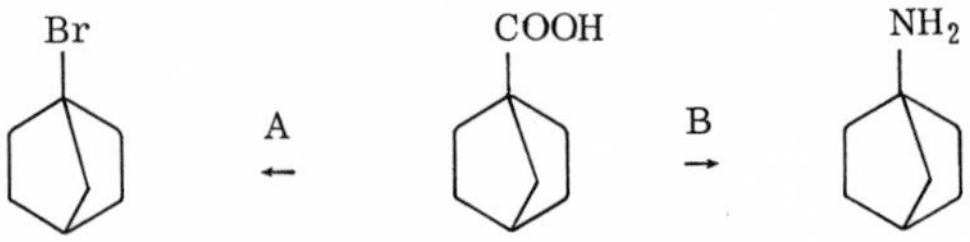

(152.3)   RCOOH → RCOCH$_3$

(152.4)

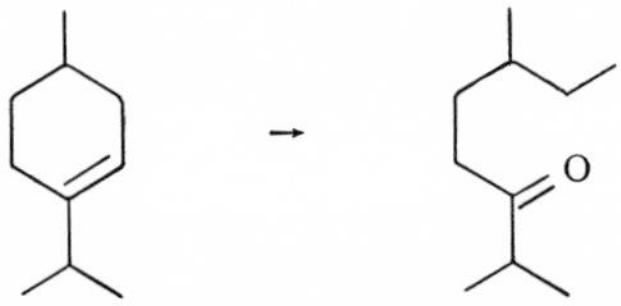

ANSWER 152.   [Excellent discussions of synthetic reactions can be found in L. F. Fieser and M. Fieser, *Advanced Organic Chemistry*, Reinhold, New York, 1961. References to experimental examples are available in R. B. Wagner and H. D. Zook, *Synthetic Organic Chemistry*, Wiley, New York, 1953.]

(152.1)   (X = Br)[1]

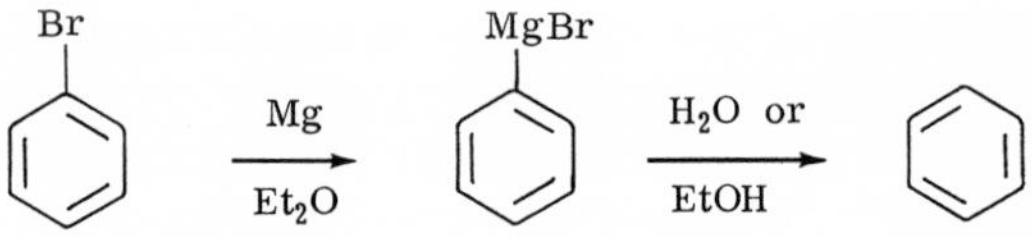

(X = OH)[2, 3]

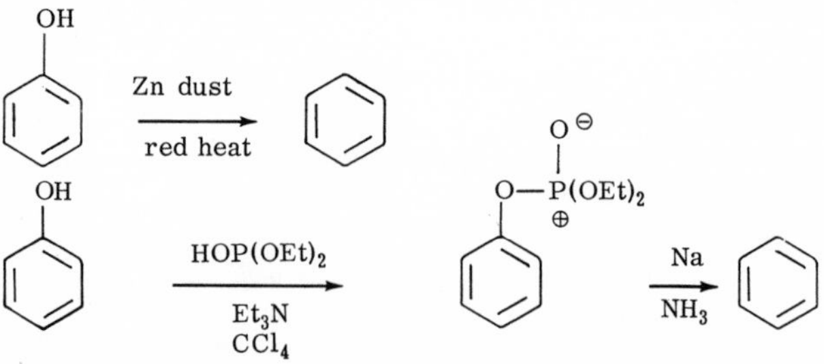

[1]Fieser and Fieser, op. cit., pp. 114–117; Wagner and Zook, op. cit., p. 9
[2]Fieser and Fieser, op. cit., pp. 667–668; Wagner and Zook, op. cit., p. 8.
[3]S. W. Pelletier and D. M. Locke, *J. Org. Chem.*, **23**, 131 (1958).

The zinc dust distillation is a brutal reaction which is useless for synthetic purposes and unreliable for degradative ones. The yields tend to be extremely poor. The reduction with hypophosphite is somewhat limited in scope but is potentially more useful.

$(X = COOH)$[4]

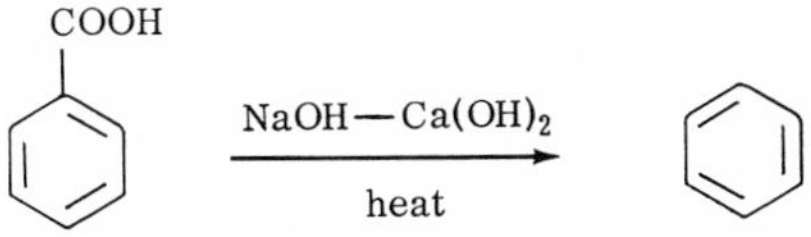

$(X = NO_2)$[5]

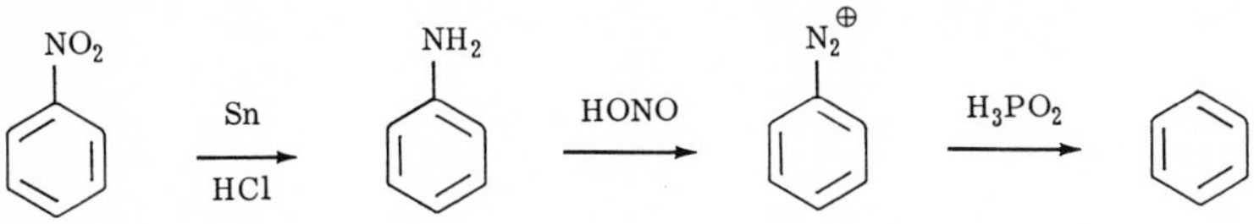

52.2) (a) [See C. V. Wilson in *Organic Reactions*, Vol. 9, Wiley, New York, 1957, p. 332.]

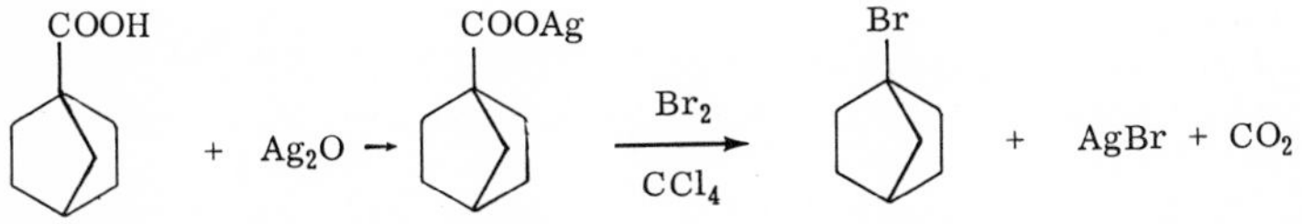

This is the Hunsdiecker reaction.

(b) [See E. S. Wallis and J. F. Lane in *Organic Reactions*, Vol. 3, Wiley, New York, 1946, p. 258; H. Wolff, ibid., p. 307; P. A. S. Smith, ibid., p. 337.]

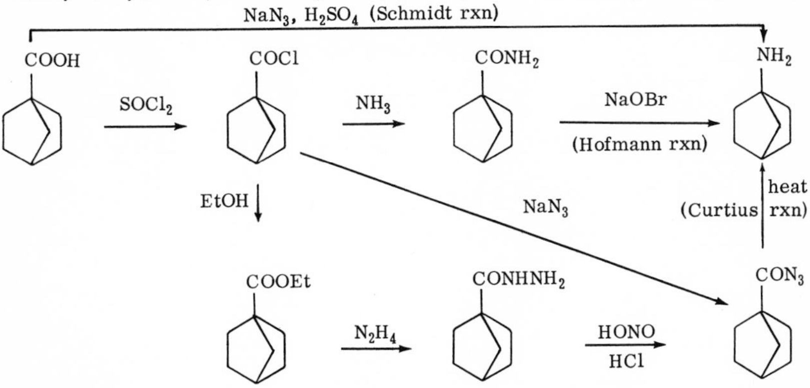

---

[4]Fieser and Fieser, op. cit., p. 667; Wagner and Zook, op. cit., p. 13.

[5]Fieser and Fieser, op. cit., pp. 706–708, 723–726, 734–736; Wagner and Zook, op. cit., pp. 14, 654, 772.

All these methods are applicable to bridgehead acids. The Schmidt is obviously the easiest for small-scale reactions on compounds which can tolerate the strongly acid conditions, but hydrazoic acid is a risky reagent for large-scale preparations.

(152.3)   (a) [D. A. Shirley in *Organic Reactions,* Vol. 8, Wiley, New York, 1954, p. 28.]

$$RCOOH \xrightarrow{SOCl_2} RCOCl \xrightarrow{(CH_3)_2Cd} RCOCH_3$$

The Grignard reagent CH_3MgI may be used as well, but the yields are generally much poorer.[6]

(b) [C. D. Gutsche in *Organic Reactions,* Vol. 8, Wiley, New York, 1954, p. 364.]

$$RCOCl \xrightarrow[\substack{Pd-BaSO_4 \\ quinoline-S}]{H_2} RCHO \xrightarrow{CH_2N_2} \left[\begin{array}{c} O^{\ominus} \\ | \\ R-C-CH_2-N\equiv N \\ | \\ H \end{array} \right]$$

$$\downarrow -N_2$$

$$\begin{array}{c} O \\ \| \\ RCCH_3 \end{array}$$

The first step is the Rosemund reduction.[7]

(c) [C. Tegner, *Acta Chem. Scand.,* **6,** 782 (1952).]

$$RCOOH + 2CH_3Li \rightarrow \begin{array}{c} O^{\ominus} \ Li^{\oplus} \\ | \\ R-C-O^{\ominus} Li^{\oplus} \\ | \\ CH_3 \end{array} \xrightarrow{H_3O^{\oplus}} \begin{array}{c} O \\ \| \\ RCCH_3 \end{array}$$

(152. 4)

---

[6]But see J. Cason and K. W. Kraus, *J. Org. Chem.,* **26,** 1768 (1961).

[7]E. Mosettig and R. Mozingo in *Organic Reactions,* Vol. 4, Wiley, New York, 1948, p. 362.

(A)　O_3; H_2O_2[8] or $KMnO_4$, HIO_4.[9]

(B)　CH_2N_2 or C_2H_5OH, $H^{\oplus}$, benzene, reflux with a water separator.[10]

(C)　$HOCH_2CH_2OH$, TsOH, benzene, reflux with a water separator.[11]

(D)　$LiAlH_4$; cautious hydrolysis with aqueous NH_4Cl.[12]

(E)　TsCl, pyridine; $LiAlH_4$.[13]

PROBLEM 153.　　Devise methods for achieving the following transformations:

(153.1)

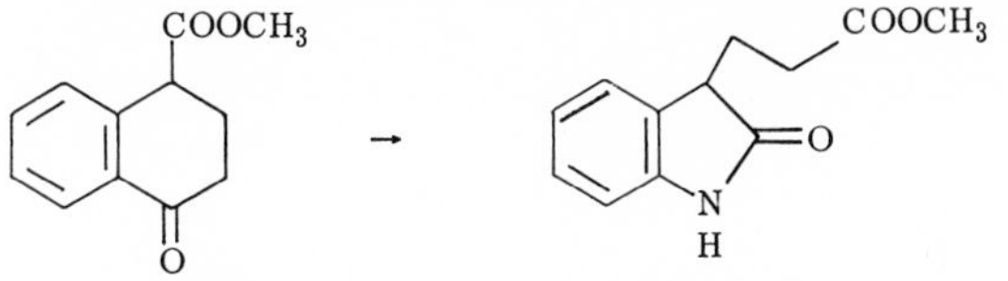

(153.2)

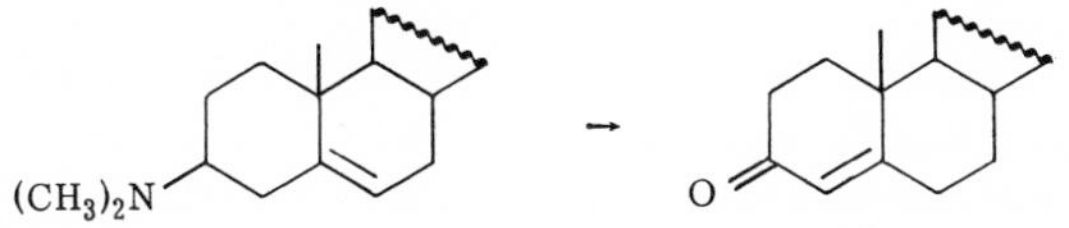

(153.3)

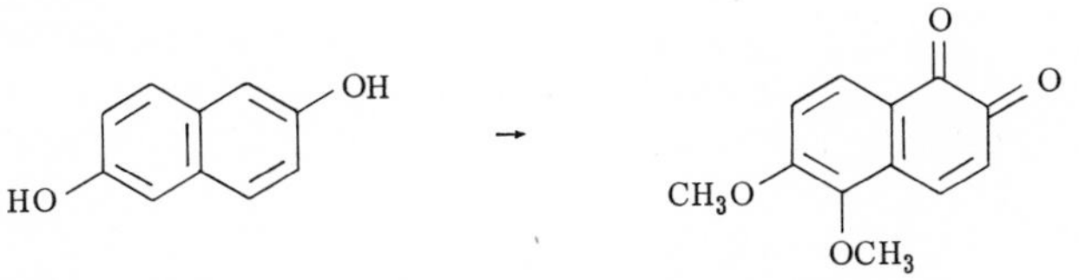

ANSWER 153.

(153.1)　　[H. A. Lloyd and E. C. Horning, *J. Am. Chem. Soc.*, **76**, 3651 (1954).]

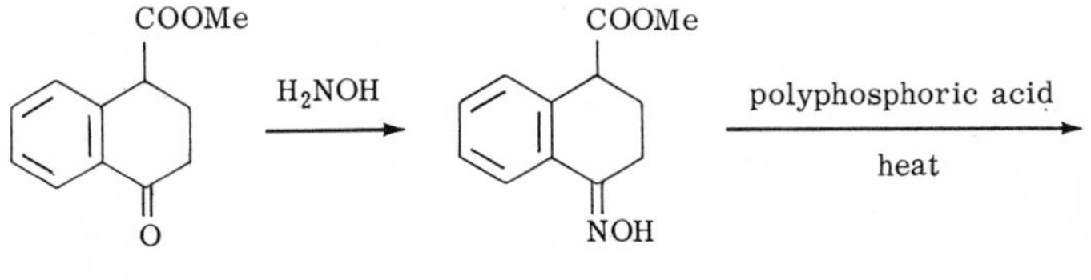

---

[8] L. Long, Jr., *Chem. Rev.*, **27**, 437 (1940).

[9] R. V. Lemieux and E. von Rudloff, *Can. J. Chem.*, **33**, 1701 (1955).

[10] C. Weygand, *Organic Preparations*, Wiley-Interscience, New York, 1945, pp. 171ff.

[11] See J. F. W. Keana in *Steroid Reactions* (C. Djerassi, ed.), Holden-Day, San Francisco, 1963, pp. 3ff.

[12] N. G. Gaylord, *Reductions with Complex Metal Hydrides*, Wiley-Interscience, New York, 1956, pp. 391ff, 1007ff.

[13] N. G. Gaylord, op. cit., p. 855.

The reaction involves a Beckmann rearrangement, followed by an ester/amide interchange which leads to the more stable five-membered ring.

(153.2)   [F. Buzzetti, W. Wicki, J. Kalvoda, and O. Jeger, *Helv. Chim. Acta*, **42**, 388 (1959); see also H. Ruschig, W. Fritsch, J. Schmidt-Thome, and W. Haede, *Ber.*, **88**, 883 (1955).]

The first step is the von Braun reaction.[1]

(153. 3)   [M. Gates, *J. Am. Chem. Soc.*, **72**, 228 (1950).]

---

[1] H. A. Hageman in *Organic Reactions*, Vol. 7, Wiley, New York, 1953, p. 198.

PROBLEM 154.   Give a rationalization of the following observations:

(154.1)   Acetylation of optically active glycylleucine with acetic anhydride or ketene gives an optically active product if the pH is maintained around 10. If it is allowed to go to 4, the product is racemic. Leucylglycine, however, gives an optically active product under either set of conditions.

(154.2)

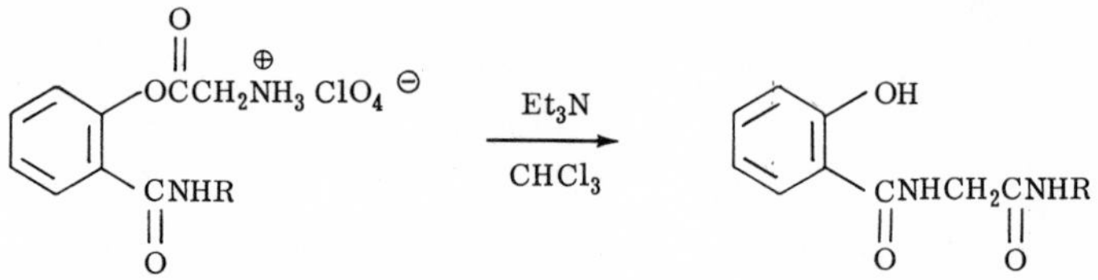

(154.3)   Treatment of a polypeptide containing tyrosine residues with aqueous NBS or bromine leads to selective cleavage at the tyrosyl-peptide links:

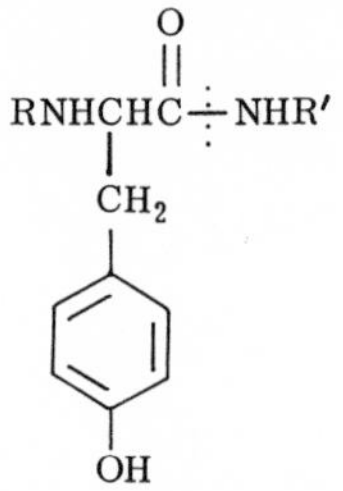

ANSWER 154.
(154.1)   [W. M. Cahill and I. F. Bunton, *J. Biol. Chem.*, **132**, 161 (1940).]

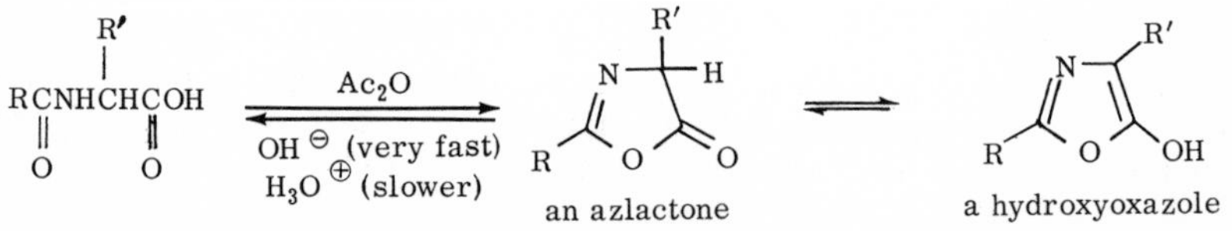

Acetylating agents readily convert α-acylamino acids to azlactones.[1] Because of the ease of tautomerism to the resonance stabilized oxazole system, an asymmetric center next to the carbonyl is then racemized very rapidly. In glycylleucine, the asymmetric carbon is adjacent to the carboxyl group and can be racemized in this way. In leucylglycine it is not, and no racemization occurs.

The differing results in acid and base appear to be due to the very rapid basic hydrolysis of the azlactone, which destroys it before racemization can occur.

---

[1]H. E. Carter in *Organic Reactions*, Vol. 3, Wiley, New York, 1946, p. 198; J. P. Greenstein and M. Winitz, *Chemistry of Amino Acids*, Vol. 2, Wiley, New York, 1961, pp. 829–838.

154.2) [M. Brenner, J. P. Zimmermann, J. Wehrmüller, P. Quitt, A. Hartmann, W. Schneider, and V. Beglinger, *Helv. Chim. Acta,* **40**, 1496 (1957).]

Alternative routes going through the diacylimide **1** may reasonably be considered, but model experiments have suggested that compounds of this type give the imidazolone **2** instead of the rearrangement product.

1   **2**

This reaction can be used as a means of extending a peptide chain by attaching additional amino acid residues to the N-terminal end.

(154.3) [G. L. Schmir, L. A. Cohen, and B. Witkop, *J. Am. Chem. Soc.*, **81**, 2228 (1959).]

It is not known whether the formation of the dienone lactone occurs through displacement from the bromodienone, path (a), or by oxidative ring closure on the phenol, path (b).

PROBLEM 155.   Rationalize the formation of B and C and give the struc-ture for D.

ANSWER 155.   [E. E. van Tamelen and J. E. Brenner, *J. Am. Chem. Soc.,*
79, 3839 (1957).]

PROBLEM 156.   Deduce structures for the following reaction products:

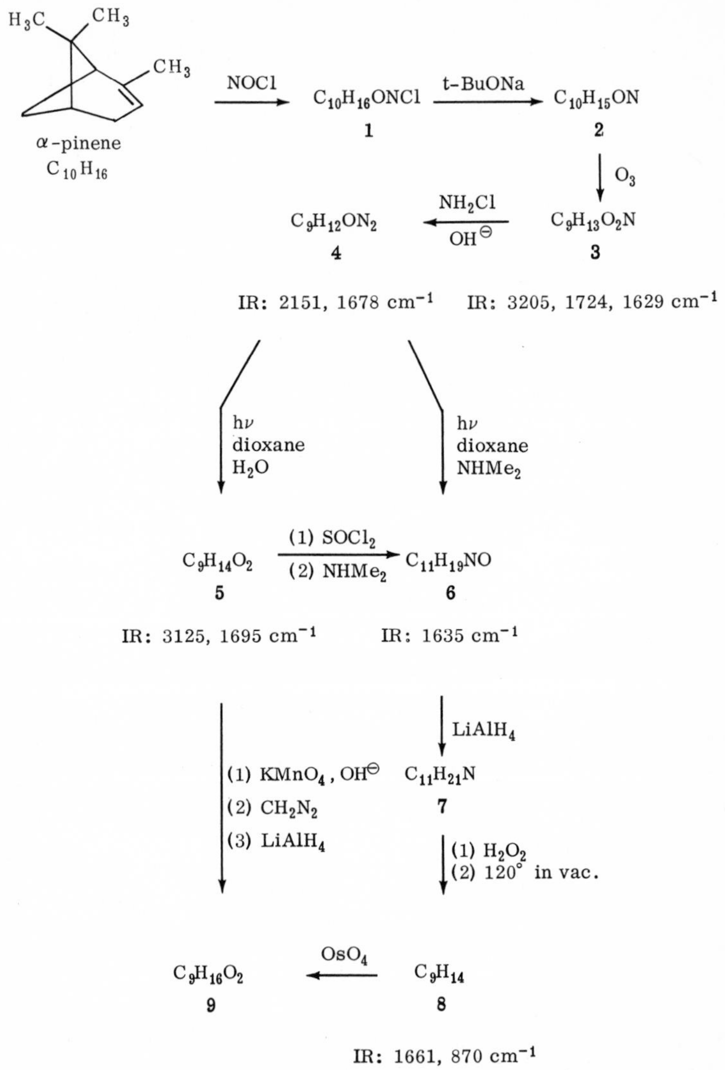

$$
\begin{array}{c}
\text{H}_3\text{C} \quad \text{CH}_3 \\
\\
\text{CH}_3 \\
\alpha\text{-pinene} \\
\text{C}_{10}\text{H}_{16}
\end{array}
\quad \xrightarrow{\text{NOCl}} \quad
\begin{array}{c}
\text{C}_{10}\text{H}_{16}\text{ONCl} \\
1
\end{array}
\quad \xrightarrow{\text{t-BuONa}} \quad
\begin{array}{c}
\text{C}_{10}\text{H}_{15}\text{ON} \\
2
\end{array}
$$

$$\downarrow \text{O}_3$$

$$
\begin{array}{c}
\text{C}_9\text{H}_{12}\text{ON}_2 \\
4
\end{array}
\quad \xleftarrow[\text{OH}^{\ominus}]{\text{NH}_2\text{Cl}} \quad
\begin{array}{c}
\text{C}_9\text{H}_{13}\text{O}_2\text{N} \\
3
\end{array}
$$

IR: 2151, 1678 cm^{-1} IR: 3205, 1724, 1629 cm^{-1}

hν
dioxane
H$_2$O

hν
dioxane
NHMe$_2$

$$
\begin{array}{c}
\text{C}_9\text{H}_{14}\text{O}_2 \\
5
\end{array}
\quad \xrightarrow[\text{(2) NHMe}_2]{\text{(1) SOCl}_2} \quad
\begin{array}{c}
\text{C}_{11}\text{H}_{19}\text{NO} \\
6
\end{array}
$$

IR: 3125, 1695 cm^{-1} IR: 1635 cm^{-1}

$$\downarrow \text{LiAlH}_4$$

(1) KMnO$_4$, OH$^{\ominus}$ $\text{C}_{11}\text{H}_{21}\text{N}$
(2) CH$_2$N$_2$ 7
(3) LiAlH$_4$

(1) H$_2$O$_2$
(2) 120° in vac.

$$
\begin{array}{c}
\text{C}_9\text{H}_{16}\text{O}_2 \\
9
\end{array}
\quad \xleftarrow{\text{OsO}_4} \quad
\begin{array}{c}
\text{C}_9\text{H}_{14} \\
8
\end{array}
$$

IR: 1661, 870 cm^{-1}

ANSWER 156.   [J. Meinwald and P. G. Gassman, *J. Am. Chem. Soc.*, **82**, 2857 (1960).]

The reactions **1 → 4** are normal; **4 → 5** is the photochemical Wolff rearrangement, which is presumed to go via a carbene which rearranges to a
ketone.[1] The ketone then reacts with water or dimethylamine to give the observed
products. Hydration of the ketene occurs from the less hindered side (unsubstituted

---

[1]See *Molecular Rearrangements* (P. de Mayo, ed.), Wiley-Interscience, New York, 1963,
pp. 528ff; Gould, pp. 627ff.

$$4 \xrightarrow{h\nu} \left[\quad O \right] \longrightarrow A$$

1-carbon bridge) to give the product with the carboxyl group up (β-configuration). Subsequent, and similar, attacks (**5 → B; 8 → 9**) also occur from the unhindered side.

PROBLEM 157.   Deduce structures for the following products:

$$\text{(pyridine)} \xrightarrow[160^\circ]{CH_2O} \underset{1}{C_9H_{13}NO_2} \xrightarrow[\text{reflux}]{Ac_2O} \underset{2}{C_{11}H_{13}NO_2}$$

IR: 1735, 1635, 1595, 1565, 1480, 1230 cm^{-1}

$$\Big\downarrow \begin{array}{l} NaH \\ CH_2(CO_2Et)_2 \end{array}$$

$$\underset{4}{C_{14}H_{23}NO_3} \xleftarrow{\text{heat}} \underset{HOAc}{\xleftarrow{H_2/Pt}} \underset{3}{C_{16}H_{21}NO_4}$$

IR: 1735, 1645 cm^{-1}

IR: 1735, 1630, 1600, 1562, 1486 cm^{-1}

$$\Big\downarrow \begin{array}{l} (1)\ conc.\,HCl \\ (2)\ EtOH,\ HCl \end{array}$$

$$\underset{5}{C_{13}H_{25}NO_2} \xrightarrow{K_2CO_3} \underset{6}{C_{18}H_{27}NO_4}$$

IR: 3300, 1735 cm^{-1}

IR: 3110, 1735, 1625, 1573, 1505, 875 cm^{-1}

$$\Big\downarrow \begin{array}{l} \text{soda lime} \\ \text{dry dist.} \end{array}$$

$$\underset{8}{C_{15}H_{23}NO} \xleftarrow[Pd]{H_2} \underset{7}{C_{15}H_{21}NO}$$

IR: 3110, 1505, 875 cm^{-1}

IR: 3110, 1645, 1588, 1505, 875 cm^{-1}

ANSWER 157. [M. Kotake, I. Kawasaki, T. Okamoto, S. Kusumoto, and T. Kaneko, *Ann.,* **636,** 158 (1960); T. Kaneko, I. Kawasaki, and T. Okamoto, *Chem. Ind. (London),* **1959,** 1191.]

The IR bands around 1600, 1560, and 1480 cm^{-1} in **2** and **3** are due to the pyridine ring. Those at 3110 (CH), ca. 1580, 1505 (C=C), and 875 in **6** and **7** are due to the furan system,[1] with the ~1580 band appearing when the ring is conjugated.

The product **8** is a mixture of the diastereomeric forms of the natural alkaloid deoxynupharidine. It has subsequently[2] been separated chromatographically into a pure dl-compound which could be resolved to give the natural product.

PROBLEM 158.   Deduce structures for the following products:

$C_{10}H_{17}N$

$\xrightarrow{\text{HClO}_4}$ $[C_{10}H_{18}N]^{\oplus} ClO_4^{\ominus}$ **1**

IR: 1665 cm^{-1}

$\xrightarrow{\text{CH}_2\text{N}_2}$ $[C_{11}H_{20}N]^{\oplus} ClO_4^{\ominus}$ **2**

IR: no band at ca. 3100 or 1665 cm^{-1}

(1) CH$_3$MgI ether
(2) HClO$_4$

H$_2$/Pt

CH$_3$OH reflux

(1) ClCH$_2$CH$_2$OH
(2) neut., reflux in ether
(3) HClO$_4$

$[C_{11}H_{22}N]^{\oplus} ClO_4^{\ominus}$ **3**

$[C_{12}H_{24}NO]^{\oplus} ClO_4^{\ominus}$ **4**

IR: 3125 cm^{-1}

$[C_{13}H_{24}NO]^{\oplus} ClO_4^{\ominus}$ **5**

(1) BrCH$_2$CH$_2$CH$_2$CH$_2$Br
(2) HClO$_4$

CH$_3$O   COCH$_3$ ‖ O

$C_9H_{16}O_3$

$\xrightarrow{\text{NH}_3}$ $C_8H_{15}NO_2$ **6**

$\xrightarrow{\text{LiAlH}_4}$ $C_8H_{17}NO$ **7**

---

[1]Nakanishi, pp. 52, 213.

[2]M. Kotake, I. Kawasaki, S. Matsutani, S. Kusumoto, and T. Kaneko, *Bull. Chem. Soc. Japan*, **35**, 698 (1962).

ANSWER 158.   [N. J. Leonard and K. Jann, *J. Am. Chem. Soc.*, **82,** 6418 (1960).]

The IR band of **1** at 1665 cm^{-1} can be ascribed to the $\overset{\oplus}{\diagdown C=N\diagup}$ group,[1] but

is probably not safely distinguishable from $\diagdown C=C\overset{\overset{\oplus}{H}}{\underset{|}{-NH-}}$. The absence of an

NH stretching band at ca. 3100 cm^{-1} (see below) eliminates the second possibility, however.

The reaction **1** → **2** resembles the formation of epoxides by the reaction of diazomethane with ketones.[2]

The difference in direction in the ring openings **2** → **3** and **2** → **4** probably arises from the difference between a solvolysis which develops positive character preferably at the tertiary center (→**4**) and a reaction on the catalyst surface which attacks the less hindered bond (→**3**).

The —N—H band in tertiary amine salts such as **4** appears to be affected by the anion present. They are reported to shift ca. 2600 → 2800 → 3100 cm^{-1} for the series Cl$^-$ → Br$^-$ → ClO$_4^-$.[1]

PROBLEM 159. Compound A, synthesized by the following reaction sequence, is the racemic form of a natural product **1**. Deduce structures for the natural product and the other products.

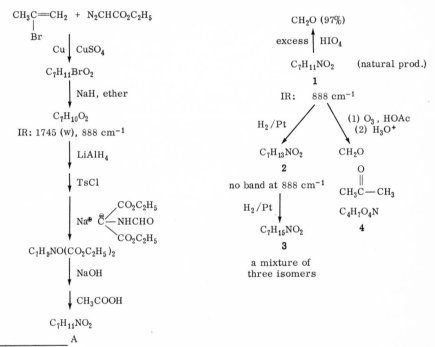

[1]Nakanishi, p. 39.
[2]See B. Eistert in *Newer Methods of Preparative Organic Chemistry*, Wiley-Interscience, New York, 1948, pp. 513–570.

ANSWER 159. [Synthesis by J. A. Carbon, W. B. Martin, and L. R. Swett, *J. Am. Chem. Soc.,* **80**, 1002 (1958); for degradation and structure see references below.]

hypoglycine

The natural product, hypoglycine, occurs in the unripe fruit of a West Indian tree and is of interest because of its marked power to decrease the concentration of sugar in the blood. Its structure was reported almost simultaneously by six laboratories.[1-6]

The synthesis is straightforward, the only significant point being the exocyclic position of the double bond. This is indicated by the band at 888 cm^{-1}

$(=\!CH_2\,;\ 1745\ \triangleright\!C\!=\!C\!\!\stackrel{H}{\underset{H}{\diagdown}}\ ?^7,\ 888\ cm^{-1}$ overtone?) and by analogy with Feist's

acid (B).[8]

$$\underset{\substack{| \\ HOOC \quad COOH \\ B}}{\overset{\displaystyle CH_2}{\triangle}}$$

The methylenecyclopropane system is apparently preferred over the methyl-cyclopropene, even if the latter can be conjugated.

The ozonolysis of hypoglycine is anomalous, giving instead of formaldehyde mainly the products of ring cleavage followed by hydrolysis. Oxidation with excess HIO_4, an apparently little-known but potentially useful alkene cleavage technique[9] (cf. the Lemieux reagent,[10] $KMnO_4 - HIO_4$), however, gives excellent yields of formaldehyde. Feist's acid shows quite similar behavior.[11,12]

Various workers[2,3] are in disagreement about the relative amounts of the ring-opened acids produced by hydrogenation of hypoglycine, but it does appear probable that all possible products are formed.

[1]S. Wilkinson, *Chem. Ind., (London)*, 1958, 17.

[2]C. von Holt and W. Leppla, *Angew. Chem.*, **70**, 25 (1958).

[3]R. S. de Rapp, J. C. von Meter, E. C. de Renzo, K. W. McKerns, C. Pidocks, P. H. Bell, E. F. Ullman, S. R. Safir, W. J. Fanshawe, and S. B. Davis, *J. Am. Chem. Soc.*, **80**, 1004 (1958).

[4]E. V. Ellington, C. H. Hassall, and J. R. Plummer, *Chem. Ind. (London)*, 1958, 329.

[5]H. V. Anderson, J. L. Johnson, J. W. Nelson, E. C. Olson, M. E. Speeter, and J. J. Vavra, *Chem. Ind. (London)*, 1958, 330.

[6]U. Renner, A. Johl, and W. G. Stoll, *Helv. Chim. Acta*, **41**, 589 (1958).

[7]J. T. Grayson, K. W. Greenlee, J. M. Derfer, and C. E. Boord, *J. Am. Chem. Soc.*, **75**, 3344 (1953).

[8]M. G. Ettlinger and F. Kennedy, *Chem. Ind. (London)*, 1956, 166.

[9]A. Chatterjee and S. G. Majumdar, *Anal. Chem.*, **28**, 878 (1956).

[10]R. U. Lemieux and E. von Rudloff, *Can. J. Chem.*, **33**, 1701, 1710 (1955).

[11]F. R. Goss, C. K. Ingold, and J. F. Thorpe, *J. Chem. Soc.*, **123**, 327 (1923).

[12]D. Lloyd, *Chem. Ind. (London)*, 1956, 874.

PROBLEM 160.   Deduce the structures of the natural product (**1**) and its derivatives.

$$C_8H_{14}O_3 \xleftarrow[\text{MeOH}]{\text{NaBH}_4} \xleftarrow{\text{H}^\oplus} C_{10}H_{14}O_5 \xrightarrow[\text{at room temp.}]{N \text{ NaOH}} \left\{ \begin{array}{l} CH_3COOH \\ C_7H_{10}O \end{array} \right.$$

5   **1**   **4**

IR: 1757 cm^{-1} IR: 1795, 1765, 1715 cm^{-1} UV: 235 mµ (log ε, 4.16)
neutral compound   (no bands at 2730,   300 mµ (log ε, 1.76)
                              1730 cm^{-1})
                              iodoform test positive
                              ferric chloride test negative
                              tetranitromethane negative
                              4 C—CH$_3$; no O—CH$_3$

OH$^\ominus$

$$\begin{array}{cc} CH_3 & CH_3 \\ | & | \\ HOOC-CH- & CH-COOH \end{array}$$

NaOI

$$C_7H_{11}N \xleftarrow{(\text{NH}_4)_2\text{CO}_3} C_7H_{12}O_2 \xrightarrow{\text{Ag}_2\text{O}} C_7H_{12}O_3$$

AcONa/H$_2$O
90–95°

6   **2**   **3**

ANSWER 160.   [L. Ettlinger, E. Gaumann, R. Hutter, W. Keller-Schierlein, F. Kradolfer, L. Neipp, V. Prelog, and H. Zahner, *Helv. Chim. Acta,* **41**, 216 (1958); W. Keller-Schierlein, M. L. Mihailovic, and V. Prelog, *Helv. Chim. Acta,* **41**, 220 (1958).]

The sequence **2** → **3** → dimethylsuccinic acid is clearly as shown, and the 1,4 dicarbonyl nature of **2** is confirmed by its ready conversion to the pyrrole derivative **6**.

An aldol condensation, followed by double-bond migration, leads from **2** to **4**.

The double bond is indicated as being in the 2,3 position by the UV spectrum, which may be calculated[1,2] as being

$$215 + 2(12) + 10 - 10 = 239 \ m\mu$$

for **4** and

$$215 + 12 - 10 = 217 \ m\mu$$

for the isomer A. (Note that ca. 10 $m\mu$ are subtracted because the system is a cyclopentenone rather than a cyclohexenone.)[2]

The loss of CO_2 on hydrolysis suggests the presence of a β-keto acid as an intermediate, i.e., B or C.

To account for the hydrolysis of acetic acid and the IR bands[3] at 1765 and 1795 cm^{-1}, the ester-lactones D and E can be proposed.

Since **1** shows ketonic rather than aldehydic properties, and since the IR spectrum does not fit an aldehyde, D is favored.

[1] L. F. Fieser and M. Fieser, *Steroids*, Reinhold, New York, 1959, pp. 15ff.
[2] H. S. French, *J. Am. Chem. Soc.*, **74**, 514 (1952).
[3] R. S. Rasmussen and R. R. Brattain, *J. Am. Chem. Soc.*, **71**, 1073 (1949).

The conversion of **1** to **5** can be visualized as hydrolysis of the ester and lactone groups in the mildly basic NaBH$_4$ solution, reduction of the aldehyde and ketone functions, and relactonization during the workup with acid.

PROBLEM 161. Deduce the structures of the natural product **1** and its derivatives.

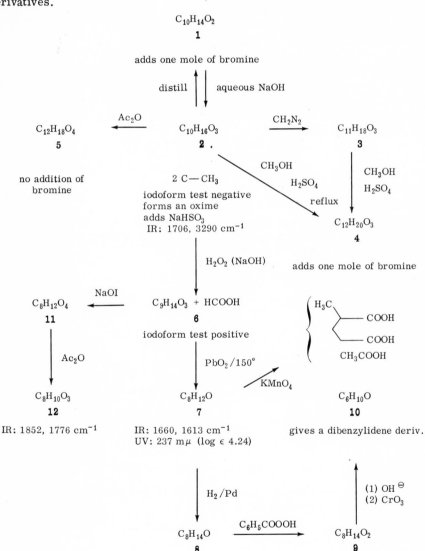

$C_{10}H_{14}O_2$

1

adds one mole of bromine

distill   aqueous NaOH

$C_{12}H_{18}O_4$ $\xleftarrow{\ Ac_2O\ }$ $C_{10}H_{16}O_3$ $\xrightarrow{\ CH_2N_2\ }$ $C_{11}H_{18}O_3$

5   **2**   **3**

no addition of
bromine

$2\ C{-}CH_3$

iodoform test negative
forms an oxime
adds NaHSO$_3$
IR: 1706, 3290 cm^{-1}

CH$_3$OH
H$_2$SO$_4$

CH$_3$OH
H$_2$SO$_4$
reflux

$C_{12}H_{20}O_3$

4

H$_2$O$_2$ (NaOH)   adds one mole of bromine

$C_8H_{12}O_4$ $\xleftarrow{\ NaOI\ }$ $C_9H_{14}O_3$ + HCOOH

11   **6**

iodoform test positive

Ac$_2$O

PbO$_2$/150°

KMnO$_4$

$C_8H_{10}O_3$ $C_8H_{12}O$ $C_6H_{10}O$

12   **7**   **10**

IR: 1852, 1776 cm^{-1} IR: 1660, 1613 cm^{-1} gives a dibenzylidene deriv.
                               UV: 237 mμ (log ϵ 4.24)

$\left\{\begin{array}{l} H_3C \\ \end{array}\right.$ COOH

COOH

CH$_3$COOH

H$_2$/Pd   (1) OH$^\ominus$
               (2) CrO$_3$

$C_8H_{14}O$ $\xrightarrow{\ C_6H_5COOOH\ }$ $C_8H_{14}O_2$

8   **9**

ANSWER 161.   [S. M. McElvain, R. D. Bright, and P. R. Johnson, *J. Am. Chem. Soc.*, **63**, 1558 (1941); S. M. McElvain and E. J. Eisenbraun, *J. Am. Chem. Soc.*, **77**, 1599 (1955).]

Compound **1** is nepetalactone and is isolated from catnip.

The analysis of this problem is probably most easily begun with the oxidation of **7**. Acetic acid and α-methylglutaric acid can be combined into three possible structures, A, B, and C:

A   B   C

Of these, only C is likely to undergo catalytic reduction of the $\underset{/}{\overset{\backslash}{C}}{=}\underset{\backslash}{\overset{/}{C}}$ to give a product (**8**) which after Baeyer-Villiger oxidation[1] (**8** → **9**) can be hydrolyzed with the loss of two carbon atoms (**9** → **10**). Structures A and B would lead to lactones on oxidation, and hydrolysis would occur without loss of carbon. The location of the methyl group in C (**7**) follows from the formation by **10** of a dibenzylidene derivative. This shows that **10** possesses the part structure

$$-CH_2\overset{\overset{\displaystyle O}{\|}}{C}CH_2- \xrightarrow[OH^{\ominus}]{\phi CHO} -\overset{\overset{\displaystyle \phi CH}{\|}}{C}-\overset{\overset{\displaystyle O}{\|}}{C}-\overset{\overset{\displaystyle HC\phi}{\|}}{C}-$$

and thus leads to C1 for **7** rather than the originally possible alternative C2.

C1   C2

The structure of **6** is suggested by the oxidative decarboxylation-dehydrogenation **6** → **7** (cf. the oxidative bis-decarboxylation[2] D → E) and the position of the double bond in **7**.

---

[1] See C. H. Hassall in *Organic Reactions*, Vol. 9, Wiley, New York, 1957, p. 74.

[2] W. von E. Doering, M. Farber, and A. Sayigh, *J. Am. Chem. Soc.*, **74**, 4370 (1952).

It is confirmed by the oxidation **6** → **11** and the formation from **11** of a dehydration product which is, from its IR spectrum, obviously a five-membered cyclic anhydride.[3]

Starting from the other end, the relationship between **1** and **2** is that of a lactone and its hydroxy acid. That the lactone is enolic is suggested by the presence of unsaturation in **1** and the apparently aldehydic properties of **2**. Given these observations and the structure of **6**, the reaction **2** → **6** may be proposed, although it is decidedly unusual. Once **2** is in hand, the further reactions serve to confirm its correctness.

The actual structure of **2** is something of a problem. In order to explain its reactions, it has been proposed that the three forms **F**, **G**, and **H**:

are in equilibrium. Although the first two are reasonable, and the second might be expected to predominate, it is difficult to see why this structure should lead to any sizable amount of enol. It is probable that the reaction **2** → **1** represents the dehydration of G and not the esterification of H, as has been suggested. The reaction **2** → **6** is difficult to account for satisfactorily with any structure, although mechanisms can be written that are based on the addition of $HOO^{\ominus}$ to the aldehyde group of F, followed by rearrangement (see the Dakin oxidation of phenolic aldehydes[4]), or the attack of HO· on the enolate anion of F and further oxidation of the resulting α-hydroxyaldehyde.

---

[3] Nakanishi, p. 45.

[4] H. D. Dakin, *Am. Chem. J.*, **42**, 474 (1909).

PROBLEM 162.   Deduce the structures of the natural product **1** and its derivatives:

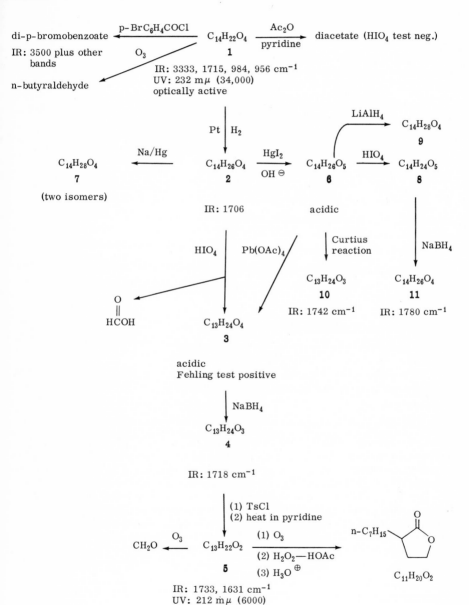

(cont.)

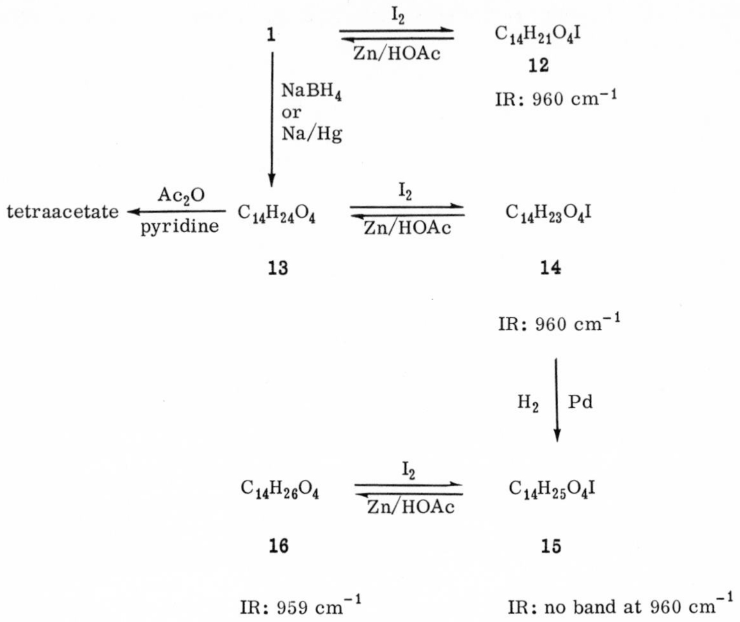

$$1 \quad \xrightarrow[\text{Zn/HOAc}]{I_2} \quad C_{14}H_{21}O_4I$$

12

IR: 960 cm^{-1}

NaBH$_4$
or
Na/Hg

$$\text{tetraacetate} \xleftarrow[\text{pyridine}]{Ac_2O} \quad C_{14}H_{24}O_4 \quad \xrightarrow[\text{Zn/HOAc}]{I_2} \quad C_{14}H_{23}O_4I$$

13   **14**

IR: 960 cm^{-1}

H$_2$ | Pd

$$C_{14}H_{26}O_4 \quad \xrightarrow[\text{Zn/HOAc}]{I_2} \quad C_{14}H_{25}O_4I$$

16   **15**

IR: 959 cm^{-1} IR: no band at 960 cm^{-1}

Notes: (a) A transformation similar to **1** → **12** is not observed on the diacetate of **1**.

(b) Products **1, 2,** and **12** all give isopropylidene derivatives when treated with ZnCl$_2$ and acetone.

(c) The IR spectra given above are frequently incomplete, and no dependence should be placed on what is *not* given.

ANSWER 162. [K. Bowden, B. Lythgoe, and D. J. S. Marsden, *J. Chem. Soc.,* **1959**, 1662.]

The compound **1** is the mold metabolite palitantin.

Consideration of the molecular formula of **1** shows the presence of four units of unsaturation. One of this is present as a $\text{C}={O}$ group (IR at 1710 cm^{-1}) and one or two as $\text{C}={C}$ (UV = C≡C—C≡O or C≡C—C≡C). The reduction with 4 H to **2**, which still contains a carbonyl, suggests the presence of a diene, and consequently a monocyclic skeleton. The formation of a diacetate and di-p-bromobenzoate indicates the presence of at least two hydroxyls, but the IR band at 3500 cm^{-1} in the latter suggests that there is also a third, hindered, one which is not esterified. This is supported, although not conclusively, by the formation of a tetraacetate after NaBH$_4$ reduction of **1**.

Starting from the other end, the formation of the α-n-heptyl-γ-lactone from **5** and the production of n-butyraldehyde by ozonolysis of **1** suggest the part structure

$$\text{CH}_3\text{CH}_2\text{CH}_2\text{CH}{=}\text{CH}-\text{CH}{=}\text{CH}-$$

for **1**.

Considering the production of CH$_2$O on the ozonolysis of **5**, two structures are possible (A, B). Either of these could give an α-keto lactone which would be readily oxidized to the observed product.

A

B

However, the relatively high frequency of the $\ce{>C=O}$ IR band and the short wavelength of the UV absorption are in much better agreement with A than with B.

Working backward from A leads via **4** to the structure given above for **3**. The IR spectrum of **4** is somewhat anomalous when compared with that of **5**, since the latter, being conjugated, would be expected to absorb at a lower frequency than its unconjugated precursor. Assuming that the values given are correct, the best explanation is that of an intramolecular hydrogen bond between the OH group and the ester carbonyl, which shifts the frequency of **4** to a lower value. This effect may be combined with steric distortions in **5**, which disturb the coplanarity of the methylene and carbonyl groups, and so reduce the spectral effects of conjugation.

C

D

The formation of **3** and HCOOH on periodic acid oxidation is consistent with either of the structures C or D for **2**, whereas the observation of two isomeric products (**7**) on the reduction of **2** suggests that the carbonyl group must be capable of giving rise to two stereoisomeric alcohols. This is possible with the secondary alcohol derived from a ketone, but not with the primary alcohol from an aldehyde, so structure D may be rejected. [The preceding argument is perhaps a little more glib than is justified by the evidence presented. It is necessary to be sure that the products really do represent stereoisomers formed by alternative modes of reduction of the carbonyl group and do not arise by stereochemical changes elsewhere, e.g., inversion at the carbon α to the carbonyl prior to the reduction. In this case, however, the α-carbon in D does not bear a proton and would be expected to be stable under the basic conditions of the reduction. Furthermore, the tetraol corresponding to D is known (**9**) and is different from either of the isomers of **7**.]

Once the structure of **2** is in hand, it only remains to explain its transformations. The formation of **6** occurs at least formally by oxidation to an α-diketone followed by a benzylic acid rearrangement.[1]

---

[1]S. Selman and J. F. Eastham, *Quart. Rev.*, **14**, 221 (1961).

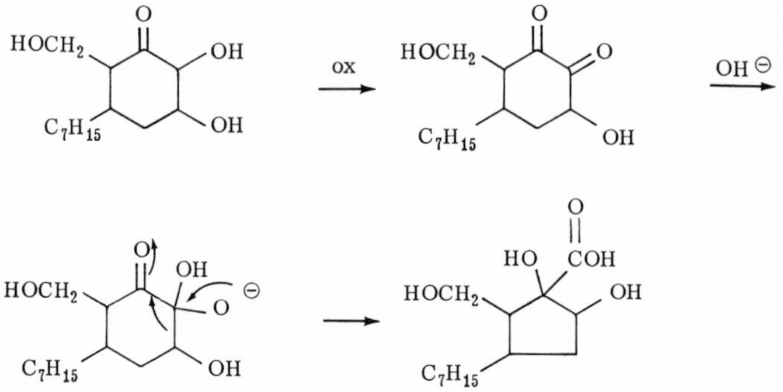

The reagent used (Doevre's reagent)[2] is another in the set of heavy metal oxidants (Tollens' reagent, Fehling's reagent) which are normally considered specific for aldehydes but which also oxidize α-ketols.

The oxidation of **6** with Pb(OAc)$_4$ cleaves both the vic-diol and the α-hydroxy acid groups, yielding **3**, but HIO$_4$ reacts only very slowly with α-hydroxy acids, and the reaction stops with the formation of **8**.[3] It is suggested, on the basis of its carbonyl stretching frequency, that the lactone **11**, formed after NaBH$_4$ reduction of **8**, has the structure shown.

The final series of reactions simply represent the reversible oxyiodination of one of the double bonds of the side chain. This reaction is undoubtedly favored by the steric arrangement of the substituents on the carbocyclic ring. The absence of such a reaction with the diacetate of **1** indicates the hydroxymethyl group is, as would be expected, acetylated. The inertness of this same acetate to periodate has led to the proposal that it can be represented as E. It is difficult to see, however, why the last hydroxyl group should be unreactive in this system but capable of being acetylated when the carbonyl group is reduced. An alternative proposal would be that the diacetate has the structure F and that the periodate cleavage of the α-ketol system fails for steric reasons.

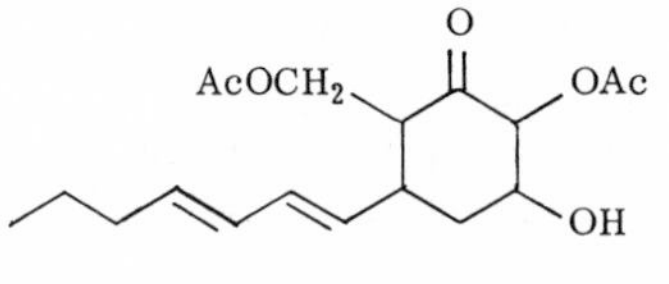

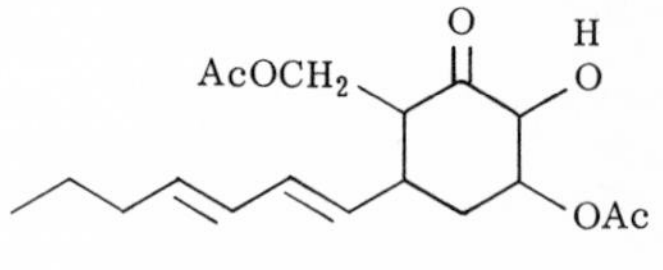

[2] J. Doeuvre, *Bull. Soc. Chim. France*, **41**, 1145 (1927).

[3] For a comparison of these two reagents, see R. Criegee in *Newer Methods of Preparative Organic Chemistry*, Wiley-Interscience, New York, 1948, p. 1.

INDEX 1

TYPES OF PROBLEMS

Problems requiring conformational and stereochemical interpretation:
    10, 11, 12, 17, 19, 30, 31, 32, 33, 35, 36, 40, 50, 51, 52, 55, 57, 60, 61, 64, 65, 69,
    74, 85, 87, 110, 112, 119, 121, 125, 127, 135, 137, 142, 146, 154, 156, 162

Problems requiring explanations:
    33, 34, 44, 45, 47, 48, 50, 51, 54, 59, 60, 62, 64, 65, 69, 74, 85, 89, 121, 129, 133,
    143, 146, 154

Problems requiring interpretation of physical organic data:
    37, 43, 60, 62, 86, 87, 109

Problems requiring interpretation of spectra:
    all of Chapter 2; 71, 117, 123, 124, 125, 134, 135, 136, 148, 156, 157, 158, 159,
    160, 161, 162

Problems requiring the prediction of products of reactions:
    20, 21, 24, 26, 27, 29, 35, 36, 40, 49, 52, 55, 56, 57, 58, 71, 72, 73, 79, 88, 99,
    101, 102, 103, 104, 108, 117, 122, 126, 132, 133, 134, 142, 143, 155

Problems requiring suggested mechanisms:
    38, 39, 41, 42, 46, 53, 61, 63, 66, 67, 68, 70, 76, 77, 78, 79, 81, 82, 83, 84, 91,
    92, 93, 94, 95, 96, 97, 98, 100, 105, 106, 110, 111, 112, 113, 114, 115, 116, 118,
    119, 120, 127, 128, 130, 131, 138, 139, 140, 141, 144, 145, 147, 149, 155

Problems requiring synthetic or degradative schemes:
    80, 90, 107, 150, 151, 152

Road-map (Compound X) problems:
    22, 23, 74, 75, 123, 124, 125, 135, 136, 148, 156, 157, 158, 159, 160, 161, 162

INDEX 2